Presented to The San Diego Branch
of the League of American Pen Women
by the author

Gail Calmerton

WHEELER'S GRADED READERS

A FIFTH READER

BY

GAIL CALMERTON

AND

WILLIAM H. WHEELER

CHICAGO

W. H. WHEELER & COMPANY

CONSIDER what you have in the smallest chosen library.
A company of the wisest and wittiest men that could be
picked out of all civil countries in a thousand years have
set in best order the results of their learning and wisdom.
The men themselves were hidden and inaccessible, solitary,
impatient of interruption, fenced by etiquette; but the
thought which they did not uncover to their bosom friend
is here written out in transparent words to us, the strangers
of another age.

RALPH WALDO EMERSON.

 39

PREFACE

A FAMOUS writer has said: "The habit of reading is one's pass to the greatest, the purest, the most perfect pleasures that have been prepared for human beings. But you cannot acquire this habit in your old age; you cannot acquire it in middle age; you must learn to read and to like reading when you are young or you cannot do so when you are old."

No one, however, can derive very great pleasure or very great profit from reading unless he is able to read well. As a rule indifferent reading is a result of indifferent appreciation. The pupil who stumbles over every hard word, or who is at a loss to know the meaning of this or that expression, is not likely to find much enjoyment in books. Growth of vocabulary is a necessary part of the daily reading lesson of all pupils. Even to read well to one's self, one must be able to read aloud in such a manner as to interest and delight those who listen to him. The ready use of the dictionary and other reference books for pronunciation and meaning of words, for historical and mythical allusions should be steadily cultivated.

A well-known college professor, in response to a school superintendent's question as to what would better the preparation of students for college, replied: "Teach them how to read." Another college instructor, a learned authority on geology, remarks that he finds occasion to say to his classes about once a month, "It's a great thing to be able to read a page of English."

Every intelligent person in the present day is impressed with the great advantages to be derived from reading. But even in this day it may be interesting and instructive to draw a contrast between the man of *no* culture and the man of *high* culture.

Look first at the poor unlettered rustic. He has never been taught to think or to read. His intellect is still confined to his five senses. It takes in nothing but the dull images of the byways along which he plods, the beasts of the fields, the forms of his relatives and neighbors, and the slow-paced routine of his narrow life. The distant and the past are to him a complete void. His soul is tied to the present and to that small spot of the earth's surface on which he moves in his daily rounds. The wonderful rocks upon which this old earth of ours has written so much of her history are to him — stones, mere stones. The plants so infinitely varied in form, color, perfume, and association are to him — flowers, mere flowers.

> " A primrose by a river's brim,
> A yellow primrose is to him,
> And it is nothing more."

Look now at the accomplished man of letters. He sits in his quiet study with clear head, sympathetic heart, and lively fancy. The walls around him are lined with books on every subject. He is indeed a man of magical powers, and these are his magical volumes full of wonder-working spells. When he opens one of these books and reads with eye and soul intent, in a few minutes the objects around him fade from his senses, and his soul is carried away into distant regions, or into bygone times.

It may be a book descriptive of other lands; and then he feels himself, perhaps, to be amid the biting frost and the blinding snow of a polar winter, or the fierce heat and the luxuriant vegetation of the equator. Or, perhaps, the book may be one of our great English classics, — Shakespeare, Emerson, or Carlyle, — and immediately he is in the closest contact with a spirit far larger than his own; his mind grasps its grand ideas, his heart imbibes its glowing sentiments, until he finds himself dilated, refined, inspired, — a greater and a nobler being. Thus does the scholar's soul grow and extend itself until it lives in every region of the earth and in every bygone age, and holds the most intimate intercourse with the mighty spirits of the dead.

Reading is thinking the line of thought established by the author. To read well is to think clearly and closely. To love good literature, to find pleasure in reading it, and to gain power to choose it with discrimination, are the supreme ends to be attained by the reading lesson. After we leave school, our information is largely gained from books, and what we get from these is largely determined by our school training. More than we at first suspect we read ourselves into the style of language we use, into the forms of thought we entertain, and into the sort of lives we live. Reading not only informs but forms the mind.

In the public schools the aim should be to produce simple, natural, expressive readers, not artistic actors and orators. It should be impressed upon

4

the pupils from the outset that they are studying the thoughts and feelings that others have expressed in words upon the printed page. They must discover the thoughts behind the words and then express them; that is all there is to reading.

In the earlier books of this series the pupils have found a wonderful collection of myths and interesting stories of fact, and fable, and fairy, and fiction. Now they are entering into companionship with some of the mighty masters of literature and with the creatures of their fancy. Here they are introduced to Little Eppie and Little Nell, the Cratchitts and the Primroses, and other charming people of the book world, with the conviction that it is better to inspire the heart with a noble sentiment than to teach the mind a truth of science, and with the hope that they will like these charming book people too well to confine their acquaintance within the brief limits necessary to this book. Better — a thousand times better — than all the material wealth the world can give, is the love for the best books — books which make us clearer in head, larger in heart, and nobler in action.

A great German, who was young when the "Vicar of Wakefield" first appeared, read the story some four years after its publication, and read it with delight and admiration; and seventy years later when he read it again with renewed delight, he told a friend how much its first reading had to do with forming his education. That great German was Goethe.

In selecting the material for this book, no selection has been accepted merely because it is new; and no selection has been rejected merely because it is old. Several familiar old pieces that have stood the test of time are included in the list. They are the songs that will always be sung and the stories that will always be told. Such selections should be studied for the pleasure that comes from reading beautiful thoughts beautifully expressed.

In this book the pupils are asked to read about some of the things which loving, watchful eyes have seen in the world of nature, with the hope that they will learn that that world is before them, full of interesting, wonderful things which they may discover for themselves; that they will learn to open their eyes and let them wander over the varied forms of flower, and tree, and rock; that they will learn to open their ears and let them delight in the sighing of the breeze, the tinkle of the brook, the hum of the bee, and the trill of the bird. Those pupils who have the good fortune to train their powers of observation in this way are not likely to be complaining that they have no taste for poetry

Poets and story-tellers live in the imagination, which is a much larger world than that found in the geographies, and into this larger region our heroes often take us. Surely travelers into the realms of poetry and fiction could not ask for more exhilarating guides. But if we wish to follow them, we must train our mental eyesight. We must see the scene, enter into the thought and feeling of the story or poem which we read. The imagination is a wonderful worker if we only trust it. It is as susceptible of improvement by exercise as our judgment or memory. But the imagination cannot be developed in a week or a month; and unless there is imagination there can be no sympathy. The greatest intellectual training afforded by reading is the training of the imagination. Without this power of mental vision, which we call imagination, we can never read well, because we can never understand well. Perhaps we have wished for the gifts of the old fairy tale, —the magic glass through which one sees distant objects and the magic rug on which one is borne to far-off scenes. Both these gifts are ours in this wonderful power of imagination.

Grateful acknowledgments are due to the critic, Josephine Turck Baker, editor of "Correct English," and to all the teachers who have given helpful suggestions.

CONTENTS

7

8

Grateful acknowledgments are due to all the publishers and the authors who have kindly given us permission to use selections from their copyright material.

The selections from the writings of Henry Wadsworth Longfellow, Alice Cary, James Russell Lowell, Nathaniel Hawthorne, Ralph Waldo Emerson, John Greenleaf Whittier, and Oliver Wendell Holmes are used by permission of and special arrangement with Houghton, Mifflin Company, the authorized publishers of the writings of these authors.

9

ILLUSTRATIONS

EVENTIDE.

B. W. Leader.

SILAS MARNER AND LITTLE EPPIE

GEORGE ELIOT

PART I

vista	revelry	flexibly	violently
impulse	solitude	repetition	instinctively
Raveloe	vocation	constraint	Silas Marner
remnants	pulsation	vibrations	contemplation

In the days when the spinning wheels hummed busily in the farmhouses, and when even great ladies, clothed in silk and thread-lace, had their toy spinning wheels of polished oak, there might be seen in districts far away among the lanes, or deep in the bosom of the hills, certain scattered linen weavers, pallid, under-sized men, who, by the side of the brawny country-folk, looked like the remnants of a disinherited race.

In the early years of this century, such a linen weaver, named Silas Marner, worked at his vocation in a stone cottage that stood among the nutty hedgerows near the village of Raveloe, and not far from the edge of a deserted stone pit. And Raveloe was a village which lay in the rich central plain of what we are pleased to call Merry England. But it was nestled in a snug, well-wooded hollow, quite an hour's journey on horseback from any turnpike, where it was never reached by the vibrations of the coach horn or of public opinion.

When Silas Marner first came to Raveloe, he was simply a pallid young man, with prominent, short-sighted brown eyes; but he had known disappointment and he still walked in the shadow of a great sorrow. He hated the thought of the past; there was nothing that called out his love and fellowship towards the strangers he had come among, and the future was all dark. Thought was arrested by utter bewilderment, and affection seemed to have died under the bruise that had fallen on its keenest nerves.

His first movement after the shock had been to work in his loom, and he went on with this, never asking himself why he worked far on into the night after he came to Raveloe. He seemed to weave like a spider, from pure impulse, without reflection. His hand satisfied itself with throwing the shuttle, and his eye with seeing the little squares in the cloth complete themselves under his effort.

At last the table linen was finished, and Silas was paid in gold. Now, for the first time in his life, he had five bright guineas put into his hand; no man expected a share of them, and he loved no man that he should offer him a share. But what were the guineas to him who saw no vista beyond countless days of weaving? It was needless for him to ask that, for it was pleasant to him to feel them in his palm, and to look at their bright faces, which were all his own. The weaver's hand had known the touch of hard-won money even before the palm had grown to its full breadth, and now as he walked homeward across the fields in the twilight, he drew out the money and thought it was brighter in the gathering gloom.

Gradually the guineas, the crowns, and the half-crowns, grew to a heap, and Marner drew less and less for his own wants, trying to solve the problem of keeping himself strong enough to work sixteen hours a day on as small an outlay as possible. Marner wanted the heaps of ten to grow into a square, and then into a larger square; and every added guinea, while it was itself a satisfaction, bred a new desire. In this strange world, made a hopeless riddle to him, he might, if he had had a less intense nature, have sat weaving, weaving — looking towards the end of his pattern, or towards the end of his web, till he forgot the riddle, and everything else but his immediate sensations; but the money had come to mark off his weaving into periods, and the money not only grew, but remained with him. He began to think it was conscious of him, as his loom was, and he would on no account have exchanged those coins for other coins with unknown faces. He handled them, he counted them, till their form and color were like the satisfying of a thirst to him; but it was only in the night, when his work was done, that he drew them out to enjoy their companionship. He had taken up some bricks in his floor underneath his loom, and here he had made a hole in which he set the iron pot that contained his guineas and silver coins, covering the bricks with sand whenever he replaced them.

So, year after year, Silas Marner had lived in this solitude, his guineas rising in the iron pot, and his life narrowing and hardening itself more and more into a mere pulsation of desire and satis-

15

faction that had no relation to any other being. His life had reduced itself to the functions of weaving and hoarding, without any contemplation of an end towards which the functions tended. Strangely, Marner's face and figure shrank and bent themselves into a constant mechanical relation to the objects of his life. The prominent eyes that used to look trusting and dreamy now looked as if they had been made to see only one kind of thing, which was very small, like tiny grains, and for which they hunted everywhere: and he was so withered and yellow, that, though he was not yet forty, the children always called him "Old Master Marner."

This is the history of Silas Marner until the fifteenth year after he came to Raveloe. The livelong day he sat in his loom, his ear filled with its monotony, his eyes bent close down on the slow growth of sameness in the brownish web, his muscles moving with such even repetition that their pause seemed almost as much a constraint as the holding of his breath. But at night came his revelry: at night he closed his shutters, and made fast his doors, and drew forth his gold. Long ago the heap of coins had become too large for the iron pot to hold them, and he had made for them two thick leather bags, which wasted no room in their resting-place, but lent themselves flexibly to every corner. How the guineas shone as they came pouring out of the dark leather mouth! The silver bore no large proportion in amount to the gold, because the long pieces of linen which formed his chief work were always partly paid for in gold, and out of the silver he supplied his own bodily wants, choosing the shillings and the sixpences to spend in this way. He loved the guineas best, but he would not change the silver, — the crowns and half-crowns that were his own earnings; he loved them all. He spread them out in heaps and bathed his hands in them; then he counted them and set them up in regular piles, and felt their rounded outline between his thumb and fingers, and thought fondly of the guineas that were only half earned by the work in his loom — thought of the guineas that were coming slowly through the coming years, through all his life, which spread far away before him, the end quite hidden by countless days of weaving.

One dark, rainy night, when a thief closed the door of the weaver's cottage, and stepped forward into the darkness carrying in his hands two thick leather bags filled with gold, Silas Marner was not more than a hundred yards away, plodding along from the village with a sack thrown round his shoulders as an overcoat, and with a lantern in his hand. His legs were weary, but his mind was at ease. What thief would find his way to the stone-pits on such a night as this? And why should he come on this particular night, when he had not come through all the fifteen years before?

He reached his door in much satisfaction that his errand was done. It was a nasty fog to turn out into, but to lose time by going on errands in the morning was out of the question. He opened his door, and to his short-sighted eyes everything remained as he had left it, except that the fire sent out a welcome increase of heat.

As soon as he was warm he began to think it would be a long

while to wait till after supper before he drew out his guineas and it would be pleasant to see them on the table before him as he ate his feast. For joy is the best of wine, and Silas's guineas were a golden wine of that sort.

He rose and placed his candle unsuspectingly on the floor near his loom, swept away the sand without noticing any change, and removed the bricks. The sight of the empty hole made his heart leap violently, but the belief that his gold was gone could not come at once — only terror, and the eager effort to put an end to the terror. He passed his trembling hand all about the hole, trying to think it possible that his eyes had deceived him; then he held the candle in the hole and examined it curiously, trembling more and more. At last he shook so violently that he let the candle fall, and lifted his hands to his head, trying to steady himself, that he might think. Had he put his gold somewhere else, by a sudden resolution last night, and then forgotten it? He searched in every corner, he turned his bed over and shook it; he looked in his brick-oven where he laid his sticks. When there was no other place to be searched, he kneeled down again and felt once more all round the hole. There was no untried refuge left for a moment's shelter from the terrible truth.

Silas got up from his knees trembling, and looked round at the table : didn't the gold lie there after all? The table was bare. Then he turned and looked behind him, — looked all round his dwelling, seemed to strain his brown eyes after some possible appearance of the bags where he had already sought them in vain. He could see every object in his cottage, and his gold was not there.

18

C. E. Brock.

HE PLACED HIS CANDLE UNSUSPECTINGLY ON THE FLOOR AND REMOVED THE BRICKS.

Again he put his trembling hands to his head, and gave a wild ringing scream, a cry of desolation. For a few moments after, he stood motionless; but the cry had relieved him from the first maddening pressure of the truth. He turned, and tottered towards his loom, and got into the seat where he worked, instinctively seeking this as the strongest assurance of reality.

Part II

Eppie	emotion	disperse	inarticulate
torpor	supreme	porridge	encountered
tension	assigned	transition	automatically
peevish	yearning	contracted	half-transparent

One dark stormy night a few weeks after Silas Marner's money was stolen, a young wife was walking with slow, uncertain steps through the snow-covered Raveloe lanes, carrying her child in her arms. She walked on and on under the breaking clouds, from which there came now and then the light of a quickly veiled star, for a freezing wind had sprung up since the snowing had ceased. But she walked always more and more drowsily and clutched more and more automatically the sleeping child at her bosom. Soon she felt nothing but a supreme immediate longing to lie down and sleep. She sank down against a bush, an easy pillow enough; and the bed of snow, too, was soft. She did not feel that the bed was cold, and she did not heed whether the child would awake and cry for her. But her arms had not yet relaxed their instinctive clutch; and the little one slumbered on as gently as if it had been rocked in a lace-trimmed cradle.

But the complete torpor came at last; the fingers lost their tension, the arms unbent; then the little head fell away from the bosom, and the blue eyes opened wide on the cold starlight. At first there was a little peevish cry of "Mamma" and an effort to regain the pillowing arm; but Mamma's ear was deaf, and the pillow seemed to be slipping away backward. Suddenly, as the child rolled downward on its mother's knees, all wet with snow, its eyes were caught by a bright glancing light on the white ground, and, with the ready transition of infancy, it was immediately absorbed in watching the bright living thing running towards it, yet never arriving. That bright living thing must be caught; and in an instant the child had slipped on all fours, and held out one little hand to catch the gleam. But the gleam would not be caught in that way, and now the head was held up to see where the cunning gleam came from. It came from a very bright place; and the little one, rising on its legs, toddled through the snow, the old shawl in which it was wrapped trailing behind it, and the queer little bonnet dangling at its back — toddled on to the open door of Silas Marner's cottage, and right up to the warm hearth, where there was a bright fire of logs and sticks, which had thoroughly warmed the old sack spread out on the bricks to dry. The little one, accustomed to be left to itself for long hours without notice from its mother, squatted down on the sack, and spread its tiny hands towards the blaze in perfect contentment, gurgling and making many inarticulate communications to the cheerful fire, like a new-hatched gosling beginning to find itself comfortable. But presently the warmth had a lulling effect, and the little golden head sank down on the old sack, and the blue eyes were veiled by their delicate, half-transparent lids.

But where was Silas Marner while this strange visitor had come to his house? He was in the cottage, but he did not see the child. During the last few weeks, since he had lost his money, he had contracted the habit of opening his door and looking out from time to time, as if he thought that his money might be somehow coming back to him, or that some trace, some news of it might be mysteriously on the road, and be caught by the listening ear or the straining eye. It was chiefly at night, when he was not occupied in his loom, that he fell into this repetition of an act for which he could have assigned no definite purpose, and which can hardly be understood except by those who have undergone a bewildering separation from a supremely loved object. In the evening twilight, and later whenever the night was not dark, Silas looked out on that narrow prospect round the stone pits, listening and gazing, not with hope, but with mere yearning and unrest.

This morning he had been told by some of his neighbors that it was New Year's Eve, and that he must sit up and hear the old year rung out and the new rung in, because that was good luck, and might bring his money back again. This was only their friendly way of jesting with the half-crazy oddities of a miser, but it had perhaps helped to throw Silas into a more than usually excited state. Since the on-coming of twilight he had opened his door again and again, though only to shut it immediately at seeing all distance veiled by the falling snow. But the last time he opened it the snow had ceased, and the clouds were parting here and there. He stood and listened, and gazed for a long while — there was really something on the road coming towards him then, but he caught no sign of it; and the stillness and the wide, trackless snow seemed to narrow his solitude, and touched his yearning with the chill of despair. He went in again, and put his right hand on the latch of the door to close it, but he did not close it: he stood in a trance, like a graven image, with wide but sightless eyes, holding open his door, powerless to resist either the good or the evil that might enter there.

When Marner's sensibility returned, he closed his door unaware of any change, except that the light had grown dim, and that he was chilled and faint. He thought he had been too long standing at the door and looking out. Turning towards the hearth, where the two logs had fallen apart, and sent forth only a red, uncertain glimmer, he seated himself on his fireside chair, and was stooping to push the logs together, when, to his blurred vision, it seemed as if there were gold on the floor in front of the hearth. Gold! — his own gold — brought back to him as mysteriously as it had been taken away! He felt his heart begin to beat violently, and for a few moments he was unable to stretch out his hand and grasp the restored treasure. The heap of gold seemed to glow and get larger beneath his agitated gaze. He leaned forward at last, and stretched forth his hand; but instead of the hard coin with the familiar resisting outline, his fingers encountered soft warm curls. In utter amazement, Silas fell down on his knees and bent his head low to examine the marvel:

it was a sleeping child — a round, fair thing, with soft, yellow rings all over its head. Could this be his little sister come back to him in a dream — his little sister whom he had carried about in his arms for a year before she died, when he was a small boy without shoes or stockings? That was the first thought that darted across Silas's blank wonderment. Was it a dream? He rose to his feet again, pushed the logs together, and, throwing on some dried leaves and sticks, raised a flame; but the flame did not disperse the vision — it only lighted up more distinctly the little round form of the child and its shabby clothing. It was very much like his little sister. Silas sank into his chair powerless. How and when had the child come in without his knowledge?

But there was a cry on the hearth: the child had awakened, and Marner stooped to lift it on his knee. It clung round his neck, and burst louder and louder into cries of " Mamma." Silas pressed it to him, and almost unconsciously uttered sounds of hushing tenderness, while he bethought himself that some of his porridge, which had got cool by the dying fire, would do to feed the child with if it were only warmed up a little.

He had plenty to do through the next hour. The porridge, sweetened with some dry brown sugar, stopped the cries of the little one, and made her lift her blue eyes with a wide quiet gaze at Silas as he put the spoon into her mouth. Presently she slipped from his knee and began to toddle about, but with a pretty stagger that made Silas jump up and follow her lest she should fall against anything that would hurt her. But she only fell in

24

THE PORRIDGE MADE HER LIFT HER BLUE EYES WITH A WIDE QUIET GAZE AT SILAS,
AS HE PUT THE SPOON INTO HER MOUTH.

a sitting posture on the ground, and began to pull at her boots, looking up at him with a crying face as if the boots hurt her. He took her on his knee again, but it was some time before it occurred to Silas's dull bachelor mind that the wet boots were the grievance, pressing on her warm ankles. He got them off with difficulty, and Baby was at once happily occupied with the primary mystery of her own toes, inviting Silas, with much chuckling, to consider the mystery, too.

And Silas Marner was trembling with an emotion, mysterious to him, at something unknown dawning on his life. Thought and feeling were so confused within him, that if he had tried to give them utterance he could only have said: "My money is gone, I don't know where, and this pretty little child is come from I don't know where. This little child has come instead of the gold — the gold has turned into the child."

But Silas soon learned the terrible truth; the little girl's mother was dead, frozen to death in the cold white snow. When Silas learned this, he said: "I shall keep her till some one shows that he has a right to take her away from me." So Silas kept the little girl and called her Eppie, lavishing on her the affection he had formerly given only to his gold. As the weeks grew to months, the child created fresh and fresh links between his life and the lives from which he had hitherto shrunk continually. Eppie was a creature of endless claims and ever growing desires, seeking and loving sunshine, and living sounds and living movements, and stirring the human kindness in all eyes that looked on her.

And when the sunshine grew strong and lasting, so that the buttercups were thick in the meadows, Silas might be seen in the midday, or the late afternoon when the shadows were lengthening under the hedgerows, strolling out with uncovered head to carry Eppie beyond the stone pits to where the flowers grew, till they reached some favorite bank where they could sit down, while Eppie toddled to pluck the flowers, and make remarks to the winged things that murmured happily above the bright petals, calling Daddy's attention continually by bringing him the flowers. Then she would turn her ear to some sudden bird note, and Silas learned to please her by making signs of hushed stillness, that they might listen for the note to come again, so that when it came, she set up her small back and laughed with gurgling triumph.

PART III

scissors	cavities	discipline	uninclosed
capacity	peculiar	engrossed	requisition
devising	adhesive	perturbed	discoursing

By the time that Eppie was three years old, she had developed a fine capacity for mischief and for devising ways of being troublesome, which found much exercise, not only for Silas's patience, but for his watchfulness. For example, he had wisely chosen a broad strip of linen as a means of fastening her to his loom when he was busy; it made a broad belt round her waist, and was long enough to allow of her reaching the low bed and

27

sitting down on it, but not long enough for her to attempt any dangerous climbing.

One bright summer morning, Silas had been more engrossed than usual in "setting up" a new piece of work, an occasion on which his scissors were in requisition. These scissors had been kept carefully out of Eppie's reach, but the click of them had a peculiar attraction for her ear. Silas had seated himself in his loom, and the noise of the weaving had begun; but he had left his scissors on the ledge, which Eppie's arm was long enough to reach; and now, like a small mouse, watching her opportunity, she stole quietly from the corner, secured the scissors, and toddled to the bed again, setting up her back as a mode of concealing the fact. She had a distinct intention as to the use of the scissors; and having cut the linen strip in a jagged but effectual manner, in two moments she had run out at the open door where the sunshine was inviting her, while poor Silas believed her to be a better child than usual. It was not until he happened to need his scissors that the terrible fact burst upon him : Eppie had run out by herself — had perhaps fallen into the stone pit.

Silas, shaken by fear, rushed out, calling "Eppie!" and ran eagerly about the uninclosed space, exploring the dry cavities into which she might have fallen, and then gazing with questioning dread at the smooth red surface of the water. The cold drops stood on his brow. How long had she been out? There was one hope, that she had crept through the stile, and had got into the fields where he usually took her to stroll. But the grass was high in the meadow, and there was no descrying her, if she were there, except by a close search. Poor Silas, after peering all round the hedgerows, traversed the grass, beginning with perturbed vision to see Eppie behind every group of red sorrel, and to see her moving farther off as he approached. The meadow was searched in vain; and he got over the stile into the next field, looking with dying hope towards a small pond which was now reduced to its summer shallowness, so as to leave a wide margin of good adhesive mud.

Here, however, sat Eppie, discoursing cheerfully to her own small boot, which she was using as a bucket to convey the water into a deep hoof mark, while her little naked foot was planted comfortably on a cushion of olive-green mud. A red-headed calf was observing her with alarmed doubt through the opposite hedge. Silas, overcome with joy at finding his treasure again, could do nothing but snatch her up and cover her with half-sobbing kisses. It was not until he had carried her home and had begun to think of the necessary washing, that he recollected the need that he should punish Eppie and "make her remember." The idea that she might run away again and come to harm gave him unusual resolution, and for the first time he determined to try the coalhole, a small closet near the hearth.

"Naughty, naughty Eppie!" he suddenly began, holding her on his knee, and pointing to her muddy feet and clothes; "naughty to cut with the scissors and run away. Eppie must go into the coalhole for being naughty. Daddy must put her in the coalhole." He half expected that this would be shock enough, and that Eppie would begin to cry. But instead of that she began to shake herself on his knee as if the plan opened a pleasing novelty. He put her in the coalhole and held the door closed, with a trembling sense that he was using a strong measure.

For a moment there was silence. Then came a little cry, "Open, open;" and Silas let her out again, saying, "Now Eppie will never be naughty again, else she must go in the coalhole, a black, naughty place." The weaving must stand still a long while this morning, for now Eppie must be washed and have clean clothes on; but it was to be hoped that this punishment would have a lasting effect, and save time in future — though, perhaps, it would have been better if Eppie had cried more.

In half an hour she was clean again. Silas, having turned his back to see what he could do with the linen band, threw it down again, with the reflection that Eppie would be good without fastening for the rest of the morning. He turned round again, and was going to place her in her little chair near the loom, when she peeped out at him with black face and hands again, and said, "Eppie in de toalhole!" This total failure of the coalhole discipline shook Silas's belief in punishment. "She'd take it all for fun," he said, "if I didn't hurt her, and that I can't do." So Eppie was reared without punishment. The stone hut was made a soft nest for her, lined with downy patience; and also in the world that lay beyond the stone hut, she knew nothing of frowns and denials.

PICTURES OF MEMORY

ALICE CARY

vale   saintlike

gnarled   coquetting

Among the beautiful pictures
  That hang on Memory's wall,
Is one of a dim old forest
  That seemeth best of all:
Not for its gnarled oaks olden,
  Dark with the mistletoe;
Not for the violets golden
  That sprinkle the vale below;
Not for the milk-white lilies
  That lean from the fragrant hedge,
Coquetting all day with the sunbeams,
  And stealing their shining edge;
Not for the vines on the upland
  Where the bright red berries be,
Nor the pinks, nor the pale sweet cowslip,
  It seemeth the best to me.

I once had a little brother,
  With eyes that were dark and deep;
In the lap of that old dim forest
  He lieth in peace asleep;
Light as the down of the thistle,

Free as the winds that blow,
We roved there the beautiful summers,
 The summers of long ago;
But his feet on the hills grew weary,
 And, one of the autumn eves,
I made for my little brother
 A bed of the yellow leaves.

Sweetly his pale arms folded
 My neck in a meek embrace,
As the light of immortal beauty
 Silently covered his face:
And when the arrows of sunset
 Lodged in the tree tops bright,
He fell, in his saintlike beauty,
 Asleep by the gates of light.
Therefore, of all the pictures
 That hang on Memory's wall,
The one of the old dim forest
 Seemeth the best of all.

HOPE, FAITH, AND LOVE

FRIEDRICH SCHILLER

surges   eternal
disport   environ

There are three lessons I would write, —
Three words, as with a burning pen,

In tracings of eternal light,
   Upon the hearts of men.

Have Hope! Though clouds environ round,
   And gladness hides her face in scorn,
Put off the shadow from thy brow —
   No night but hath its morn.

Have Faith! Where'er thy bark is driven —
   The calm's disport, the tempest's mirth —
Know this: God rules the hosts of heaven,
   The inhabitants of earth.

Have Love! Not love alone for one;
   But man, as man, thy brother call;
And scatter, like the circling sun,
   Thy charities on all!

Thus grave these lessons on thy soul —
   Hope, Faith, and Love — and thou shalt find
Strength when life's surges rudest roll,
   Light when thou else wert blind.

WILLIAM WORDSWORTH

Rydal	Calais	Grasmere
verily	Dorothy	Switzerland

   William Wordsworth, one of the Lake Poets, was born in England, in 1770. He had three brothers, and one sister, Dorothy, who was his constant companion. His father and mother died when he was a mere boy.

   "Of my earliest days at school," said he, "I have little to say, but that

WILLIAM WORDSWORTH.

they were very happy ones, chiefly because I was left at liberty then, and in vacations, to read whatever books I liked. For example, I read all of Fielding's works, 'Don Quixote,' 'Gil Blas,' and any part of Swift that I liked, 'Gulliver's Travels,' and 'The Tale of a Tub' being both much to my taste."

In the autumn of 1790 Wordsworth and a young friend made a journey, mostly on foot, to Calais, visiting Switzerland. They wandered across a mountainous country, and were greatly disappointed when a peasant told them that they had crossed the Alps without knowing it.

In 1803 Wordsworth and his sister Dorothy went to Scotland, and there met Sir Walter Scott. Two years later Scott and his wife returned this visit and were delighted with their reception at the humble Dove Cottage at Grasmere. Dove Cottage is still standing by the roadside close to the lake, with a garden, where some of the plants which Wordsworth set out may still be found. It was here that he wrote "To the Cuckoo," and "The Daffodils." In *Dorothy Wordsworth's Journal,* we find the following : " I never saw daffodils so beautiful. They grew among the mossy stones ; some rested their heads on the stones as on a pillow ; the rest tossed and reeled, and seemed as if they verily danced with the wind, they looked so gay and glancing."

In 1813, the family moved to Rydal Mount, where they remained the rest of Wordsworth's life. The home at Rydal was a gray cottage, almost hidden by ivy and roses, with an old-fashioned garden.

A stranger who once visited Wordsworth's home asked to see where he worked. The servant took him first into a room filled with books. "This," said she, " is my master's library, but his study is out of doors." He was made poet laureate when he was seventy-three years old. His life closed gently and quietly in 1850, and he was laid in the quiet churchyard at Grasmere.

THE DAFFODILS

WILLIAM WORDSWORTH

pensive   jocund

I wandered lonely as a cloud
That floats on high o'er vales and hills

RYDAL MOUNT.

When all at once I saw a crowd,
  A host of golden daffodils;
Beside the lake, beneath the trees,
Fluttering and dancing in the breeze.

Continuous as the stars that shine
  And twinkle on the milky way,
They stretched in never-ending line
  Along the margin of the bay:
Ten thousand saw I at a glance,
Tossing their heads in sprightly dance.

The waves beside them danced, but they
  Outdid the sparkling waves in glee.
A poet could not but be gay
  In such a jocund company;
I gazed and gazed, but little thought
What wealth the show to me had brought.

For oft, when on my couch I lie
  In vacant or in pensive mood,
They flash upon that inward eye
  Which is the bliss of solitude,
And then my heart with pleasure fills,
And dances with the daffodils.

MY HEART LEAPS UP

piety

My heart leaps up when I behold
A rainbow in the sky.
So was it when my life began;
So is it now I am a man;
So be it when I shall grow old,
Or let me die!
The child is father of the man;
And I could wish my days to be
Bound each to each by natural piety.

TO THE CUCKOO

WILLIAM WORDSWORTH

unsubstantial

O blithe Newcomer! I have heard,
I hear thee and rejoice.
O Cuckoo! shall I call thee Bird,
Or but a wandering Voice?

While I am lying on the grass
Thy twofold shout I hear,
From hill to hill it seems to pass,
At once far off, and near.

Though babbling only to the Vale,
　　Of sunshine and of flowers,
Thou bringest unto me a tale
　　Of visionary hours.

Thrice welcome, darling of the Spring!
　　Even yet thou art to me
No bird, but an invisible thing,
　　A voice, a mystery;

The same whom in my schoolboy days
　　I listened to; that Cry
Which made me look a thousand ways
　　In bush, and tree, and sky.

To seek thee did I often rove
　　Through woods and on the green;
And thou wert still a hope, a love;
　　Still longed for, never seen.

And I can listen to thee yet;
　　Can lie upon the plain
And listen, till I do beget
　　That golden time again.

O blessed Bird! the earth we pace
　　Again appears to be
An unsubstantial fairy place,
　　That is fit home for thee!

BARBOX BROTHERS

Charles Dickens

Part I

Mugby	sacrifice	initiative	refrigerated
Barbox	gluttony	ridiculous	whimsically
apology	blotched	obliterated	portmanteaus
luggage	suspicion	multiplied	photographed
Junction	ascending	retirement	superannuated

The hero of this story is first a clerk in the firm of Barbox Brothers, then a partner, and finally the firm itself. He prevented the gradual retirement of an old business from him, by taking the initiative and retiring from it. With enough to live on (though, after all, with not too much), he obliterated the firm of Barbox Brothers from the pages of the Post-office Directory and the face of the earth, leaving nothing of it but its name on two portmanteaus. "For one must have some name in going about, for people to pick up," he explained at Mugby Junction.

"Guard! What place is this?"

"Mugby Junction, sir."

"A windy place!"

"Yes, sir."

"Is it a rainy night still?"

"Pours, sir."

"Open the door. I'll get out."

"You'll have, sir," said the guard, glistening with drops of wet, and looking at the tearful face of his watch by the light of his lantern, "three minutes here."

40

"More, I think; for I am not going on."

"Thought you had a through ticket, sir?"

"So I have, but I shall sacrifice the rest of it. I want my luggage."

"Please to come to the van and point it out, sir. Be good enough to look very sharp, sir. Not a moment to spare."

The guard hurried to the luggage van, and the traveler hurried after him. The guard got into it, and the traveler looked into it.

"Those two large, black portmanteaus in the corner where your light shines. Those are mine."

"Name upon them, sir?"

"Barbox Brothers."

"Stand clear, sir, if you please. One. Two. Right!"

Lamp waved — signal lights ahead already changing — shriek from engine — train gone.

"Mugby Junction!" said the traveler, pulling up the woolen muffler round his throat with both hands. "At past three o'clock of a tempestuous morning! So!"

He spoke to himself. There was no one else to speak to. Perhaps, even though there had been any one else to speak to, he would have preferred to speak to himself. Speaking to himself, he spoke to a man within five years of fifty either way, who had turned gray too soon, like a neglected fire; a man with many indications on him of having been much alone.

He stood unnoticed on the dreary platform, except by the rain and by the wind. But with a steady step, he went up and down, up and down, up and down, seeking nothing, and finding it.

41

"Yours, sir?"

The traveler recalled his eyes from the waste into which they had been staring, and fell back a step or so under the abruptness of the question.

"Oh! My thoughts were not here for the moment. Yes; yes; those two portmanteaus are mine. Are you a porter?"

"On porter's wages, sir; but I am Lamps."

The traveler looked a little confused.

"Who did you say you were?"

"Lamps, sir," showing an oily cloth in his hand, as further explanation.

"Surely, surely. Is there any hotel or tavern here? I suppose I can put up in the town? There is a town here?"

"Oh, yes; there's a town, sir. Anyway, there's town enough to put up in. But," following the glance of the other at his luggage, "this is a very dead time of the night with us, sir. The deadest time."

"No porters about?"

"Well, sir, you see," returned Lamps, "they generally go off with the gas. That's how it is. And they seem to have overlooked you, through your walking to the farther end of the platform. But in about twelve minutes or so, she may be up."

"Who may be up?"

"The three forty-two, sir."

He then explained that porters were required to be on duty when the three forty-two came up, and that they would doubtless turn up with the gas. In the meantime, if the gentleman would

42

not very much object to the smell of lamp-oil, and would accept the warmth of his little room; — the gentleman being by this time very cold, instantly closed with the proposal.

A greasy little cabin it was, suggestive to the sense of smell of a cabin in a Whaler. But there was a bright fire burning in its rusty grate, and on the floor there stood a wooden stand of newly trimmed and lighted lamps, ready for service.

As Barbox Brothers (so to call the traveler by the name on his luggage) took his seat and warmed his hands at the fire, he glanced aside at a little desk, much blotched with ink, which his elbow touched. Upon it were some scraps of coarse paper, and a superannuated steel pen in very reduced and gritty circumstances.

From glancing at the scraps of paper, he turned to his host, and said, with some roughness : —

" Why, you are never a poet, man! "

Lamps had certainly not the appearance of one. He was a spare man of about the Barbox Brothers time of life, with his features whimsically drawn upward as if they were attracted by the roots of his hair. And his attractive hair, being cut short, and being grizzled, and standing straight up on end as if it in its turn were attracted by some invisible magnet above it, the top of his head was not very unlike a lampwick.

" But to be sure it's no business of mine," said Barbox Brothers. " Be what you like."

" Some people, sir," remarked Lamps, in a tone of apology, " are sometimes what they don't like."

"Nobody knows that better than I do," sighed the other. "I have been what I don't like, all my life."

"When I first took, sir," resumed Lamps, "to composing little Comic-Songs —"

Barbox Brothers eyed him with great disfavor.

"— To composing little Comic-Songs — and what was more hard — to singing them afterwards," said Lamps, "it went against the grain at that time, it did indeed."

Something that was not all oil here shining in Lamps's eye, Barbox Brothers looked at the fire, and put a foot on the top bar.

"Why did you do it, then?" he asked, after a short pause; abruptly enough, but in a softer tone. "If you didn't want to do it, why did you do it? Where did you sing them?"

To which Mr. Lamps returned the curious reply: "Bedside."

At this moment Mugby Junction started suddenly, trembled violently, and opened its gas eyes. "She's up! The three forty-two!" Lamps announced excitedly.

The legend "Barbox Brothers" in large white letters on two black surfaces was very soon afterwards trundling on a truck through a silent street, and, when the owner of the legend had shivered on the pavement half an hour, while the porter's knocks at the Inn door woke up the whole town first, and the Inn last, he groped his way into the close air of a shut-up house, and so groped between the sheets of a shut-up bed that seemed to have been expressly refrigerated for him when last made.

The next morning Barbox Brothers took up his hat and walked out, just in time to see, passing along on the opposite side of the

44

way, a man, carrying his day's dinner in a small bundle that might have been larger without suspicion of gluttony, and pelting away towards the Junction at a great pace.

"There's Lamps!" said Barbox Brothers. "And by the bye—"

Ridiculous, surely, that a man so serious should stand rubbing his chin in the street, in a brown study about Comic-Songs.

"Bedside?" said Barbox Brothers, testily. "Sings them at the bedside? Why at the bedside? But it's no business of mine. Let me see. Mugby Junction! Mugby Junction! Where shall I go next? As it came into my head last night when I woke from an uneasy sleep and found myself here, I can go anywhere from here. Where shall I go? I'll go and look at the Junction by daylight. There's no hurry, and I may like the looks of one Line better than another."

But there were so many Lines that Barbox Brothers stood puzzled on the bridge, passing his right hand across the lines on his forehead, which multiplied while he looked down, as if the railway Lines were getting themselves photographed on that sensitive plate.

"I have not made my next move much clearer by this. No hurry. No need to make up my mind to-day, or to-morrow, nor yet the day after. I'll take a walk."

Ascending a gentle hill he came to a few cottages. There, looking about him as a very reserved man might who had never looked about him in his life before, he saw some six or eight young children come merrily trooping and whooping up from one of the cottages, and disperse. But not until they had all turned at the little garden gate and kissed their hands to a face at the upper window; a low window enough, although the upper, for the cottage had but a story of one room above the ground.

Now that the children should do this was nothing; but that they should do this to a face lying on the sill of the open window, turned towards them in a horizontal position, and apparently only a face, was something noticeable. He looked up at the window again. But he could see only a fragile though a very bright face, lying on one cheek on the window sill; the delicate, smiling face of a girl or a woman.

PART II

gesture	relished	diffident	humiliation
fluently	ethereal	perceived	embarrassed
swarthy	emphasis	irresolute	acknowledged
taciturn	passively	deprivation	misinterpreted

He walked on, turned back, passed the window again, shyly glanced up again. There was no change. He struck off by a winding branch road at the top of the hill, keeping the cottages in view, and worked his way round at a distance so as to come out once more into the main road and so be obliged to pass the cottages again. The face still lay on the window sill, but not so much inclined towards him. And now there was a pair of delicate hands, too. They had the action of performing on some musical instrument, and yet it produced no sound that reached his ears.

"Mugby Junction must be the maddest place in England," said Barbox Brothers, pursuing his way down the hill. "The

46

first thing I find here is a railway porter who composes Comic-Songs to sing at his bedside. The second thing I find here is a face, and a pair of hands playing a musical instrument that *don't* play!"

He relished his walk so well, that he repeated it the next day. He was a little earlier at the cottage than on the day before, and he could hear the children upstairs singing to a regular measure and clapping out the time with their hands.

Then there was the stir of little feet, and the children came trooping and whooping out, as on the previous day. And again, as on the previous day, they all turned at the garden gate, and kissed their hands — evidently to the face on the window sill, though Barbox Brothers from his retired post at the corner could not see it.

But as the children dispersed, he cut off one small straggler, a brown-faced boy with flaxen hair, and said to him : —

" Come here, little one. Tell me, whose house is that?"

The child, with one swarthy arm held up across his eyes, half in shyness, and half ready for defense, said from behind the inside of his elbow : —

" Phœbe's."

" And who," said Barbox Brothers, quite as much embarrassed by his part in the dialogue as the child could possibly be by his, " is Phœbe ?"

To which the child made answer: " Why, Phœbe, of course."

" Phœbe," said the child, " can't be anybody else but Phoebe, can she?"

"No, I suppose not."

"Well," returned the child, "then why did you ask me?"

"What do you do there? Up there in that room where the open window is. What do you do there?"

"Cool," said the child.

"Eh?"

"C-o-o-l," the child repeated in a louder voice, lengthening out the word with a fixed look and great emphasis, as much as to say: "What's the use of your having grown up, if you're such a donkey as not to understand me?"

"Ah! school, school," said Barbox Brothers. "Yes, yes, yes. And Phœbe teaches you?"

The child nodded.

"Good boy."

"Tound it out, have you?" said the child.

"Yes, I have found it out. What would you do with two-pence, if I gave it to you?"

"Pend it."

Barbox Brothers produced the twopence and withdrew in a state of humiliation.

But, seeing the face on the window sill as he passed the cottage, he acknowledged its presence there with a gesture, which was not a nod, not a bow, not a removal of his hat from his head, but was a diffident compromise between or struggle with all three. The eyes in the face seemed amused, or cheered, or both, and the lips modestly said: "Good day to you, sir."

"I find I must stick for a time to Mugby Junction," said

48

Barbox Brothers, "I can't make up my mind yet which iron road to take. In fact, I must get a little accustomed to the Junction before I can decide."

But he did not so wholly devote himself to the study of Mugby Junction as to neglect exercise. On the contrary, he took a walk every day, and always the same walk. But the weather turned cold and wet again, and the window was never open.

At length, after a lapse of some days, there came another streak of fine bright hardy autumn weather. It was a Saturday. The window was open, and the children were gone. Not surprising, this, for he had patiently watched and waited at the corner until they were gone.

"Good day," he said to the face; absolutely getting his hat clear off his head this time.

"Good day to you, sir."

"I am glad you have a fine sky again to look at."

"Thank you, sir. It is kind of you."

"You are an invalid, I fear?"

"No, sir; I have very good health."

"But are you not always lying down?"

"Oh, yes! I am always lying down, because I cannot sit up. But I am not an invalid."

The laughing eyes seemed highly to enjoy his great mistake.

"Would you mind taking the trouble to come in, sir? There is a beautiful view from this window. And you would see that I am not at all ill — being so good as to care."

49

It was said to help him, as he stood irresolute, but evidently desiring to enter, with his diffident hand on the latch of the garden gate. It did help him, and he went in.

The room upstairs was a very clean, white room, with a low roof. Its only inmate lay on a couch that brought her face to a level with the window. The couch was white, too; and her simple dress or wrapper being light blue, like the band around her hair, she had an ethereal look, and a fanciful appearance of lying among clouds. He felt that she instinctively perceived him to be by habit a downcast, taciturn man; it was another help to him to have established that understanding so easily.

There was an awkward constraint upon him, nevertheless, as he touched her hand, and took a chair at the side of her couch.

"I see now," he began, not at all fluently, "how you occupy your hands. Seeing you only from the path outside, I thought you were playing upon something."

She was engaged in very nimbly making lace. A lace pillow lay upon her breast, and the quick movements and changes of her hands upon it as she worked, had given them the action he had misinterpreted.

"That is curious," she answered, with a bright smile, "for I often fancy, myself, that I play tunes while I am at work."

"Have you any musical knowledge?"

She shook her head.

"I think I could pick out tunes if I had any instrument that could be made as handy to me as my lace pillow. But I dare say I deceive myself. At all events, I shall never know."

50

"You have a musical voice. Pardon me; I have heard you sing."

"With the children?" she answered, slightly coloring. "Oh, yes. I sing with the dear children, if it can be called singing."

All this time her hands were busy at her lace pillow. As they still continued so, and as there was a kind of substitute for conversation in the click and play of its pegs, Barbox Brothers took the opportunity of observing her. He guessed her to be thirty. The charm of her transparent face and large bright brown eyes was, not that they were passively resigned, but that they were actively and thoroughly cheerful. Even her busy hands, which of their own thinness alone might have besought compassion, plied their task with a gay courage.

He saw her eyes in the act of rising towards his, and he directed his towards the prospect, saying: "Beautiful indeed!"

"Most beautiful, sir. I have sometimes had a fancy that I should like to sit up, for once, only to try how it looks to an erect head. But what a foolish fancy that would be to encourage! It cannot look more lovely to any one than it does to me."

Her eyes were turned to it as she spoke, with a most delighted admiration and enjoyment. There was not a trace in it of any sense of deprivation.

"And those threads of railway, with their puffs of smoke and steam changing places so fast, make it so lively for me," she went on. "I think of the number of people who *can* go where they wish, on their business, or their pleasure; I remember that the puffs make signs to me that they are actually going while I look; and that enlivens the prospect with abundance of company, if I want company. There is the great Junction, too. I don't see it under the foot of the hill, but I can very often hear it, and I always know it is there. It seems to join me, in a way, to I don't know how many places and things that *I* shall never see."

With an abashed kind. of idea that it might have already joined him to something he had never seen, he said, " Just so."

" And so you see, sir," pursued Phœbe, " I am not the invalid you thought me, and I am very well off indeed."

" You have a happy disposition," said Barbox Brothers.

" Ah! But you should know my father," she replied. " His is the happy disposition! This is my father coming."

PART III

obtuse	interval	expedient	ramifications
offense	protested	interposed	unintelligible
argument	velveteen	comprehended	complimentary

The door opened, and the father paused there.

" Why, Lamps!" exclaimed Barbox Brothers, starting from his chair. " How do you do, Lamps?"

To which Lamps responded: " The gentleman for Nowhere! How do you *do*, sir?"

And they shook hands, to the greatest admiration and surprise of Lamps's daughter.

Arthur Jules Goodman.

"Why, Lamps!" exclaimed Barbox Brothers, starting from his chair.

"I have looked you up half a dozen times since that night," said Barbox Brothers, "but have never found you."

"So I've heard, sir, so I've heard," returned Lamps. "It's your being noticed so often down at the Junction, without taking any train, that has begun to get you the name among us of the gentleman for Nowhere. No offense in my having called you by it when taken by surprise, I hope, sir?"

"None at all. It's as good a name for me as any other you could call me by. But may I ask you a question in the corner here?"

Lamps suffered himself to be led aside from his daughter's couch, by one of the buttons of his velveteen jacket.

"Is this the bedside where you sing your songs?"

Lamps nodded.

The gentleman for Nowhere clapped him on the shoulder, and they faced about again.

"Your daughter tells me," said Barbox Brothers, "that she never sits up."

"No, sir, nor never has done so. You see, her mother, who died when she was a year and two months old, dropped her when a baby, and this happened."

"I wish you would tell me a little more about yourselves," said Barbox Brothers. "I hardly know how to ask it of you, for I am conscious that I have a bad stiff manner, a dull discouraging way with me, but I wish you would."

"With all our hearts, sir," returned Lamps, gayly, for both. "And first of all, that you may know my name —"

54

"Stay!" interposed the visitor, with a slight flush. "What signifies your name! Lamps is name enough for me. I like it. It is bright and expressive. What do I want more!"

"Why to be sure, sir," returned Lamps. "I have in general no other name down at the Junction."

"You are hard-worked, I take for granted?" said Barbox Brothers.

Lamps was beginning, "Not particularly so," when his daughter took him up.

"Oh, yes, sir, he is very hard-worked. He works fourteen, fifteen, eighteen hours a day, and sometimes twenty-four hours at a time."

"And you," said Barbox Brothers, "what with your school, Phœbe, and what with your lace making — "

"But my school is a pleasure to me," she interrupted, opening her brown eyes wider, as if surprised to find him so obtuse. "I began it when I was but a child, because it brought me and other children into company, don't you see? *That* was not work. I carry it on still, because it keeps the children about me. *That* is not work. I do it as love, not as work. Then my lace pillow;" her busy hands had stopped, as if her argument required all her cheerful earnestness, but now went on again at the name; "it goes with my thoughts when I think, and it goes with my tunes when I hum any, and *that's* not work. Why you yourself thought it was music, you know, sir. And so it is, to me."

"Everything is!" cried Lamps, radiantly. "Everything is music to her, sir."

55

"My father is at any rate," said Phœbe, exultingly pointing her thin forefinger at him.

"I say! My dear! you are flattering your father," he protested sparkling.

"No; I am not, sir, I assure you. No; I am not. If you could hear my father sing, you would know I am not. But you will never hear him sing, because he never sings to any one but me. However tired he is, he always sings to me when he comes home. When I lay here long ago, quite a poor little broken doll, he used to sing to me. More than that, he used to make songs, bringing in whatever little jokes we had between us. More than that, he often does so to this day. Oh! I'll tell of you, Father, as the gentleman has asked about you! He is a poet, sir."

"I shouldn't wish the gentleman, my dear," observed Lamps, for the moment turning grave, "to carry away that opinion of your father, because it might look as if I were given to asking the stars in a melancholy manner what they were up to."

"My father," resumed Phœbe, "is always on the bright side, and the good side. You told me just now, I had a happy disposition. How can I help it?"

"Well, but my dear," returned Lamps, "how can *I* help it? Put it to yourself, sir. Look at her. Always as you see her now. Always working—and after all, sir, for but a few shillings a week —always contented, always lively, always interested in others, of all sorts. I said, this moment, she was always as you see her now. So she is, with a difference that comes to much the same. For, when it's my Sunday off and the morning bells have done

56

ringing, I hear the prayers and thanks read in the touchingest way, and I have the hymns sung to me — so soft, sir, that you couldn't hear them out of this room — in notes that seem to me, I am sure, to come from Heaven and go back to it."

" When my father, sir," she said brightly, " tells you about my being interested in other people even though they know nothing about me — which, by the bye, I told you myself, you ought to know how that comes about. That's my father's doing."

" No, it isn't ! " he protested.

" Don't you believe him, sir ; yes, it is. He tells me of everything he sees down at his work. You would be surprised what a quantity he gets together for me every day. He looks into the carriages, and tells me how the ladies are dressed, so that I know all the fashions ! · He looks into the carriages, and tells me what pairs of lovers he sees, and what new-married couples on their wedding trip, so that I know all about that ! He collects chance newspapers and books, so that I have plenty to read ! He tells me about the sick people who are traveling to try to get better, so that I know all about them ! In short, as I began by saying, he tells me everything he sees and makes out, down at his work, and you can't think what a quantity he does see and make out."

" As to the young pairs, married and unmarried," said Lamps, "it's only natural that I should bring home what little I can about *them*, seeing that there's not a couple of either sort in the neighborhood that don't come of their own accord to confide in Phœbe."

She raised her eyes triumphantly to Barbox Brothers, as she said : —

"Indeed, sir, that is true. If I could have got up and gone to church, I don't know how often I should have been a bridesmaid. But if I could have done that, some girls in love might have been jealous of me, and as it is, no girl is jealous of me. And my pillow would not have been half as ready to put the piece of cake under, as I always find it," she added, turning her face on it with a light sigh, and a smile at her father.

Barbox Brothers rose to take his leave, and took it, saying that if Phœbe had no objection, he would come again.

He had muttered that he would come "in the course of his walks." The course of his walks must have been highly favorable to his return, for he returned after an interval of a single day.

"You thought you would never see me any more, I suppose?" he said to Phœbe as he touched her hand, and sat down by her couch.

"Why should I think so?"

"I took it for granted you would mistrust me."

"For granted, sir? Have you been so much mistrusted?"

"I think I am justified in answering yes. But I may have mistrusted, too, on my part; no matter just now. We were speaking of the Junction last time. I have passed hours there since the day before yesterday."

"Are you now the gentleman for Somewhere?" she asked with a smile.

"Certainly for Somewhere; but I don't know yet Where. You would never guess what I am traveling from. Shall I tell you? I am traveling from my birthday."

Her hands stopped in her work, and she looked at him with astonishment.

"Yes," said Barbox Brothers, not quite easy in his chair, "from my birthday. I am to myself an unintelligible book with the earlier chapters all torn out, and thrown away. My childhood had no grace of childhood, my youth had no charm of youth, and what can be expected from such a lost beginning?"

As he paused, she looked at him; but only shook her head as being quite at a loss.

"This is unintelligible to your happy disposition," he pursued; "I knew it would be, and I am glad it is. However, on this travel of mine (in which I mean to pass the rest of my days), I stopped, as you heard from your father, at the Junction here. The extent of its ramifications quite confused me as to whither I should go *from* here. I have not yet settled, being still perplexed among so many roads. What do you think I mean to do? How many of the branching roads can you see from your window?"

Looking out, full of interest, she answered, "Seven."

"Seven," said Barbox Brothers, watching her with a grave smile. "Well! I propose to myself at once to reduce the gross number to those very seven, and gradually to fine them down to one — the most promising for me — and to take that."

"But how will you know, sir, which *is* the most promising?" she asked, with her brightened eyes roving over the view.

"Ah!" said Barbox Brothers, with another grave smile, considerably improving in his ease of speech. "To be sure; in this way. The gentleman for Nowhere must become still better known at the Junction. He shall continue to explore it, until he attaches something that he has seen, heard, or found out, at the head of each of the seven roads, to the road itself. And so his choice of a road shall be determined by his choice among his discoveries."

Her hand still busy, she again glanced at the prospect, as if it comprehended something that had not been in it before, and laughed as if it yielded her new pleasure. ·

"But I must not forget," said Barbox Brothers, "to ask a favor. I want your help in this expedient of mine. I want to bring you what I pick up at the heads of the seven roads that you lie here looking out at, and to compare notes with you about it. May I? They say two heads are better than one. I should say myself that probably depends upon the heads concerned. But I am quite sure, though we are so newly acquainted, that your head and your father's have found out better things, Phœbe, than ever mine of itself has discovered."

She gave him her sympathetic right hand in perfect rapture with his proposal, and eagerly and gratefully thanked him.

"That's well!" said Barbox Brothers. "Again I must not forget to ask a favor. Will you shut your eyes?"

Laughing playfully at the strange nature of the request, she did so.

"Keep them shut," said Barbox Brothers, going softly to the

door, and coming back. "You are on your honor, mind, not to open your eyes until I tell you that you may?"

"Yes! on my honor."

"Good. May I take your lace pillow from you for a minute?"

Still laughing and wondering, she removed her hands from it, and he put it aside.

"Tell me. Did you see the puffs of smoke and steam made by the morning fast train yesterday on road number seven from here?"

"Behind the elm trees and the spire?"

"That's the road," said Barbox Brothers, directing his eyes towards it.

"Yes; I watched them melt away."

"Anything unusual in what they expressed?"

"No!" she answered, merrily.

"Not complimentary to me, for I was in that train. I went — don't open your eyes — to fetch you this, from the great town. It is not half so large as your lace pillow, and lies easily and lightly in its place. These little keys are like the keys of a miniature piano. May you pick out delightful music from it, my dear! For the present — you may open your eyes now — good-by!"

In his embarrassed way, he closed the door upon himself and only saw, in doing so, that she took the present to her bosom and caressed it. The glimpse gladdened his heart, and yet saddened it.

deduce	incident	brooding	confirming
Trivits	elevated	tributary	authorities
forcible	external	researches	intervention
venture	hazarded	preference	consumption
vaguely	commenced	culminated	Constantinople

With good will and earnest purpose, the gentleman for Nowhere began, on the very next day, his researches at the heads of the seven roads.

It must be admitted, however, that Barbox Brothers by no means hurried himself. For he had connected this interest with this road, or that interest with the other, but could deduce no reason from it for giving any road the preference. Consequently, when the last council was held, that part of the business stood, in the end, exactly where it had stood in beginning.

" But, sir," remarked Phœbe, " we have only six roads after all. Is the seventh road dumb ?"

" The seventh road ? Oh !" said Barbox Brothers, rubbing his chin, " that is the road I took, you know, when I went to get your little present. That is *its* story, Phœbe."

" Would you mind taking that road again, sir ?" she asked with hesitation.

" Not in the least; it is a great highroad after all."

" I should like you to take it," returned Phœbe, with a persuasive smile, "for the love of that little present which must ever be so dear to me. I should like you to take it, because that road can never be again like any other road to me. I should like you to take it in remembrance of your having made me so much happier! If you leave me by the road you traveled when you went to do me this great kindness, I shall feel, lying here watching at my window, as if it must conduct you to a prosperous end, and bring you back some day."

"It shall be done, my dear; it shall be done."

So at last the gentleman for Nowhere took a ticket for Somewhere, and his destination was the great town.

He had loitered so long about the Junction that it was the eighteenth of December when he left it. "High time," he reflected, as he seated himself in the train, "that I started in earnest! Only one clear day remains between me and the day I am running away from. I'll push onward for the hill-country to-morrow. I'll go to Wales."

But surely, here not far ahead, must be the great town. This crashing and clashing that the train was undergoing could mean nothing less than approach to the great station. It did mean nothing less. After some stormy flashes of town lightning, there came the thundering in at the journey's end.

Having seen his portmanteaus safely housed in the hotel that he chose, and having appointed his dinner hour, Barbox Brothers went out for a walk in the busy streets. And now it began to be suspected by him that Mugby Junction was a Junction of many branches, invisible as well as visible, and had joined him to an endless number of byways. For, whereas he would, but a little while ago, have walked these streets blindly brooding, he now had eyes and thoughts for a new external world. How the many toiling people lived, and loved, and died; how wonderful it was to consider the various trainings of eye and hand, the nice distinctions of sight and touch, that separated them into classes of workers!

These considerations, and a host of such, made his walk a memorable one. "I too am but a little part of a great whole," he began to think; "and to be serviceable to myself and others, or to be happy, I must cast my interest into, and draw it out of, the common stock."

Although he had arrived by noon at his journey's end for the day, he had since insensibly walked about the town so far and so long that the lamplighters were now at their work in the streets, and the shops were sparkling up brilliantly. Thus reminded to turn towards his quarters, he was in the act of doing so, when a very little hand crept into his, and a very little voice said: —

"Oh! If you please, I am lost!"

He looked down, and saw a very little, fair-haired girl.

"Yes," she said, confirming her words with a serious nod. "I am indeed. I am lost."

Greatly perplexed, he stopped, looked about him for help, and said, bending low, "Where do you live, my child?"

"I don't know where I live," she returned. "I am lost."

"What is your name?"

"Polly."

" What is your other name ? "

The reply was prompt, but unintelligible.

Imitating the sound, as he caught it, he hazarded the guess, " Trivits ? "

" Oh, no ! " said the child. " Nothing like that."

" Say it again, little one."

An unpromising business. For this time it had quite a different sound.

He made the venture, " Paddens ? "

" Oh, no ! " said the child. " Nothing like that."

" Ah ! I think," said Barbox Brothers, with a desperate air of resignation, " that we had better give it up."

" But I am lost," said the child, nestling her little hand more closely in his, " and you'll take care of me, won't you ? "

" Lost ! " he repeated, looking down at the child. " I am sure *I* am. What is to be done ! "

" Where do you live ? " asked the child, looking up at him wistfully.

" Over there," he answered, pointing vaguely in the direction of the hotel.

" Hadn't we better go there ? " said the child.

" Really," he replied, " I don't know but that we had."

So they set off, hand in hand. He, through comparison of himself against his little companion, with a clumsy feeling on him as if he had just developed into a foolish giant. She, clearly elevated in her own tiny opinion by having helped him so neatly out of his embarrassment.

"We are going to have dinner when we get there, I suppose?" said Polly.

"Well," he rejoined, "I — yes, I suppose we are."

"Do you like your dinner?" asked the child.

"Why, on the whole," said Barbox Brothers, "yes, I think I do."

"I do mine," said Polly. "Have you any brothers and sisters?"

"No; have you?"

"Mine are dead."

"Oh!" said Barbox Brothers.

"What," she asked, turning her soft hand coaxingly in his, "are you going to do to amuse me, after dinner?"

"Upon my soul, Polly," exclaimed Barbox Brothers, very much at a loss, "I have not the slightest idea!"

"Then I'll tell you what," said Polly. "Have you any cards at your house?"

"Plenty," said Barbox Brothers, in a boastful vein.

"Very well. Then I'll build houses, and you shall look at me. You mustn't blow, you know."

"Oh, no!" said Barbox Brothers. "No, no, no! No blowing. Blowing's not fair."

He flattered himself that he had said this pretty well for an idiotic monster; but the child, instantly perceiving the awkwardness of his attempt to adapt himself to her level, utterly destroyed his hopeful opinion of himself by saying, compassionately, "What a funny man you are!"

Feeling, after this melancholy failure, as if every minute he grew bigger and heavier in person, and weaker in mind, Barbox Brothers gave himself up for a bad job. No giant ever submitted more meekly to be led in triumph by an all-conquering Jack, than he to be bound in slavery to Polly.

"Do you know any stories?" she asked him.

He was reduced to the humiliating confession, "No."

"What a dunce you must be, mustn't you?" said Polly.

He was reduced to the humiliating confession, "Yes."

"Would you like me to teach you a story? But you must remember it, you know, and be able to tell it right to somebody else afterwards."

He professed that it would afford him the highest mental gratification to be taught a story, and that he would humbly endeavor to retain it in his mind. Whereupon Polly, giving her hand a new little turn in his, expressive of settling down for enjoyment, commenced a long romance, of which every relishing clause began with the words: "So this" or "And so this." As, "So this boy;" or, "So this fairy;" or "And so this pie was four yards round, and two yards and a quarter deep." The interest of the romance was derived from the intervention of this fairy to punish this boy for having a greedy appetite. To achieve which purpose, this fairy made this pie, and this boy ate and ate and ate, and his cheeks swelled and swelled and swelled. There were many tributary circumstances, but the forcible interest culminated in the total consumption of this pie, and the bursting of this boy. Truly he was a fine sight, Barbox Brothers, with serious attentive face, an ear bent down, much jostled on the pavements of the busy town, but afraid of losing a single incident of the story, lest he should be examined in it by and by and found deficient.

Thus they arrived at the hotel. And there he had to say at the office, and said awkwardly enough, "I have found a little girl."

The whole establishment turned out to look at the little girl. Nobody knew her; nobody could make out her name, as she set it forth — except one chambermaid, who said it was Constantinople, which it wasn't.

"I will dine with my young friend in a private room," said Barbox Brothers to the hotel authorities, "and perhaps you will be so good as to let the police know that the pretty baby is here. I suppose she is sure to be inquired for, soon, if she has not been already. Come along, Polly."

PART V

epoch	ecstatic	program	consultation
diffuse	detected	deference	sheepishness
truism	pinafores	languidly	transcendent
vestige	execution	assortment	anticipations
ignoble	wheedling	approbation	constitutions
flourish	impending	accumulated	indispensable

Perfectly at ease and peace Polly came along, but, finding the stairs rather stiff work, was carried up by Barbox Brothers. The dinner was a most transcendent success, and the Barbox

68

Brothers' sheepishness, under Polly's directions how to mince her meat for her, and how to diffuse gravy over the plate with a liberal and equal hand, was another fine sight.

"And now," said Polly, "while we are at dinner, you be good, and tell me that story I taught you."

With tremors of a civil service examination on him, and very uncertain indeed, not only as to the epoch at which the pie appeared in history, but also as to the measurements of that indispensable fact, Barbox Brothers made a shaky beginning, but under encouragement did fairly well. There was a want of breadth observable in his rendering of the cheeks, as well as the appetite, of the boy; and there was a certain tameness in his fairy. Still, as the first lumbering performance of a good-humored monster, it passed muster.

"I told you to be good," said Polly, "and you are good, aren't you?"

"I hope so," replied Barbox Brothers.

Such was his deference that Polly, elevated on a platform of sofa cushions in a chair at his right hand, encouraged him with a pat or two on the face from the greasy bowl of her spoon, and even with a gracious kiss. In getting on her feet upon the chair, however, to give him this last reward, she toppled forward among the dishes, and caused him to exclaim as he effected her rescue: "Gracious! Whew! I thought we were in the fire, Polly!"

"What a coward you are, aren't you?" said Polly, when replaced.

"Yes, I am rather nervous," he replied. "Whew! Don't, Polly! Don't flourish your spoon, or you'll go over sideways. Don't tilt up your legs when you laugh, Polly, or you'll go over backwards. Whew! Polly, Polly, Polly," said Barbox Brothers, nearly succumbing to despair, "we are environed with dangers!"

Indeed, he could descry no security from the pitfalls that were yawning for Polly, but in proposing to her, after dinner, to sit upon a stool. So, as peace of mind should go before all, he begged the waiter to wheel aside the table, bring a pack of cards, a couple of footstools, and a screen, and close in Polly and him before the fire, as it were in a snug room within the room. Then, finest sight of all, was Barbox Brothers on his footstool, contemplating Polly as she built successfully, and growing blue in the face with holding his breath, lest he should blow the house down.

"How you stare, don't you?" said Polly, in a houseless pause.

Detected in the ignoble fact, he felt obliged to admit, apologetically, "I am afraid I was looking rather hard at you, Polly."

"Why do you stare?" asked Polly.

"I cannot," he murmured to himself, "recall why; I don't know, Polly."

"You must be a simpleton to do things and not know why, mustn't you?" said Polly.

In spite of which reproof, he looked at the child again, intently, as she bent her head over her card-structure, her rich curls shading her face.

He then went into the building trade as a journeyman under Polly, and they built three stories high, four stories high, even five.

"I say. Who do you think is coming?" asked Polly, rubbing her eyes after tea.

He guessed, "The waiter?"

"No," said Polly, "the dustman. I am getting sleepy."

A new embarrassment for Barbox Brothers!

"I don't think I am going to be fetched to-night," said Polly; "what do you think?"

He thought not, either. After another quarter of an hour, the dustman not merely impending but actually arriving, the chambermaid cheerily undertook that the child should sleep in a comfortable and wholesome room, which she herself would share.

"And I know you will be careful, won't you," said Barbox Brothers, as a new fear dawned upon him, "that she doesn't fall out of bed."

Polly found this so highly entertaining that she was under the necessity of clutching him around the neck with both arms as he sat on his footstool picking up the cards, and rocking him to and fro, with her dimpled chin on his shoulder.

"Oh, what a coward you are, aren't you!" said Polly. "Do *you* fall out of bed?"

"No; not generally, Polly."

"No more do I."

With that, Polly gave him a reassuring hug or two to keep

him going, and then giving that confiding mite of a hand of hers to be swallowed up in the hand of the chambermaid, trotted off, chattering without a vestige of anxiety.

"Hallo!" cried Polly, putting her saucy sunny face in at the door next morning when breakfast was ready, "I thought I was fetched last night?"

"So you were, Polly, but I asked leave to keep you here for the day, and to take you home in the evening."

"Upon my word!" said Polly. "You are very cool, aren't you?"

However, Polly seemed to think it a good idea, and added, "I suppose I must give you a kiss though you *are* cool." The kiss given and taken, they sat down to breakfast in a highly conversational tone.

"Of course, you are going to amuse me?" said Polly.

"Oh, of course!" said Barbox Brothers.

In the pleasurable height of her anticipations, Polly found it indispensable to put down her piece of toast, cross one of her little fat knees over the other, and bring her little fat right hand down into her left hand with a business-like slap. After this gathering of herself together, Polly, by that time, a mere heap of dimples, asked in a wheedling manner, "What are we going to do, you dear old thing?"

"Why, I was thinking," said Barbox Brothers, " — but are you fond of horses, Polly?"

"Ponies, I am," said Polly, "especially when their tails are long. But horses — no — too big, you know."

72

" Well," pursued Barbox Brothers, in a spirit of grave mysterious confidence adapted to the importance of the consultation, "I did see yesterday, Polly, on the walls, pictures of two long-tailed ponies, speckled all over!"

"No, no, no!" cried Polly, in an ecstatic desire to linger on the charming details. "Not speckled all over!"

"Speckled all over. Which ponies jump through hoops—"

"No, no, no!" cried Polly, as before. "They never jump through hoops!"

"Yes, they do. Oh, I assure you they do. And eat pie in pinafores—"

"Ponies eating pie in pinafores!" said Polly. "What a story-teller you are, aren't you?"

"Upon my honor!—and fire off guns."

"And I was thinking," pursued Barbox Brothers, "that if you and I were to go to the Circus where these ponies are, it would do our constitutions good."

"Does that mean, amuse us?" inquired Polly. "What long words you use, don't you?

"That means amuse us. That is exactly what it means. There are many other wonders besides the ponies, and we shall see them all. Ladies and gentlemen in spangled dresses, and elephants and lions and tigers."

Polly became observant of the teapot, with a curled-up nose indicating some uneasiness of mind. "They never get out, of course," she remarked as a mere truism.

"The elephants and lions and tigers?—Oh, dear no!"

"Oh, dear no!" said Polly. "And of course nobody's afraid of the ponies shooting anybody."

"Not the least in the world."

"No, no! not the least in the world," said Polly.

"I was also thinking," proceeded Barbox Brothers, "that if we were to look in at the toy-shop, to choose a doll ——"

"Not dressed!" cried Polly, with a clap of her hands. "No, no, no! not dressed!"

"Full dressed. Together with a house, and all things necessary for housekeeping ——"

Polly gave a little scream, and seemed in danger of falling into a swoon of bliss. "What a darling you are!" she languidly exclaimed, leaning back in her chair. "Come and be hugged, or I must come and hug you."

This grand program was carried into execution with the utmost rigor of the law. Polly in the magic warehouse, with a doll as large as herself under each arm, and a neat assortment of some twenty more on view upon the counter, did indeed present a spectacle of indecision, but the light cloud passed. The lovely specimen oftenest chosen, oftenest rejected, and finally abided by, was graciously pleased to express her entire approbation of the Circus, and so was Polly; for the ponies *were* speckled, and brought down nobody when they fired.

But by evening Polly had become unable to look upon such accumulated joys with waking eyes, and had withdrawn her consciousness into the wonderland Paradise of a child's sleep. "Sleep, Polly, sleep," said Barbox Brothers, as her head dropped

74

on his shoulder; " you shall not fall out of this bed, easily, at any rate!'"

What rustling piece of paper he took from his pocket, and carefully folded into the bosom of Polly's frock, shall not be mentioned. He said nothing about it, and nothing shall be said about it. They drove to a modest suburb of the great town, and stopped at a small house. " Do not wake the child," said Barbox Brothers, softly, to the driver, " I will carry her in as she is."

He kissed her again and again, and gave her up gently to both her parents, and went out.

But he went not to Wales. No, he never went to Wales. He went straightway for another stroll about the town, and he looked in upon the people at their work, and at their play, here, there, everywhere, and where not. For he was Barbox Brothers and Company now, and had taken thousands of partners into the solitary firm.

He had at length got back to his hotel room, and was standing before his fire, when he heard the town clocks striking, and, referring to his watch, found the evening to have so slipped away, that they were striking twelve. As he put up his watch again, his eyes met those of his reflection in the chimney-glass.

" Why it's your birthday already," he said, smiling. " You are looking very well. I wish you many happy returns of the day."

He had never before bestowed that wish upon himself. " It alters the whole case of running away from one's birthday! It's a thing to explain to Phœbe. Besides, here is quite a long story to tell her, that has sprung out of the road with no story. I'll go back, instead of going on."

THE ARROW AND THE SONG

Henry Wadsworth Longfellow

I shot an arrow into the air,
It fell to earth, I knew not where;
For, so swiftly it flew, the sight
Could not follow it in its flight.

I breathed a song into the air,
It fell to earth, I knew not where,
For who has sight so keen and strong,
That it can follow the flight of song?

Long, long afterwards, in an oak
I found the arrow, still unbroke;
And the song, from beginning to end,
I found again in the heart of a friend.

Robert Burns

| quaint | bulrushes | exquisite | constructed |
| annually | monument | enshrined | contributions |

Robert Burns, the national poet of Scotland, was born in 1759, in a small clay cottage, which his father's own hands had constructed, about a mile and a half south of Ayr. It is said that more than thirty thousand persons

ROBERT BURNS.

annually visit this low, whitewashed cottage with its quaint windows and thatched roof in which the great poet first saw the light.

Robert Burns was the son of a poor farmer, and many of his best songs came to him when following the plow. One beautiful little gem is addressed "To a Mouse," on turning one up in her nest with the plow in November; and another is addressed "To a Mountain Daisy," on turning one down with the plow in April.

He loved the hills, the streams, and the flowers of his native land, and the songs that he wrote about them have enshrined him not only in the hearts of his countrymen but also in the hearts of the entire English-speaking race. Emerson says: "Every man's, every boy's, every girl's head carries snatches of his songs, and they say them by heart, and what is strangest of all, they never learned them from a book, but from mouth to mouth. The wind whispers them, the birds whistle them, and the corn, barley, and bulrushes hoarsely rustle them."

Although it is difficult for many readers to understand the Scotch dialect, Burns' poems are familiar to all students of literature. "Auld Lang Syne," with its exquisite lines on friendship, and "A Man's a Man for a' That," with its splendid appreciation of man's true worth, will live forever.

Robert Burns died in 1796, at the early age of thirty-seven years, but he still lives in the hearts and the memories of all who sing his songs. Near the banks of the Doon upon a lovely hillside stands a monument to his memory. It cost nearly seventeen thousand dollars, and was paid for largely by sixpenny and shilling contributions from the poor.

MY HEART'S IN THE HIGHLANDS

Robert Burns

valor   straths   torrents

My heart's in the Highlands, my heart is not here;
My heart's in the Highlands a-chasing the deer;
Chasing the wild deer and following the roe,
My heart's in the Highlands wherever I go.

78

Farewell to the Highlands, farewell to the North,
The birthplace of valor, the country of worth;
Wherever I wander, wherever I rove,
The hills of the Highlands forever I love.

Farewell to the mountains high covered with snow;
Farewell to the straths and green valleys below;
Farewell to the forests and wild hanging woods;
Farewell to the torrents and loud-pouring floods.

My heart's in the Highlands, my heart is not here,
My heart's in the Highlands a-chasing the deer;
Chasing the wild deer and following the roe,
My heart's in the Highlands wherever I go.

PLEASURES

ROBERT BURNS

poppies   borealis

But pleasures are like poppies spread,
You seize the flow'r, its bloom is shed;
Or like the snow falls in the river,
A moment white — then melts forever;
Or like the borealis race,
That flit ere you can point their place;
Or like the rainbow's lovely form
Evanishing amid the storm.

—From "Tam O'Shanter."

SCOTIA

Robert Burns

coronets   contagion

O Scotia! my dear, my native soil!
   For whom my warmest wish to Heaven is sent!
Long may thy hardy sons of rustic toil
   Be blest with health, and peace, and sweet content!
   And Oh! may Heaven their simple lives prevent
From luxury's contagion, weak and vile!
   Then, howe'er crowns and coronets be rent,
   A virtuous populace may rise the while,
And stand a wall of fire around their much-lov'd isle.

                — From " The Cotter's Saturday Night."

FLOW GENTLY, SWEET AFTON

Robert Burns

braes   theme   primroses   resounds

Flow gently, sweet Afton, among thy green braes,
Flow gently, I'll sing thee a song in thy praise;
My Mary's asleep by thy murmuring stream,
Flow gently, sweet Afton, disturb not her dream.

Thou stock-dove whose echo resounds thro' the glen,
Ye wild whistling blackbirds in yon thorny den,
Thou green crested lapwing, thy screaming forbear,
I charge you disturb not my slumbering fair.

How lofty, sweet Afton, thy neighboring hills,
Far mark'd with the courses of clear, winding rills;
There daily I wander as noon rises high,
My flocks and my Mary's sweet cot in my eye.

How pleasant thy banks and green valleys below,
Where wild in the woodlands the primroses blow;
There oft, as mild ev'ning weeps over the lea,
The sweet-scented birk shades my Mary and me.

Thy crystal stream, Afton, how lovely it glides,
And winds by the cot where my Mary resides;
How wanton thy waters her snowy feet lave,
As gathering sweet flow'rets she stems thy clear wave.

Flow gently, sweet Afton, among thy green braes,
Flow gently, sweet river, the theme of my lays;
My Mary's asleep by thy murmuring stream,
Flow gently, sweet Afton, disturb not her dream.

WHO WROTE "THE ARABIAN NIGHTS"?

Donald G. Mitchell

edict	Sultan	deceitful	sulphurous
Persia	Aladdin	narration	enchanting
Genius	Ali-Baba	abolished	fascinating
Cracow	murderous	manuscript	morocco-bound

Who knows? You could never guess who wrote "The
Arabian Nights," for nobody knows when those stories were first

written. It seems very odd that a book should be made, and no one be able to tell when it was made. Yet it is even so with the book we are talking of.

More than two hundred years ago, a learned Frenchman found an old manuscript written in the language of Arabia, and called "The Thousand and One Nights." He translated it into his own language, and the schoolboys throughout France all came to know the wonderful stories of Aladdin and of Ali-Baba.

But why the title of "The Thousand and One Nights"? I will tell you why. And in telling you why, I shall tell you a story; and this is the way it runs : —

Once there lived a wicked Sultan of Persia who had many wives.

Well, this old Sultan found that his wives were deceitful, and he vowed that he would cut off all chance of their sinning by making an end of them. So it happened that whatever new wife he married one day, he killed upon the next.

You will think that the brides were foolish to marry him; but all the women of the East were slaves, and had to obey whatever orders the Sultan might make.

It happened that this old Sultan had a chief officer under him who carried out all his murderous orders, and who was horrified by the cruelties he had to commit. And this same officer had a beautiful and accomplished daughter who was even more horrified than her father ; and she plotted how she might stop the bloody actions of the Sultan.

She could not meet him, and could hope to win no influence

over him, except by becoming his bride. But if she became his bride, she would have but one day to live. So, at least, thought her sister and her father.

She, of course, found it very hard to win the consent of her father to her plan; but at last she succeeded, and so arranged matters that the wicked Sultan should command her to be his bride.

At last the marriage day came, and the officer was in an agony of grief and alarm. The morning after the marriage he waited for the usual order for the execution of the innocent bride; but to his surprise the order was postponed to the following day.

This bride was most winning of speech, and a most charming story-teller. And on the day of her marriage she had commenced the telling of a most interesting story to her husband, and she had so artfully timed it, and measured out its length, that, when the hour came for the Sultan to set about his cares of office, she should be at its most interesting part.

The Sultan had been so delighted by her interesting story and was so eager to hear the rest of it that he put off the execution in order to hear the end of the story on the following night.

And so rich was the narration, and so great was the art of the princess, that she kept alive the curiosity and wonder of the Sultan, day after day, and week after week, and month after month, until her fascinating stories had lasted for a thousand and one nights.

If you count up these, you will find that they make a period of two years and nine months, during which time she had put off the order for her execution.

In the meantime she had so won her husband that he abolished his cruel edict forever, on condition that from time to time she should tell over again those enchanting stories. And the stories she told on those thousand and one nights, and which have been told since in every language thousands and thousands of times, are the tales of "The Arabian Nights."

If this account is not all true, it is at least as true as the stories are.

But, after all, the question is not answered as to who wrote "The Arabian Nights." I doubt if it ever will be answered truly. Who cares, indeed? I know well I cared or thought nothing about the authorship in those old school days when I caught my first reading of Aladdin and the Wonderful Lamp.

What a night it was! What a feast! I think I could have kissed the hand that wrote it.

A little red morocco-bound book it was, with gilt edges to the leaves, that I had borrowed from Tom Spooner; and Tom Spooner's aunt had lent it to him, and she thought all the world of it, and had covered it in brown paper, and I mustn't soil it, or dog's-ear it. And I sat down with it — how well I remember! — at a little square-legged red table, and read about the sulphurous clouds rolling up round the wonderful lamp, and the Genius coming forth in smoke and flames!

What delight! If I could only fall in with an old peddler with a rusty lamp, — such as Aladdin's, — wouldn't I rub it!

And with my elbows fast on the little red table, and my knees fast against the square legs, I thought what I would order the Genius to do, if I ever had a chance: A week's holiday to begin with; Saturday afternoons should come twice a week — at the very least; turkey with stuffing every day except oyster day. I would have a sled, brought by the Genius, that would beat Ben Brace's "Reindeer" he bragged so much about, — by two rods at least. I would have a cavern, like the salt mines in Cracow, Poland, as pictured in my geography; only, instead of salt, it should be all rock-candy; and I would let in clever fellows and pretty girls, and the homely ones, too — well, as often as every Wednesday.

Ah, well-a-day! we never come to the ownership of such caverns! We never find a peddler with the sort of lamp that will bring any sort of riches — with wishing.

But, there is a Genius that will come to any boy's command, and will work out amazing things for him all through boyhood and all through life; and his name is — Industry.

— From "About Old Story-Tellers"; published by Charles Scribner's Sons.

ALADDIN, OR THE WONDERFUL LAMP

PART I

| niche | variety | consisted |
| liquor | incense | Mustapha |

In one of the large cities of China, there once lived a boy named Aladdin. He was the son of a poor tailor, who could hardly, by his daily labor, maintain himself and his family, which consisted only of his wife and son.

Aladdin was a very careless and idle boy. He was disobedient to his father and mother, and would go out early in the morning and stay out all day playing in the streets and public places with idle children of his own age.

When he was old enough to learn a trade, his father took him into his own shop, and taught him how to use the needle; but all his father's endeavors to keep him to his work were vain, for no sooner was his back turned, than the boy was gone for the day. When Aladdin was about fifteen years old, his father, Mustapha, died, leaving him in the care of his mother. But he still continued his foolish ways, and his mother was forced to spin cotton night and day in order to keep herself and him.

One day while Aladdin was playing in the street, a strange-looking man who was going by stopped and looked at him. This stranger was a famous African magician, who had arrived from Africa only a few days before. The magician, observing in Aladdin's countenance something which assured him that he was a fit boy for his purpose, artfully inquired his name and character of some persons standing near. And when he had learned all he desired to know, he went in among the crowd of lads, clapped his hand on Aladdin's shoulder, and said, "My good lad, art thou not the son of Mustapha, the tailor?"

"Yes, sir," said Aladdin; "but my father has been dead a long time."

The African magician then threw his arms about Aladdin's neck and kissed him, saying, with tears in his eyes, "I am your uncle. Your worthy father was my own brother. You are so like my dear brother that I knew you at first sight." Then he gave Aladdin a handful of money, and said: "Give my love to your mother, and tell her that I will visit her to-morrow, that I may see where my good brother lived and died."

Pleased with the money, Aladdin ran home to his mother. "Mother," said he, "I have just seen a man who says that he is my uncle and my father's brother. He cried and kissed me when I told him that my father was dead; he gave me some money, and sent his love to you, and promised to come and pay you a visit, that he might see the house my father lived and died in."

"Indeed, my child," replied his mother, "your father had no brother, and so you have no uncle."

The next day the magician found Aladdin playing in the streets again; and embracing him as before, put two pieces of gold into his hand and said to him: "Carry this to your mother. Tell her to get us something good for supper, and that I will come to see you to-night; but you must first show me where you live."

Aladdin showed the African magician the house, and carried the two pieces of gold to his mother. His mother went out and bought provisions, and then spent nearly the whole day in preparing the supper. And just as they had begun to fear that he might not find the house, the African magician knocked at the door and came in, bringing wine and fruits of every sort. After a few words of greeting to them both, he asked them to show him the sofa on which his brother, Mustapha, used to sit; and when they had done so, he exclaimed, with tears in his eyes: "My poor brother! how unhappy I am not to have come soon enough to give you one last embrace!"

As soon as they had sat down to supper, the magician said to Aladdin's mother: "My good sister, do not be surprised at your never having seen me during all the time that you were married to my brother, Mustapha. I have been out of this country for more than forty years, and during that time I traveled to see the wonders of distant countries, and finally made my home in Africa." Then turning toward Aladdin, he said, "Well, Aladdin, what business do you follow?"

At this question Aladdin hung down his head, and was not a little abashed when his mother said, "Aladdin is an idle boy; his father tried to teach him his trade, but could not succeed; and since his death, in spite of all that I can say to him, he does nothing but idle away his time in the streets, so that I despair of his ever coming to any good."

With these words the poor woman burst into tears, and the magician, turning to Aladdin, said, "This is not well, Nephew; you must think of helping yourself and getting your livelihood, and I will help you as far as I can. There are many different trades; perhaps you do not like your father's, and would prefer another; I will endeavor to help you. If you do not wish to learn any trade, I will take a shop for you, furnish it with all sorts of fine stuffs and linens; and then with the money you make you can buy more goods, and live in an honorable way. Tell me frankly what you think of my proposal; you shall always find me ready to keep my word."

This plan just suited Aladdin, who hated work. He thought that there was very little labor in keeping a shop, and so he told his uncle that this would suit him better than anything else.

" Well, then," said the magician, " I will take you with me to-morrow, clothe you as handsomely as the best merchants in the city, then we will open a shop."

Aladdin's mother no longer doubted that the magician was her husband's brother. She thanked him very heartily, and begged Aladdin to render himself worthy of the good fortune promised by his kind uncle.

Soon after supper the magician took his leave. But he came again the next day, as he had promised, and took Aladdin with him to a merchant, who sold all sorts of clothing for different ages and ranks, and a variety of fine stuffs; the magician then told Aladdin to choose the suits which he preferred.

When Aladdin found himself so handsomely clothed, he thanked his uncle, who thus addressed him: " As you are soon to be a merchant, it is proper you should visit some of the shops and become acquainted with them." He then showed him some of the largest and finest of them, and gave him a merry feast in the evening. When he brought Aladdin home to his mother at night, and she saw him so well dressed, she was transported with joy, and bestowed a thousand blessings upon the magician.

The next morning Aladdin got up and dressed himself very early, so impatient was he to see his uncle. Presently he saw him coming, and ran to meet him. The magician greeted him very kindly : " Come, my good boy," he said with a smile ; " we will spend the day in the country, but to-morrow we will purchase the shop." So away they walked through the gardens and palaces outside one of the gates of the city. Each palace seemed more beautiful than the last, and Aladdin did nothing but exclaim at their beauty ; and so his uncle, by degrees, led him on farther and farther into the country. They had gone very far before Aladdin thought the morning even half gone.

They rested by a fountain to eat the cakes and fruit which they had brought with them. Then they went on again, still farther into the country, till they reached a place between two mountains of equal size, where the work was to be done that had brought the magician from Africa to China.

" We will go no farther now," said he to Aladdin. " I will show you here some strange things which no one but you has ever seen. I am now going to strike a light, and in the meantime, you gather up all the loose dry sticks you can find, to kindle a fire with."

Aladdin found so many dry sticks that he soon collected a great heap. The magician then set them on fire ; and when they were in a blaze, he threw in some incense, and spoke several magical words, which Aladdin did not understand.

A dense smoke rose up while the magician was speaking the mysterious words. At the same instant, the earth opened just

90

before the magician, and they both saw a stone in which was fixed a brass ring. Aladdin was so frightened that he would have run away, but the magician held him. "Do not be afraid, Aladdin," said the magician. "I shall ask nothing but for you to obey me promptly, if you would have the good things I intend for you. Under this stone there is a treasure that will make you richer than the greatest monarch on earth. No one but yourself may lift this stone or enter the cave; so you must do instantly whatever I command, for this is a matter of great importance to both of us."

"Well, Uncle, what is to be done?" said Aladdin, losing his fear. "Command me; I am ready to obey you."

"Take hold of the ring and lift up that stone."

"Indeed, Uncle, I am not strong enough; you must help me."

"No," said the magician; "if I help you, we shall be able to do nothing. Take hold of the ring and lift it up; you will find that it will come easily." Aladdin obeyed, and to his great surprise raised the stone with ease, and lifted it on one side.

When the stone was pulled up there appeared a staircase, about four feet deep, leading to a door. "Descend those steps and open that door," said the magician. "It will lead you into a palace divided into three great halls. In each of these halls you will see large bronze vases full of gold and silver, but you must not touch any of it; and above all things, do not touch the walls, even with your clothes. If you do, you will die instantly.

"At the end of the third hall you will find a door opening into a garden planted with trees loaded with fine fruit. Walk directly across the garden to a terrace, where you will see a niche before you, and in the niche you will see a lighted lamp. Take the lamp down and put it out. When you have thrown away the wick and poured out the liquor, put the lamp in your waistband, and bring it to me. Do not be afraid that the liquor will spoil your clothes, for it is not oil, and the lamp will be dry as soon as the liquor is thrown out."

PART II

ALADDIN FINDS THE WONDERFUL LAMP

hideous	deceived	amethysts
prudent	emeralds	turquoises
dungeon	sapphires	pomegranates

When the magician had given these directions, he took a ring from his finger and put it on one of Aladdin's, saying, "This is a charm against all evil, so long as you obey me. Go boldly, and we shall both be rich all our lives."

Aladdin went down, found all to be just as the magician had said, and carefully obeyed his orders. When he had put the lamp into his waistband, he returned to the garden to look at the fruit which he had seen as he passed along. Each tree bore fruits of a different color. The white were pearls; the sparkling and transparent were diamonds; the deep red were rubies; the green, emeralds; the blue, turquoises; the violet, amethysts; those tinted with yellow, sapphires. All were of the largest size, and more perfect than had ever been seen before in the whole world. These fruits were really precious jewels, but Aladdin, not knowing their great value, would have preferred figs, grapes, or pomegranates. But as he had his uncle's permission, he decided to gather some of each kind. He filled the two purses his uncle had given him, and he also filled the skirts of his vest.

W. L. Haskell.

THE AFRICAN MAGICIAN WAS DETERMINED THAT HE WOULD HAVE THE LAMP BEFORE HE WOULD HELP ALADDIN UP.

He then returned with the greatest care, and found the magician anxiously waiting for him.

As soon as Aladdin saw his uncle, he said, " Pray, Uncle, lend me your hand to help me out."

"Give me the lamp, first," replied the magician, "as it will only hinder you."

"Indeed, Uncle, I cannot give it to you now, but I will as soon as I am up. It is not at all in my way."

The African magician was determined that he would have the lamp before he would help him up; but Aladdin refused to give it up till he was out of the cave. This drove the magician into such a rage that he threw more incense into the fire, spoke two magic words, and instantly the stone moved back into its place, with the earth over it, as it had been when they first reached the spot.

Aladdin now saw that he had been deceived by one who was not his uncle, but a cruel enemy. The fact is, this magician had learned from his magic books about the secret and value of this wonderful lamp, which would make him richer than any earthly ruler if it were given into his hands by another person. He had chosen Aladdin for this purpose, and when his scheme failed, he set out immediately to return to Africa; but he did not go back to the town, that none might ask him what had become of the boy.

When Aladdin found himself buried alive, he called aloud a thousand times to his uncle, telling him he was ready to give him the lamp. But his cries were useless; the earth was closed above him, and also the palace door below him. His cries and tears brought him no help; and he sat down upon the step of his dungeon without the least hope ever again to see the light of day.

In this great emergency he said: "There is no strength or power but in the great high God;" and in joining his hands to pray, he happened to rub the ring which the magician had put upon his finger. Instantly a Genius of frightful aspect appeared, and said : " What wouldst thou have ? I am ready to obey thee. I serve him who possesses the ring on thy finger; I, and the other slaves of that ring."

At another time Aladdin would have been frightened at the sight of such an extraordinary figure, but the danger he was in made him answer without hesitation, " Whoever thou art, deliver me from this place."

He had no sooner spoken these words than he found himself outside the cave, of which no sign was to be seen on the surface of the earth. He lost no time in making his way home, where he fainted from weakness; but as soon as he recovered, he told his mother all that had happened to him.

They were both very bitter against the cruel magician, but this did not prevent Aladdin from sleeping until late the next morning.

When Aladdin awoke, his first thought was that he was very hungry, and that he would like some breakfast. " Alas, my child," replied his mother, " I have not a morsel of bread to give you ; but I have a little cotton which I have spun. I will go and sell it and buy something for our dinner."

" Keep your cotton, Mother," said Aladdin, " for another time, and give me the lamp which I brought with me yesterday. I will go and sell it, and the money I get for it will serve for both breakfast and dinner, and perhaps supper, too."

" Here it is," said his mother, " but it is very dirty. If I rub it clean, I believe it will be worth more money." She took some fine sand and water to clean it; but she had no sooner begun to rub it, than a hideous Genius of great size appeared before her, and said in a voice of thunder: " What wouldst thou have? I am ready to obey thee as thy slave, and the slave of all those who have that lamp in their hands; I, and the other slaves of the lamp."

Aladdin's mother was so terrified at the sight that she fainted. But the boy, who had already seen a Genius in the cave, did not lose his presence of mind. He took the lamp out of his mother's hand, and said in a firm tone of voice, " I am hungry; bring me something to eat."

The Genius disappeared immediately, and returned in an instant with a large silver tray, holding twelve covered silver dishes filled with tempting food, six large white cakes, two skins of wine, and two silver cups. All these were placed upon a carpet, and the Genius disappeared before Aladdin's mother had recovered from her swoon.

When Aladdin's mother was herself again, she was much surprised to see the great treat. They both satisfied their hunger, and still there was food enough for the rest of the day. This they put aside, and Aladdin's mother made him tell her all that had passed between him and the Genius during the time that she was in a swoon. The simple woman thought it all a dangerous and wicked business and begged Aladdin to sell both the lamp and the ring; but he persuaded her to let him keep both on the condition that she should have nothing to do with the Genius again.

When they had eaten all the food left from the feast that the

Genius brought, Aladdin sold the silver plates one by one to a dealer, who cheated him by paying only a small part of their value, and yet made the boy think himself rich. At last he sold the tray; and when the money it brought was spent, he rubbed the lamp again. Again the Genius appeared, and provided the mother and son with another feast and with other silver dishes. These kept them in money for some time longer. In this way they lived happily for some years, for Aladdin now behaved with the greatest wisdom and prudence. He took care to visit the principal shops and public places, speaking only with wise and prudent persons; and in this way he gathered much wisdom and grew to be a courteous and handsome youth. From the jewelers he learned that the fruits he had gathered when he got the lamp were not merely colored glass, but precious stones of untold value, the rarest in the city.

— From " The Arabian Nights."

The foregoing selection is only the first part of the story, but we believe that it will give the reader a fairly good idea of the whole story, and also some idea of the style of the " Arabian Nights Stories."

ALADDIN

JAMES RUSSELL LOWELL

When I was a beggarly boy,
    And lived in a cellar damp,
I had not a friend nor a toy,
    But I had Aladdin's lamp;
When I could not sleep for the cold,
    I had fire enough in my brain,

And builded, with roofs of gold,
  My beautiful castles in Spain!

Since then I have toiled day and night,
  I have money and power good store,
But I'd give all my lamps of silver bright
  For the one that is mine no more;
Take, Fortune, whatever you choose,
  You gave, and may snatch again;
I have nothing 'twould pain me to lose,
  For I own no more castles in Spain!

THE DAYS GONE BY

James Whitcomb Riley

truant   reposing   nightingale

Oh, the days gone by! Oh, the days gone by!
The apples in the orchard, and the pathway through the rye;
The chirrup of the robin, and the whistle of the quail
As he piped across the meadows sweet as any nightingale;
When the bloom was on the clover, and the blue was in the
    sky,
And my happy heart brimmed over, in the days gone by.

In the days gone by, when my naked feet were tripped
By the honeysuckle tangles where the water lilies dipped,
And the ripples of the river lipped the moss along the brink
Where the placid-eyed and lazy-footed cattle came to drink,

98

And the tilting snipe stood fearless of the truant's wayward cry
And the splashing of the swimmer, in the days gone by.

Oh, the days gone by! Oh, the days gone by!
The music of the laughing lip, the luster of the eye;
The childish faith in fairies, and Aladdin's magic ring —
The simple, soul-reposing, glad belief in everything, —
When life was like a story holding neither sob nor sigh,
In the golden olden glory of the days gone by.

— From " Rhymes of Childhood," by James Whitcomb Riley. Copyright, 1890.
Used by special permission of the publishers, The Bobbs-Merrill Company.

NATHANIEL HAWTHORNE

Salem   hermit   fiction   seclusion

Nathaniel Hawthorne was born at Salem, Massachusetts, on the Fourth
of July, 1804. When this little boy was only four years old, his father died.
His mother was a gifted and beautiful woman; but after the death of her
husband, she shut herself up in the house and hardly ever appeared in public, though she lived many years. There is no doubt that this seclusion on
her part had its effect on the children.

The happiest years of his boyhood were spent at his uncle's home in the
forests of Maine. He loved to wander all alone through the woods, and here
his life was as free as a bird in the air and as wild as a wandering brook.

After he left college, he went back to his home in Salem, and lived the
life of a hermit for twelve years. He lived as a shadow in a shadowy world.
He walked alone by night and wrote wild tales by day. He burned most of
the stories, but some of them were published in various magazines. No one
seemed to read them, however, and no one seemed to know that he wrote
them.

These stories were afterwards collected and published in two volumes
and were called "Twice-Told Tales." In a letter written to Longfellow, he

NATHANIEL HAWTHORNE.

said, "I have made a captive of myself and put me into a dungeon; and now I cannot find the key to let myself out." But the key was found. In these quiet years, when he burned almost every line that he wrote, he was learning how to write and how to think. Little by little he saw the greatness in everything. He saw the value of the most hidden deeds of the humblest persons. He taught us that dreams are real. His life was a very quiet one. But what a world his imagination created! He was almost an old man before he became famous, but now all agree that he was one of the most celebrated American writers of prose fiction. He is called "America's Prose Poet."

He loved children, and he wrote several charming books for them. His "Twice-Told Tales," "A Wonder Book," "Tanglewood Tales," and "Grandfather's Chair," are especially interesting to the young. His imagination found only sunshine in the lives of the children; and there are no children's books so dipped in morning dews.

During his last illness, in 1864, his old friend Franklin Pierce came to see him. The two friends started for the White Mountains in the hope of getting benefit for the sufferer. But in a little hotel where they had stopped for a rest on the way, Hawthorne passed away.

The following selection is taken from " A Wonder Book "

THE PARADISE OF CHILDREN

NATHANIEL HAWTHORNE

PART I

defied	mingled	intricate	mosquitoes
foliage	serpents	pettishly	disentangle
society	profusion	positively	disquietude
juiciest	roguishly	multitude	Epimetheus
Pandora	threshold	provoking	perseveringly

Long, long ago, when this old world was in its tender infancy, there was a child, named Epimetheus, who never had either father or mother; and, in order that he might not be lonely, another child, fatherless and motherless like him, was sent from a far country to live with him and be his playfellow and helpmate. Her name was Pandora.

The first thing that Pandora saw when she entered the cottage where Epimetheus dwelt was a great box. And almost the first question which she put to him, after crossing the threshold, was this, —

"Epimetheus, what have you in that box?"

"My dear little Pandora," answered Epimetheus, "that is a secret, and you must be kind enough not to ask any questions about it. The box was left here to be kept safely, and I do not myself know what it contains."

"But who gave it to you?" asked Pandora; "and where did it come from?"

"That is a secret, too," replied Epimetheus.

"How provoking!" exclaimed Pandora, pouting her lip. "I wish the great ugly box were out of the way!"

"Oh, come! don't think of it any more," cried Epimetheus. "Let us run out of doors, and have some nice play with the other children."

It is thousands of years since Epimetheus and Pandora were alive; and the world, nowadays, is a very different sort of thing from what it was in their time. Then, everybody was a child. There was no need of fathers and mothers to take care of the children; because there was no danger nor trouble of any kind, and no clothes to be mended, and there was always plenty to eat and drink. Whenever a child wanted his dinner, he found it growing on a tree; and, if he looked at the tree in the morning, he could see the expanding blossom of that night's supper; or at eventide he saw the tender bud of to-morrow's breakfast. It was a very pleasant life indeed. No labor to be done, no tasks to be studied; nothing but sports and dances, and sweet voices of children talking, or caroling like birds, or gushing out in merry laughter, throughout the livelong day.

What was most wonderful of all, the children never quarreled among themselves; neither had they any crying fits; nor, since time first began, had a single one of these little mortals ever gone apart into a corner, and sulked. Oh, what a good time was that to be alive in! The truth is, those ugly little winged monsters, called Troubles, which are now almost as numerous as mosquitoes, had never yet been seen on earth. It is probable that the very greatest disquietude which a child had ever experienced was Pandora's vexation at not being able to discover the secret of the mysterious box.

This was at first only the faint shadow of a Trouble; but every day it grew more and more substantial, until, before a great while, the cottage of Epimetheus and Pandora was less sunshiny than those of the other children.

"Whence can the box have come?" Pandora continually kept saying to herself and to Epimetheus. "And what in the world can be inside of it?"

"Always talking about that box!" said Epimetheus, at last; for he had grown extremely tired of the subject. "I wish, dear

Pandora, you would try to talk of something else. Come, let us go and gather some ripe figs, and eat them under the trees, for our supper. And I know a vine that has the sweetest and juiciest grapes that you have ever tasted."

"Always talking about grapes and figs!" cried Pandora, pettishly.

"Well, then," said Epimetheus, who was a very good-tempered child, like a multitude of children in those days, "let us run out and have a merry time with our playmates."

"I am tired of merry times, and I don't care whether I ever have any more!" answered our pettish little Pandora. "And, besides, I never do have any. This ugly box! I am so taken up with thinking about it all the time. I insist upon your telling me what is inside of it."

"As I have already said, fifty times over, I do not know!" replied Epimetheus, getting a little vexed. "How, then, can I tell you what is inside?"

"You might open it," said Pandora, looking sidewise at Epimetheus, "and then we could see for ourselves."

"Pandora, what are you thinking of?" exclaimed Epimetheus.

And his face expressed so much horror at the idea of looking into a box which had been confided to him on the condition of his never opening it, that Pandora thought it best not to suggest it any more. Still, however, she could not help thinking and talking about the box.

"At least," said she, "you can tell me how it came here."

"It was left at the door," replied Epimetheus, "just before you came, by a person who looked very smiling and intelligent, and who could hardly forbear laughing as he put it down. He was dressed in an odd kind of cloak, and had on a cap that seemed to be made partly of feathers, so that it looked almost as if it had wings."

"What sort of staff had he?" asked Pandora.

"Oh, the most curious staff you ever saw!" cried Epimetheus. "It was like two serpents twisting around a stick, and was carved so naturally that I, at first, thought the serpents were alive."

"I know him," said Pandora, thoughtfully. "Nobody else has such a staff. It was Quicksilver; and he brought me hither, as well as the box. No doubt he intended it for me; and, most probably, it contains pretty dresses for me to wear, or toys for you and me to play with, or something very nice for us both to eat!"

"Perhaps so," answered Epimetheus, turning away; "but until Quicksilver comes back and tells us so, we have neither of us any right to lift the lid of the box."

"What a dull boy he is!" muttered Pandora, as Epimetheus left the cottage. "I do wish he had a little more enterprise!"

For the first time since her arrival, Epimetheus had gone out without asking Pandora to accompany him. He went to gather figs and grapes by himself, or to seek whatever amusement he could find in other society than his little playfellow's. He was tired to death of hearing about the box, and heartily wished

105

that Quicksilver, or whatever was the messenger's name, had left it at some other child's door, where Pandora would never have set eyes on it. So perseveringly did she babble about this one thing! The box, the box, and nothing but the box! It seemed as if the box were bewitched, and as if the cottage were not big enough to hold it, without Pandora's continually stumbling over it, and making Epimetheus stumble over it likewise, and bruising all four of their shins.

Well, it was really hard that poor Epimetheus should have a box in his ears from morning till night; especially as the little people of the earth were so unaccustomed to vexations in those happy days that they knew not how to deal with them. Thus, a small vexation made as much disturbance, then, as a far bigger one would in our own time.

After Epimetheus was gone, Pandora stood gazing at the box. She had called it ugly more than a hundred times; but in spite of all that she had said against it, it was positively a very handsome article of furniture, and would have been quite an ornament to any room in which it should be placed. It was made out of a beautiful kind of wood, with dark and rich veins spreading over its surface, which was so highly polished that little Pandora could see her face in it. As the child had no other looking-glass, it is odd that she did not value the box merely on this account.

The edges and the corners of the box were carved with most wonderful skill. Around the margin there were figures of graceful men and women, and of the prettiest children ever seen, reclining or sporting amid a profusion of flowers and foliage; and these various objects were so exquisitely represented, and were wrought together in such harmony, that flowers, foliage, and human beings seemed to combine into a wreath of mingled beauty. But here and there, peeping forth from behind the carved foliage, Pandora once or twice fancied that she saw a face not so lovely, or something or other that was disagreeable, and which stole the beauty out of all the rest. Nevertheless, on looking more closely, and touching the spot with her finger, she could discover nothing of the kind. Some face, that was really beautiful, had been made to look ugly by her catching a sidewise glimpse at it.

The most beautiful face of all was done in what is called high relief, in the center of the lid. There was nothing else, save the dark, smooth richness of the polished wood, and this one face in the center, with a garland of flowers about its brow. Pandora had looked at this face a great many times, and had imagined that the mouth could smile if it liked, or be grave when it chose, the same as any living mouth. The features, indeed, all wore a very lively and rather mischievous expression, which looked almost as if it needs must burst out of the carved lips, and utter itself in words.

Had the mouth spoken, it would probably have been something like this : —

"Do not be afraid, Pandora! What harm can there be in opening the box? Never mind that poor, simple Epimetheus! You are wiser than he, and have ten times as much spirit. Open the box, and see if you do not find something very pretty!"

The box, I had almost forgotten to say, was fastened; not by a lock, nor by any other such contrivance, but by a very intricate knot of gold cord. There appeared to be no end to this knot, and no beginning. Never was a knot so cunningly twisted, nor with so many ins and outs which roguishly defied the skillfullest fingers to disentangle them. And yet, by the very difficulty that there was in it, Pandora was the more tempted to examine the knot, and just see how it was made. Two or three times already she had stooped over the box, and had taken the knot between her thumb and forefinger, but without positively trying to undo it.

"I really believe," said she to herself, "that I begin to see how it was done. Nay, perhaps I could tie it up again, after undoing it. There would be no harm in that, surely. Even Epimetheus would not blame me for that. I need not open the box, and should not, of course, without the foolish boy's consent, even if the knot were untied."

PART II

odious	intercept	obscurity
affright	ingenious	lamentable

It might have been better for Pandora if she had had a little work to do, or anything else to employ her mind upon, so as not to be so constantly thinking of this one subject. But children led so easy a life, before any Troubles came into the world, that they had really a great deal too much leisure. They could not be forever playing at hide and seek among the flower shrubs, or at blindman's buff with garlands over their eyes, or at whatever other games had been found out while Mother Earth was in her babyhood. When life is all sport, toil is the real play. There was absolutely nothing to do. A little sweeping and dusting about the cottage, I suppose, and the gathering of fresh flowers (which were only too abundant everywhere), and arranging them in vases, — and poor little Pandora's day's work was over. And then, for the rest of the day, there was the box !

After all, I am not quite sure that the box was not a blessing to her in its way. It supplied her with such a variety of ideas to think of, and to talk about, whenever she had anybody to listen ! When she was in good humor, she could admire the bright polish of its sides, and the rich border of beautiful faces and foliage that ran all around it. Or, if she chanced to be ill-tempered, she could give it a push, or kick it with her naughty little foot. And many a kick did the box (but it was a mischievous box, as we shall see, and deserved all it got) — many a kick did it receive. But, certain it is, if it had not been for the box, our active-minded little Pandora would not have known half so well how to spend her time as she now did.

For it was really an endless employment to guess what was inside. What could it be, indeed? Just imagine, my little hearers, how busy your wits would be, if there were a great box in the house, which, as you might have reason to suppose, contained something new and pretty for your Christmas or New Year's gifts. Do you think that you should be less curious than Pandora? If you were left alone with the box, might you not feel a little tempted to lift the lid? But you would not do it. Oh, fie! No, no! Only, if you thought there were toys in it, it would be so very hard to let slip an opportunity of taking just one peep! I know not whether Pandora expected any toys; for none had yet begun to be made, probably, in those days, when the world itself was one great plaything for the children that dwelt upon it. But Pandora was convinced that there was something very beautiful and valuable in the box; and, therefore, she felt just as anxious to take a peep as any of these little girls here around me would have felt. And, possibly, a little more so; but of that I am not quite so certain.

On this particular day, however, which we have so long been talking about, her curiosity became so much greater than it usually had been, that at last she approached the box. She was more than half determined to open it, if she could. Ah, naughty Pandora!

First, however, she tried to lift it. It was heavy; much too heavy for the slender strength of a child like Pandora. She raised one end of the box a few inches from the floor and let it fall again, with a pretty loud thump. A moment afterwards, she almost fancied that she heard something stir inside of the box. She applied her ear as closely as possible, and listened. Positively, there did seem to be a kind of stifled murmur within! Or was it merely the singing in Pandora's ears? Or could it be the beating of her heart? The child could not quite satisfy herself whether she had heard anything or no. But, at all events, her curiosity was stronger than ever.

As she drew back her head, her eyes fell upon the knot of gold cord.

"It must have been a very ingenious person who tied this knot," said Pandora to herself. "But I think I could untie it, nevertheless. I am resolved, at least, to find the two ends of the cord."

So she took the golden knot in her fingers and pried into its intricacies as sharply as she could. Almost without intending it, or quite knowing what she was about, she was soon busily engaged in attempting to undo it. Meanwhile, the bright sunshine came through the open window, as did likewise the merry voices of the children, playing at a distance, with perhaps the voice of Epimetheus among them. Pandora stopped to listen. What a beautiful day it was! Would it not be wiser to let the troublesome knot alone, and think no more about the box, but run and join her little playfellows, and be happy?

All this time, however, her fingers were half unconsciously busy with the knot; and happening to glance at the flower-wreathed face on the lid of the enchanted box, she seemed to perceive it slyly grinning at her.

"That face looks very mischievous," thought Pandora. "I wonder whether it smiles because I am doing wrong! I have the greatest mind in the world to run away!"

But just then, by the merest accident, she gave the knot a kind of a twist, which produced a wonderful result. The gold cord untwined itself, as if by magic, and left the box without a fastening.

"This is the strangest thing I have ever known!" said

Pandora. "What will Epimetheus say? And how can I possibly tie it up again?"

She made one or two attempts to restore the knot, but soon found it quite beyond her skill. It had disentangled itself so suddenly that she could not in the least remember how the strings had been doubled into one another; and when she tried to recollect the shape and appearance of the knot, it seemed to have gone entirely out of her mind. Nothing was to be done, therefore, but to let the box remain as it was until Epimetheus should come in.

"But," said Pandora, "when he finds the knot untied, he will know that I have done it. How shall I make him believe that I have not looked into the box?"

And then the thought came into her naughty little heart, that, since she would be suspected of having looked into the box, she might just as well do so at once. O very naughty and foolish Pandora! You should have thought only of doing what was right, and of leaving undone what was wrong, and not of what your playfellow Epimetheus would have said or believed. And so perhaps she might, if the enchanted face on the lid of the box had not looked so bewitchingly persuasive at her, and if she had not seemed to hear, more distinctly than before, the murmur of small voices within. She could not tell whether it was fancy or no; but there was quite a little tumult of whispers in her ear, or else it was her curiosity that whispered, "Let us out, dear Pandora! Pray let us out! We will be such nice pretty playfellows for you! Only let us out!"

W. L. Haskell.

PANDORA.

" What can it be ? " thought Pandora. " Is there something alive in the box ? Well ! yes ! I am resolved to take just one peep ! Only one peep ; and then the lid shall be shut down as safely as ever ! There cannot possibly be any harm in just one little peep ! "

But it is now time for us to see what Epimetheus was doing.

This was the first time, since his little playmate had come to dwell with him, that he had attempted to enjoy any pleasure in which she did not partake. But nothing went right ; nor was he nearly so happy as on other days. He could not find a sweet grape or a ripe fig (if Epimetheus had a fault, it was a little too much fondness for figs) ; or if ripe at all, they were overripe, and so sweet as to be distasteful. There was no mirth in his heart, such as usually made his voice gush out of its own accord, and swell the merriment of his companions. In short, he grew so uneasy and discontented, that the other children could not imagine what was the matter with Epimetheus. Neither did he himself know what ailed him, any better than they did ; for you must recollect that at the time we are speaking of, it was everybody's nature, and constant habit, to be happy. The world had not yet learned to be otherwise. Not a single soul or body, since these children were first sent to enjoy themselves on the beautiful earth, had ever been sick, or out of sorts.

At length, discovering that somehow or other he put a stop to all the play, Epimetheus judged it best to go back to Pandora, who was in a humor better suited to his own. But with a hope of giving her pleasure, he gathered some flowers and made them into a wreath, which he meant to put upon her head. The flowers were very lovely, — roses, and lilies, and orange blossoms, and a great many more, which left a trail of fragrance behind as Epimetheus carried them along; and the wreath was put together with as much skill as could reasonably be expected of a boy. The fingers of little girls, it has always appeared to me, are the fittest to twine flower wreaths; but boys could do it, in those days, rather better than they can now.

And here I must mention that a great black cloud had been gathering in the sky for some time past, although it had not yet overspread the sun. But just as Epimetheus reached the cottage door, this cloud began to intercept the sunshine, and thus to make a sudden and sad obscurity.

He entered softly; for he meant, if possible, to steal behind Pandora, and fling the wreath of flowers over her head before she should be aware of his approach. But, as it happened, there was no need of treading so very lightly. He might have trod as heavily as he pleased, — as heavily as a grown man, — as heavily, I was going to say, as an elephant, — without much probability of Pandora's hearing his footsteps. She was too intent upon her purpose. At the moment of his entering the cottage, the naughty child had put her hand to the lid, and was on the point of opening the mysterious box. Epimetheus beheld her. If he had cried out, Pandora would probably have withdrawn her hand, and the fatal mystery of the box might never have been known.

But Epimetheus himself, although he said very little about it, had his own share of curiosity to know what was inside. Perceiving that Pandora was resolved to find out the secret, he determined that his playfellow should not be the only wise person in the cottage. And if there were anything pretty or valuable in the box, he meant to take half of it to himself. Thus, after all his sage speeches to Pandora about restraining her curiosity, Epimetheus turned out to be quite as foolish, and nearly as much in fault, as she. So, whenever we blame Pandora for what happened, we must not forget to shake our heads at Epimetheus likewise.

As Pandora raised the lid, the cottage grew very dark and dismal; for the black cloud had now swept quite over the sun, and seemed to have buried it alive. There had, for a little while past, been a low growling and muttering, which all at once broke into a heavy peal of thunder. But Pandora, heeding nothing of all this, lifted the lid nearly upright, and looked inside. It seemed as if a sudden swarm of winged creatures brushed past her, taking flight out of the box, while, at the same instant, she heard the voice of Epimetheus, with a lamentable tone, as if he were in pain.

"Oh, I am stung!" cried he. "I am stung! Naughty Pandora! why have you opened this wicked box?"

Pandora let fall the lid, and, starting up, looked about her to see what had befallen Epimetheus. The thundercloud had so darkened the room that she could not very clearly see what was in it. But she heard a disagreeable buzzing, as if a great many huge flies, or gigantic mosquitoes, or those insects which we call dor bugs and pinching dogs, were darting about. And, as her eyes grew more accustomed to the imperfect light, she saw a crowd of ugly little shapes, with bats' wings, looking very spiteful, and armed with terribly long stings in their tails. It was one of these that had stung Epimetheus. Nor was it a great while before Pandora herself began to scream, in no less pain and affright than her playfellow, and making a vast deal more hubbub about it. An odious little monster had settled on her forehead, and would have stung her I know not how deeply, if Epimetheus had not run and brushed it away.

Part III

species	pestered	infinite	intolerable
anguish	Diseases	molested	abominable
calamity	knuckles	venomous	spiritualizes

Now, if you wish to know what these ugly things might be which had made their escape out of the box, I must tell you that they were the whole family of earthly Troubles. There were evil Passions; there were a great many species of Cares; there were more than a hundred and fifty Sorrows; there were Diseases, in a vast number of miserable and painful shapes; there were more kinds of Naughtiness than it would be of any use to talk about. In short, everything that has since afflicted the souls and bodies of mankind had been shut up in the mysterious box which had been given to Epimetheus and Pandora to be kept safely, in order that the happy children of the world might never be molested by Troubles. Had they been faithful to their trust, all would have gone well. No grown person would ever have been sad, nor any child have had cause to shed a single tear from that hour until this moment.

But — and you may see by this how a wrong act of any one mortal is a calamity to the whole world — by Pandora's lifting the lid of that miserable box, and by the fault of Epimetheus, too, in not preventing her, these Troubles have obtained a foothold among us, and do not seem very likely to be driven away in a hurry. For it was impossible, as you will easily guess, that the two children should keep the ugly swarm in their own little cottage. On the contrary, the first thing that they did was to fling open the doors and windows, in hopes of getting rid of them; and, sure enough, away flew the winged Troubles all abroad, and so pestered and tormented the small people everywhere about, that none of them so much as smiled for many days afterwards. And, what was very singular, all the flowers and dewy blossoms on earth, not one of which had hitherto faded, now began to droop and shed their leaves after a day or two. The children, moreover, who before seemed immortal in their childhood, now grew older day by day, and came soon to be youths and maidens, and men and women by and by, and aged people, before they dreamed of such a thing.

Meanwhile, the naughty Pandora, and hardly less naughty Epimetheus, remained in their cottage. Both of them had been grievously stung, and were in a good deal of pain, which seemed the more intolerable to them because it was the very first pain that had ever been felt since the world began. Of course they were entirely unaccustomed to it, and could have no idea what it meant. Besides all this, they were in exceedingly bad humor, both with themselves and with each other. In order to indulge it to the utmost, Epimetheus sat down sullenly in a corner with his back towards Pandora; while Pandora flung herself upon the floor and rested her head on the fatal and abominable box. She was crying bitterly, and sobbing as if her heart would break.

Suddenly there was a gentle little tap on the inside of the lid.

"What can that be?" cried Pandora, lifting her head.

But either Epimetheus had not heard the tap, or was too much out of humor to notice it. At any rate, he made no answer.

"You are very unkind," said Pandora, sobbing anew, "not to speak to me."

Again the tap! It sounded like the tiny knuckles of a fairy's hand, knocking lightly and playfully on the inside of the box.

"Who are you?" asked Pandora, with a little of her former curiosity. "Who are you, inside of this naughty box?"

A sweet little voice spoke from within, —

"Only lift the lid, and you shall see."

"No, no," answered Pandora, again beginning to sob, "I have had enough of lifting the lid! You are inside of the box, naughty creature, and there you shall stay! There are plenty of your ugly brothers and sisters already flying about the world. You need never think that I shall be so foolish as to let you out!"

She looked towards Epimetheus as she spoke, perhaps expecting that he would commend her for her wisdom. But the sullen boy only muttered that she was wise a little too late.

"Ah!" said the sweet little voice again, "you had much better let me out. I am not like those naughty creatures that have stings. They are no brothers and sisters of mine, as you would see at once if you were only to get a glimpse of me. Come, come, my pretty Pandora! I am sure you will let me out!"

And, indeed, there was a kind of cheerful witchery in the tone that made it almost impossible to refuse anything which this little voice asked. Pandora's heart had insensibly grown lighter at every word that came from within the box. Epimetheus, too, though still in the corner, had turned half round, and seemed to be in rather better spirits than before.

"My dear Epimetheus," cried Pandora, "have you heard this little voice?"

"Yes, to be sure I have," answered he, but in no very good humor as yet. "And what of it?"

"Shall I lift the lid again?" asked Pandora.

"Just as you please," said Epimetheus. "You have done so much mischief already that perhaps you may as well do a little more. One other Trouble, in such a swarm as you have set adrift about the world, can make no very great difference."

"You might speak a little more kindly!" murmured Pandora, wiping her eyes.

"Ah, naughty boy!" cried the little voice within the box, in an arch and laughing tone. "He knows he is longing to

120

see me. Come, my dear Pandora, lift up the lid. I am in a great hurry to comfort you. Only let me have some fresh air, and you will soon see that matters are not quite so dismal as you think them!"

"Epimetheus," exclaimed Pandora, "come what may, I am resolved to open the box!"

"And as the lid seems very heavy," cried Epimetheus, running across the room, "I will help you!"

So with one consent the two children again lifted the lid. Out flew a sunny and smiling little personage, and hovered about the room, throwing a light wherever she went. Have you never made the sunshine dance into dark corners by reflecting it from a bit of looking-glass? Well, so looked the winged cheerfulness of this fairylike stranger amid the gloom of the cottage. She flew to Epimetheus, and laid the least touch of her finger on the inflamed spot where the Trouble had stung him, and immediately the anguish of it was gone. Then she kissed Pandora on the forehead, and her hurt was cured likewise.

After performing these good offices, the bright stranger fluttered sportively over the children's heads, and looked so sweetly at them that they both began to think it not so very much amiss to have opened the box, since otherwise their cheery guest must have been kept a prisoner among those naughty imps with stings in their tails.

"Pray, who are you, beautiful creature?" inquired Pandora.

"I am to be called Hope!" answered the sunshiny figure.

"And because I am such a cheery little body, I was packed into the box to make amends to the human race for that swarm of ugly Troubles which was destined to be let loose among them. Never fear! we shall do pretty well in spite of them all."

"Your wings are colored like the rainbow!" exclaimed Pandora. "How very beautiful!"

"Yes, they are like the rainbow," said Hope, "because, glad as my nature is, I am partly made of tears as well as smiles."

"And will you stay with us," asked Epimetheus, "forever and ever?"

"As long as you need me," said Hope, with her pleasant smile, — "and that will be as long as you live in the world, — I promise never to desert you. There may come times and seasons, now and then, when you will think that I have utterly vanished. But again, and again, and again, when perhaps you least dream of it, you shall see the glimmer of my wings on the ceiling of your cottage. Yes, my dear children, and I know something very good and beautiful that is to be given you hereafter!"

"Oh, tell us!" they exclaimed, "tell us what it is!"

"Do not ask me," replied Hope, putting her finger on her rosy mouth. "But do not despair even if it should never happen while you live on this earth. Trust in my promise, for it is true."

"We do trust you!" cried Epimetheus and Pandora, both in one breath.

And so they did; and not only they, but so has everybody that has since been alive, trusted Hope. And to tell you the truth, I cannot help being glad (though, to be sure, it was an uncommonly naughty thing for her to do) — but I cannot help being glad that our foolish Pandora peeped into the box. No doubt — no doubt — the Troubles are still flying about the world, and have increased in multitude, rather than lessened, and are a very ugly set of imps, and carry most venomous stings in their tails. I have felt them already, and expect to feel them more as I grow older. But then that lovely and lightsome little figure of Hope! What in the world could we do without her? Hope spiritualizes the earth ; Hope makes it always new ; and, even in the earth's best and brightest aspect, Hope shows it to be only the shadow of an infinite bliss hereafter.

PERCY BYSSHE SHELLEY

| Leigh | stress | Bysshe | miracle |
| Thames | lyrics | Shelley | achievement |

Percy Bysshe Shelley was born at Field Place, England, in 1792. In 1818, after an alarming illness, he went to Italy, where the brief remainder of his life was spent. Here in the companionship of a few choice friends and in reposeful enjoyment of the lofty skies and purple fields, the broad visions of beauty, the romantic witchery of this land of poetry, his genius found its best and truest inspiration.

On the afternoon of July 8, 1822, while returning from a visit of welcome to Leigh Hunt at Leghorn, his frail yacht was capsized in a gale and all on board perished. His life was short and full of storm and stress, but in view of the achievement of the life thus brought to an untimely end, it may well be called "a miracle of thirty years."

This ode, the most popular and the most perfect of his lyrics, was written in his twenty-ninth year, two years before his death. This poem and

PERCY BYSSHE SHELLEY.

"The Cloud," says Mrs. Shelley, "were written as his mind prompted, listening to the caroling of the bird, aloft in the azure sky of Italy, or watching the cloud as it sped across the heavens, as he floated in his boat on the Thames." Describing the song of a skylark may be compared to an artist's attemp to paint a rainbow; yet in this attempt Shelley has not failed.

TO A SKYLARK

PERCY BYSSHE SHELLEY

vaunt	sprite	satiety	sincerest
vernal	aërial	languor	Hymeneal
chaunt	surpass	fraught	unpremeditated

Hail to thee, blithe spirit!
  Bird thou never wert,
That from heaven, or near it,
  Pourest thy full heart
In profuse strains of unpremeditated art.

Higher still and higher
  From the earth thou springest
Like a cloud of fire;
  The blue deep thou wingest,
And singing still dost soar, and soaring ever singest.

In the golden lightening
  Of the sunken sun,
O'er which clouds are brightening,
  Thou dost float and run;
Like an unbodied joy whose race is just begun.

125

The pale purple even
Melts around thy flight;
Like a star of heaven
In the broad daylight
Thou art unseen, but yet I hear thy shrill delight,

Keen as are the arrows
Of that silver sphere,
Whose intense lamp narrows
In the white dawn clear,
Until we hardly see, we feel that it is there.

All the earth and air
With thy voice is loud,
As, when night is bare,
From one lonely cloud
The moon rains out her beams, and heaven is overflowed.

What thou art we know not;
What is most like thee?
From rainbow clouds there flow not
Drops so bright to see
As from thy presence showers a rain of melody.

Like a poet hidden
In the light of thought,
Singing hymns unbidden,
Till the world is wrought
To sympathy with hopes and fears it heeded not:

Like a highborn maiden
  In a palace tower,
Soothing her love-laden
  Soul in secret hour
With music sweet as love, which overflows her bower:

Like a glowworm golden
  In a dell of dew,
Scattering unbeholden
  Its aerial hue
Among the flowers and grass which screen it from the view:

Like a rose embowered
  In its own green leaves,
By warm winds deflowered,
  Till the scent it gives
Makes faint with too much sweet these heavy-wingéd thieves.

Sound of vernal showers
  On the twinkling grass,
Rain-awakened flowers,
  All that ever was
Joyous, and clear, and fresh, thy music doth surpass.

Teach us, sprite or bird,
  What sweet thoughts are thine;
I have never heard
  Praise of love or wine
That panted forth a flood of rapture so divine:

Chorus Hymeneal,
  Or triumphal chaunt,
Matched with thine, would be all
  But an empty vaunt,
A thing wherein we feel there is some hidden want.

What objects are the fountains
  Of thy happy strain?
What fields, or waves, or mountains?
  What shapes of sky or plain?
What love of thine own kind? what ignorance of pain?

With thy clear keen joyance
  Languor cannot be —
Shadow of annoyance
  Never came near thee:
Thou lovest — but ne'er knew love's sad satiety.

Waking or asleep,
  Thou of death must deem
Things more true and deep
  Than we mortals dream,
Or how could thy notes flow in such a crystal stream?

We look before and after
  And pine for what is not:
Our sincerest laughter
  With some pain is fraught;
Our sweetest songs are those that tell of saddest thought.

Yet if we could scorn
  Hate, and pride, and fear;
If we were things born
  Not to shed a tear,
I know not how thy joy we ever should come near.

  Better than all measures
   Of delightful sound —
Better than all treasures
   That in books are found —
Thy skill to poet were, thou scorner of the ground!

  Teach me half the gladness
   That thy brain must know,
Such harmonious madness
   From my lips would flow,
The world should listen then — as I am listening now.

LITTLE NELL AND HER GRANDFATHER

CHARLES DICKENS

PART I

oriel	resources	vigilance	profligate
Quilp	privation	converted	moldering
drained	unsullied	cultivated	subsistence
creaked	shattered	precarious	transferred
sagacity	temporary	Kit Nubles	interruption

129

About three weeks after her father's death Little Nell's mother died, leaving to her father's care two orphans, one a son of ten or twelve years of age; the other a girl, such another infant child (the same in helplessness, in age, in form, in feature) as she had been herself when her young mother died.

The grandfather of these two children was now a broken man, crushed and borne down less by the weight of years than by the hand of sorrow. With the wreck of his possessions he began to trade, in pictures first, and then in curious antique things. He had a fondness for such matters from a boy; and the tastes he had cultivated were now to yield him an anxious and precarious subsistence.

The boy grew like his father in mind and person; and the girl so like her mother that when the old man had her on his knee, and looked into her mild blue eyes, he felt as if awakening from a wretched dream, and as if his daughter were a little child again. The wayward boy soon spurned the shelter of his roof, and sought associates more congenial to his taste. The old man and the child dwelt alone together.

It was then, when the love of two dead persons who had been nearest and dearest to his heart was all transferred to this slight creature; when her face, constantly before him, reminded him from hour to hour of the too early change he had seen in such another, of all the suffering he had watched and known, and all his child had undergone; when the young man's profligate and hardened course had drained him of money, as his father's had, and even sometimes had occasioned them temporary privation

130

and distress, it was then that there began to beset him, and to be ever in his mind, a gloomy dread of poverty and want. He had no thought of himself in this. His fear was for the child. It was a specter in his house, and it haunted him night and day.

Feeling that fortune must finally favor him, he borrowed from time to time sums of money from Quilp, a cruel and ugly but rich dwarf, pledging his little stock as security for the debt. His resources, however, were soon all exhausted, his shop and its contents were taken on execution, and he himself was thrown upon the world, a beggar, shattered in intellect, and tottering on the verge of the grave.

"Let us go away from this place, and never turn back or think of it again," said Little Nell, earnestly. "Let us wander barefoot through the world, rather than linger here."

"Let us steal away to-morrow, early and softly, so that we may not be seen or heard," said the old man, "and leave no trace or track for them to follow by. Poor Nell! thy cheek is pale, and thine eyes are heavy with watching and weeping for me, but thou wilt be well again, and merry, too, when we are far away. To-morrow morning, dear, we will turn our faces from this scene of sorrow, and be as free and happy as the birds."

The next morning Little Nell took her grandfather by the hand, and they trod lightly and cautiously down the stairs, trembling whenever a board creaked, and often stopping to listen. They got the door open without noise, and passing into the street, stood still.

"Which way?" said the child.

The old man looked, irresolutely and helplessly, first at her, then to the right and left, then at her again, and shook his head. It was plain that she was thenceforth his guide and leader. The child felt it, but had no doubts or misgivings, and putting her hand in his, led him gently away.

It was the beginning of a day in June, the deep blue sky, unsullied by a cloud, teemed with brilliant light. The streets were, as yet, nearly free from passengers, the houses and shops were closed, and the healthful air of morning fell like breath from angels on the sleeping town.

The old man and the child passed on through the glad silence, elate with hope and pleasure. They were alone together; and forth from the city, while it yet slumbered, went the two poor adventurers, wandering they knew not whither.

They came at length to the open country, and the freshness of the day, the singing of the birds, the beauty of the waving grass, the deep green leaves, the wild flowers, and the thousand scents and sounds that floated in the air, sank into their breasts and made them very glad. And in the seclusion of a quiet village, where they at last found a home, the old man's hopes and fears, and all his thoughts, were turned to the gentle object of his love, who soon began to sink under the effects of her past trials and sufferings.

In the meantime the old man's younger brother, who had left his home in early youth and had been a traveler in many countries, and had made his pilgrimage through life alone, began to dream of their young, happy life, and every night, a boy again,

LITTLE NELL AND HER GRANDFATHER.

he was at his brother's side. With the utmost speed that he could exert, he settled his affairs; converted into money all the goods that he had, and with honorable wealth enough for both, with open heart and hand, with limbs that trembled as they bore him on, with emotion such as men can hardly bear and live, arrived one evening at his brother's door, only to find the wanderers gone.

By dint of such inquiries as the utmost vigilance and sagacity could set on foot, he at last discovered the place of the wanderers' retreat. And the grandfather's old servant, Kit Nubles, and the younger brother lost no time in starting on a journey to the peaceful village where Little Nell and her grandfather were hidden.

When they reached the quiet village very late one stormy night, they saw, among some ruined buildings at a distance, one single solitary light. It shone from what appeared to be an oriel window, and, being surrounded by deep shadows of overhanging walls, sparkled like a star.

Kit made his way to where the light was shining. He approached as softly as he could and listened. There was no sound inside. The church itself was not more quiet. Touching the glass with his cheek, he listened again; no: and yet there was such silence all around, that he felt sure he could have heard even the breathing of a sleeper, if there had been one there.

A strange circumstance it was, — a light in such a place at that time of night, with no one near it. A curtain was drawn across the lower part of the window, and he could not see into the room. But there was no shadow thrown upon it from the room. Again and again he listened ; again and again the same wearisome blank.

Leaving the spot with slow and cautious steps, he came at length to a door. He knocked. There was no answer, but there was a curious noise inside. It was difficult to determine what it was. It bore a resemblance to the low moan of one in pain, but it was not that, being far too regular and constant.

The listener's blood ran colder now than ever it had done in frost and snow, but he knocked again. There was no answer, and the sound went on without any interruption. He laid his hand softly upon the latch, and put his knee against the door. It was secured on the inside, but yielded to the pressure, and turned upon its hinges. He saw the glimmering of a fire upon the old walls, and entered.

The dull, red glow of a wood-fire showed him a figure seated on the hearth, with its back towards him, bending over the fitful light. The attitude was that of one who sought the heat. It was, and yet was not. The stooping posture and the cowering form were there, but no hands were stretched out to meet the grateful warmth, no shrug or shiver compared its luxury with the piercing cold outside. With limbs huddled together, head bowed down, arms crossed upon the breast, and fingers tightly clenched, it rocked to and fro upon its seat without a moment's pause, accompanying the action with the mournful sound he had heard.

The heavy door had closed behind him on his entrance with

a crash that made him start. The figure neither spoke nor turned to look, nor gave in any other way the faintest sign of having heard the noise. The form was that of an old man, his white head akin in color to the moldering embers upon which he gazed. He, and the failing light and the dying fire, the time-worn room, the solitude, the wasted life, and the gloom, were all in fellowship. Ashes, and dust, and ruin!

PART II

| console | fatigues | imploring |
| subsided | replenish | communing |

Kit tried to speak, and did pronounce some words, though what they were he hardly knew. Still the same terrible low cry went on; still the same rocking in the chair; the same stricken figure was there, unchanged and heedless of his presence. He advanced a pace — another — another still. Another, and he saw the face. Yes! changed as it was, he knew it well.

"Master!" he cried, stooping on one knee and catching at his hand. "Dear Master! Speak to me!"

The old man turned slowly towards him, and muttered in a hollow voice, "This is another! How many of these spirits there have been to-night!"

"No spirit, Master. No one but your old servant. You know me now, I am sure? Little Nell! Where is she? Where is she?"

"They all say that!" cried the old man. "They all ask the same question."

"Where is she?" demanded Kit. "Oh, tell me but that,— but that, dear Master!"

"She is asleep — yonder — in there."

"Thank God!"

"Aye! Thank God!" returned the old man. "I have prayed to Him many, and many, and many a livelong night, when she has been asleep; He knows. Hark! Did she call?"

"I heard no voice."

"You did. You hear her now. Do you tell me that you don't hear *that?*" He started up and listened again.

"Nor that?" he cried, with a triumphant smile; "can anybody know that voice so well as I! Hush! Hush!"

Motioning to him to be silent, he stole away into another chamber. After a short absence, during which he could be heard to speak in a soft, soothing tone, he returned, bearing in his hand a lamp.

"She is still asleep," he whispered. "You were right. She did not call — unless she did so in her slumber. She has called to me in her sleep before now, sir; as I have sat by, watching, I have seen her lips move, and have known, though no sound came from them, that she spoke of me. I feared the light might dazzle her eyes and wake her, so I brought it here."

He spoke rather to himself than to the visitor, but when he had put the lamp upon the table, he took it up, as if impelled by some momentary recollection or curiosity, and held it near the visitor's face. Then, as if forgetting his motive in the very action, he turned away and put it down again.

"She is sleeping soundly," he said; "but no wonder. Angel hands have strewn the ground deep with snow, that the lightest footstep may be lighter yet; and the very birds are dead, that they may not wake her. She used to feed them, sir. Though never so cold and hungry, the timid things would fly from us. They never flew from her!"

Again he stopped to listen, and hardly drawing breath, listened for a long, long time. That fancy passed, he opened an old chest, took out some clothes as fondly as if they had been living things, and began to smooth and brush them with his hand.

"Why dost thou lie so idle there, dear Nell," he murmured, "when there are bright red berries out of doors waiting for thee to pluck them! Why dost thou lie so idle there, when thy little friends come peeping to the door, crying 'Where is Nell — sweet Nell?' — and sob, and weep, because they do not see thee. She was always gentle with children. The wildest would do her bidding; she had a tender way with them, indeed she had!"

Kit had no power to speak. His eyes were filled with tears.

"Her little homely dress, — her favorite!" cried the old man, pressing it to his breast, and patting it with his shriveled hand. "She will miss it when she wakes. They have hid it here in sport, but she shall have it — she shall have it. I would not vex my darling, for the wide world's riches. See here — these shoes — how worn they are — she kept them to remind her of our last long journey. You see where the little feet went bare upon the ground. They told me, afterwards, that the stones had cut and bruised

138

them. *She* never told me that. No, no, God bless her! and, I have remembered since, she walked behind me, sir, that I might not see how lame she was — but yet she had my hand in hers, and seemed to lead me still."

He pressed them to his lips, and having carefully put them back again, went on communing with himself, looking wistfully from time to time towards the chamber he had lately visited.

"We must have patience. When she is well again, she will rise early, as she used to do, and ramble abroad in the fresh morning time. I often tried to track the way she had gone, but her small footsteps left no print upon the dewy ground to guide me. Who is that? Shut the door. Quick! Have we not enough to do to drive away the cold, and keep her warm!"

The door was indeed opened for the entrance of Mr. Garland and the younger brother, accompanied by two other persons. These were the schoolmaster and the bachelor. The former held a light in his hand. He had, it seemed, but gone to his own cottage to replenish the exhausted lamp at the moment when Kit had come up and had found the old man alone.

He softened again at sight of these two friends; and, laying aside the angry manner, — if to anything so feeble and so sad the term can be applied, — in which he had spoken when the door opened, resumed his former speech, and subsided, little by little, into the old action, and the old, dull, wandering sound.

Of the strangers, he took no heed whatever. He had seen them, but appeared quite incapable of interest or curiosity. The younger brother stood apart. The bachelor drew a chair towards

139

the old man, and sat down close beside him.   After a long silence, he ventured to speak.

"Another night, and not in bed!" he said softly; "I had hoped you would be more mindful of your promise to me.   Why do you not take some rest?"

"Sleep has left me," returned the old man.   "It is all with her!"

They watched him as he rose and stole on tiptoe to the other chamber, where the lamp had been replaced.   They listened as he spoke again within its silent walls.   They looked into the faces of one another, and no man's cheek was free from tears.   He came back, whispering that she was still asleep, but that he thought she had moved.   It was her hand, he said — a little — a very, very little — but he was pretty sure she had moved it — perhaps in seeking his.   He had known her do that, before now, though in the deepest sleep the while.   And when he had said this, he dropped into his chair again, and clasping his hands above his head, uttered a cry never to be forgotten.

"Let us not talk of her in her sleep, but as she used to be when you were journeying together, far away — as she was at home, in the old house from which you fled together — as she was in the old cheerful time," said the schoolmaster.

"She was always cheerful — very cheerful," cried the old man, looking steadfastly at him.   "You do well to speak softly. We will not wake her.   There was ever something mild and quiet about her, I remember, from the first; but she was of a happy nature."

"We have heard you say," pursued the schoolmaster, "that in this and in all goodness, she was like her mother. You can think of, and remember her?"

He maintained his steadfast look, but gave no answer.

"Or even before her," said the bachelor. "It is many years ago, and affliction makes the time longer, but you have not forgotten her whose death contributed to make this child so dear to you, even before you knew her worth or could read her heart? Say, that you could carry back your thoughts to very distant days — to the time of your early life — when, unlike this fair flower, you did not pass your youth alone Say, that you could remember, long ago, another child who loved you dearly, you being but a child yourself. Say, that you had a brother, long forgotten, long unseen, long separated from you, who now, at last, in your utmost need, came back to comfort and console you —"

"To be to you what you were once to him," cried the younger brother, falling on his knee before him; "to repay your old affection, Brother dear, by constant care, solicitude, and love; to be, at your right hand, what he has never ceased to be when oceans rolled between us. Give me but one word of recognition, Brother — and never — no never, in the brightest moment of our youngest days, when, poor silly boys, we thought to pass our lives together — have we been half so dear and precious to each other as we shall be from this time hence!"

By little and little, the old man had drawn back towards the inner chamber while these words were spoken. He pointed there, as he replied, with trembling lips.

"You plot among you to wean my heart from her. You never will do that — never while I have life. I have no relative or friend but her — I never had — I never shall have. She is all in all to me. It is too late to part us now."

Waving them off with his hand, and calling softly to her as he went, he stole into the room. They who were left behind drew close together, and after a few whispered words, — not unbroken by emotion, or easily uttered, — followed him. They moved so gently that their footsteps made no noise; but there were sobs from among the group, and sounds of grief and mourning.

For she was dead. There, upon her little bed, she lay at rest. The solemn stillness was no marvel now.

She was dead: no sleep so beautiful and calm, so free from trace of pain, so fair to look upon. She seemed a creature fresh from the hand of God, and waiting for the breath of life; not one who had lived and had suffered death.

Her couch was dressed with here and there some winter berries and green leaves, gathered in a spot she had been used to favor. "When I die, put near me something that has loved the light, and had the sky above it always." Those were her words.

She was dead. Dear, gentle, patient, noble Nell was dead. Her little bird — a poor, slight thing the pressure of a finger would have crushed — was stirring nimbly in its cage; and the strong heart of its child mistress was mute and motionless forever.

Where were the traces of her early cares, her sufferings and fatigues? All were gone. Sorrow was dead indeed in her, but peace and perfect happiness were born, imaged in her tranquil beauty and profound repose.

And still her former self lay there, unaltered in this change. Yes; the old fireside had smiled upon that same sweet face; it had passed, like a dream, through haunts of misery and care; at the door of the poor schoolmaster on the summer evening, before the furnace fire upon the cold wet night, at the still bedside of the dying boy, there had been the same mild, lovely look.

The old man held one languid arm in his, and had the small hand tightly folded to his breast for warmth. It was the hand she had stretched out to him with her last smile; the hand that had led him on, through all their wanderings. Ever and anon he pressed it to his lips, then hugged it to his breast again, murmuring that it was warmer now; and, as he said it, he looked in agony to those who stood around, as if imploring them to help her.

She was dead, and past all help, or need of it. The ancient room she had seemed to fill with life, even while her own was waning fast — the garden she had tended — the eyes she had gladdened — the noiseless haunts of many a thoughtful hour — the paths she had trodden, as it were, but yesterday — could know her nevermore.

"It is not," said the schoolmaster, as he bent down to kiss her on the cheek, and gave his tears full vent, "it is not on earth that Heaven's justice ends. Think what earth is, compared with the world to which her young spirit has winged its early flight, and say, if one deliberate wish expressed in solemn terms above this bed could call her back to life, which of us would utter it!"

143

fervor	artifice	deferred	protracted
espied	knapsack	distracted	submissive
decrepit	paroxysm	endearment	remorseless

When morning came, and they could speak more calmly on the subject of their grief, they heard how her life had closed.

She had been dead two days. They were all about her at the time, knowing that the end was drawing on. She died soon after daybreak. They had read and talked to her in the earlier part of the night, but as the hours crept on, she had sunk to sleep. They could tell, by what she faintly uttered in her dreams, that they were of her journeyings with the old man; they were of no painful scenes, but of people who had helped and used them kindly, for she had often said "God bless you!" with great fervor. Waking, she never wandered in her mind but once, and that was of beautiful music that she said was in the air. God knows. It may have been.

Opening her eyes at last, from a very quiet sleep, she begged that they would kiss her once again. That done, she turned to the old man with a lovely smile upon her face — such, they said, as they had never seen, and never could forget — and clung with both her arms about his neck. They did not know that she was dead, at first.

The child who had been her little friend came there, almost as soon as it was day, with an offering of dried flowers which he begged them to lay upon her breast. Up to that time, the old man had not spoken once, except to her, nor had stirred from the bedside. But, when he saw her little favorite, he was moved as they had not seen him yet, and made as though he would have him come nearer. Then, pointing to the bed, he burst into tears for the first time; and they who stood by, knowing that the sight of this child had done him good, left them alone together.

Soothing him with his artless talk of her, the child persuaded him to take some rest, to walk abroad, to do almost as he desired him. And when the day came on, which must remove her in her earthly shape from earthly eyes forever, he led him away, that he might not know when she was taken from him.

They were to gather fresh leaves and berries for her bed. It was Sunday, a bright, clear, wintry afternoon; and, as they traversed the village street, those who were walking in their path drew back to make room for them, and gave them a softened greeting. Some shook the old man kindly by the hand, some stood uncovered while he tottered by, and many cried "God bless him!" as he passed along.

And now the bell — the bell she had so often heard, by night and by day, and had listened to with solemn pleasure almost as to a living voice — rang its remorseless toll for her, so young, so beautiful, so good.

Decrepit age, and vigorous life, and blooming youth, and helpless infancy, poured forth, — on crutches, in the pride and strength of health, and in the full blush of promise, in the mere dawn of life, — to gather round her tomb.

Along the crowded path they bore her now; pure as the newly fallen snow that covered it, whose day on earth had been as fleeting. Under the porch, where she had sat when Heaven in its mercy brought her to that peaceful spot, she passed again; and the old church received her in its quiet shade.

They carried her to one old nook, where she had many and many a time sat musing, and laid their burden softly on the pavement. The light streamed on it through the colored window, — a window, where the boughs of trees were ever rustling in the summer, and where the birds sang sweetly all day long. With every breath of air that stirred among those branches in the sunshine, some trembling, changing light would fall upon her grave.

Earth to earth, ashes to ashes, dust to dust! Many a young hand dropped in its little wreath, many a stifled sob was heard. Some, and they were not a few, knelt down. All were sincere and truthful in their sorrow.

Then, when the dusk of evening had come on, and not a sound disturbed the sacred stillness of the place, when the bright moon poured in her light on tomb and monument, on pillar, wall, and arch, and most of all (it seemed to them) upon her quiet grave, in that calm time, when outward things and inward thoughts teem with assurances of immortality, and worldly hopes and fears are humbled in the dust before them, then, with tranquil and submissive hearts they turned away, and left the child with God.

Oh! it is hard to take to heart the lesson that such deaths

will teach, but let no man reject it, for it is one that all must learn, and is a mighty, universal Truth. When Death strikes down the innocent and young, for every fragile form from which he lets the panting spirit free, a hundred virtues arise, in shapes of mercy, charity, and love, to walk the world, and bless it. Of every tear that sorrowing mortals shed on such green graves, some good is born, some gentler nature comes. In the Destroyer's steps there spring up bright creations that defy his power, and his dark path becomes a way of light to Heaven.

It was late when the old man came home. The boy had led him to his own dwelling, under some pretense, on their way back; and, rendered drowsy by his long ramble and late want of rest, he had sunk into a deep sleep by the fireside. He was perfectly exhausted, and they were careful not to rouse him. The slumber held him a long time, and when he at length awoke the moon was shining.

His younger brother, uneasy at his protracted absence, was watching at the door for his coming, when he appeared in the pathway with his little guide. He advanced to meet them, and tenderly obliging the old man to lean upon his arm, conducted him with slow and trembling steps towards the house.

He repaired to her chamber, straight. Not finding what he had left there, he returned with distracted looks to the room in which they were assembled. From that, he rushed into the schoolmaster's cottage, calling her name. They followed close upon him, and when he had vainly searched it, brought him home.

With such persuasive words as pity and affection could suggest, they prevailed upon him to sit among them and hear what they should tell him. Then endeavoring by every little artifice to prepare his mind for what must come, and dwelling with many fervent words upon the happy lot to which she had been removed, they told him, at last, the truth. The moment it had passed their lips, he fell down among them like a murdered man.

For many hours, they had little hope of his surviving; but grief is strong, and he recovered.

If there be any who have never known the blank that follows death — the weary void — the sense of desolation that will come upon the strongest minds, when something familiar and beloved is missed at every turn — if there be any who have not known this, and proved it by their own experience, they can never faintly guess how, for many days, the old man pined and moped away his time, and wandered here and there as seeking something, and had no comfort.

Whatever power of thought or memory he retained, was all bound up in her. He never understood, or seemed to care to understand, about his brother. To every endearment and attention he continued listless. If they spoke to him on this, or any other thing, save one, he would hear them patiently for a while, then turn away, and go on seeking as before.

On that one theme, which was in his and all their minds, it was impossible to touch. Dead! He could not hear or bear the word. The slightest hint of it would throw him into a paroxysm like that he had had when it was first spoken. In what hope he lived, no man could tell; but that he had some hope of finding her again — some faint and shadowy hope, deferred from day to day, and making him from day to day more sick and sore at heart — was plain to all.

They bethought them of a removal from the scene of this last sorrow; of trying whether change of place would rouse or cheer him. His brother sought the advice of those who were accounted skillful in such matters, and they came and saw him. Some of the number stayed upon the spot, conversed with him when he would converse, and watched him as he wandered up and down, alone and silent. Move him where they might, they said, he would ever seek to get back there. His mind would run upon that spot. If they confined him closely, and kept a strict guard upon him, they might hold him prisoner, but if he could by any means escape, he would surely wander back to that place, or die upon the road.

At length they found, one day, that he had risen early, and, with his knapsack on his back, his staff in hand, her own straw hat, and a little basket full of such things as she had been used to carry, was gone. As they were making ready to pursue him far and wide, a frightened schoolboy came who had seen him, but a moment before, sitting in the church upon her grave, he said.

They hastened there, and going softly to the door espied him in the attitude of one who waited patiently. They did not disturb him then, but kept a watch upon him all that day. When it grew quite dark, he arose and returned home, and went to bed, murmuring to himself, " She will come to-morrow ! "

Upon the morrow he was there again from sunrise until night;

and still at night he laid him down to rest, and murmured, "She will come to-morrow!"

And thenceforth, every day, and all day long, he waited at her grave for her. How many pictures of new journeys over pleasant country, of resting places under the free broad sky, of rambles in the fields and woods, and paths not often trodden; how many tones of that one well-remembered voice, how many glimpses of the form; the fluttering dress, the hair that waved so gayly in the wind; how many visions of what had been, and what he had hoped was yet to be — rose up before him, in the old, dull, silent church! He never told them what he thought, or where he went. He would sit with them at night, pondering with a secret satisfaction, they could see, upon the flight that he and she would take before night came again; and still they would hear him whisper in his prayers, "Lord! Let her come to-morrow!"

The last time was on a genial day in spring. He did not return at the usual hour, and they went to seek him. He was lying dead upon the stone.

They laid him by the side of her whom he had loved so well; and, in the church where they had often prayed, and mused, and lingered hand in hand, the child and the old man slept together.

THE DEATHBED

Thomas Hood

We watched her breathing through the night,
Her breathing soft and low,

As in her breast the wave of life
    Kept heaving to and fro.

So silently we seemed to speak,
    So slowly moved about,
As we had lent her half our powers
    To eke her living out.

Our very hopes belied our fears,
    Our fears our hopes belied, —
We thought her dying when she slept,
    And sleeping when she died.

For when the morn came dim and sad,
    And chill with early showers,
Her quiet eyelids closed ; — she had
    Another morn than ours.

HANGING A PICTURE

JEROME K. JEROME

sneer	Æolian	reference	formalities
liable	Goggles	criminal's	ostentation
grovel	essential	navigation	precipitated
discuss	discarded	commotion	cumbersome
Podger	catalogue	charwoman	merchandise

This selection is taken from a book entitled " Three Men in a Boat."

On the following evening, we again assembled, to discuss and arrange our plans. Harris said : —

" Now, the first thing to settle is what to take with us. Now, you get a bit of paper and write down, Jerome, and you get the grocery catalogue, George, and somebody give me a bit of pencil, and then I'll make out a list."

That's Harris all over — so ready to take the burden of every thing himself, and then put it on the backs of other people.

He always reminds me of my poor Uncle Podger. You never saw such a commotion up and down a house, in all your life, as when my Uncle Podger undertook to do a job. A picture would have come home from the frame-maker's and be standing in the dining room, waiting to be put up ; and Aunt Podger would ask what was to be done with it, and Uncle Podger would say : —

" Oh, you leave that to *me*. Don't you, any of you, worry yourselves about that. *I'll* do all that."

And then he would take off his coat and begin. He would send the girl out for nails, and then one of the boys after her to tell her what size to get ; and, from that, he would gradually work down, and start the whole house.

" Now you go and get me my hammer, Will," he would shout ; " and you bring me the rule, Tom ; and I shall want the stepladder, and I had better have a kitchen chair, too ; and, Jim ! you run round to Mr. Goggles, and tell him, ' Pa's kind regards, and hopes his leg's better ; and will he lend him his spirit level ?' And don't you go, Maria, because I shall want somebody to hold me the light ; and when the girl comes back, she must go out again for a bit of picture cord ; and Tom — where's Tom ? — Tom, you come here ; I shall want you to hand me up the picture."

152

And then he would lift up the picture, and drop it, and it would come out of the frame, and he would try to save the glass, and would cut himself; and then he would spring round the room, looking for his handkerchief. He could not find his handkerchief, because it was in the pocket of the coat he had taken off, and he did not know where he had put the coat, and all the house had to leave off looking for his tools, and start looking for his coat, while he would dance round and hinder them.

"Doesn't anybody in the whole house know where my coat is? I never came across such a set in all my life — upon my word I didn't. Six of you! and you can't find a coat that I put down not five minutes ago! Well, of all the — "

Then he'd get up, and find that he had been sitting on it, and would call out : —

"Oh, you can give it up! I've found it myself now. Might just as well ask the cat to find anything as expect you people to find it."

And, when half an hour had been spent in tying up his finger, and a new glass had been got, and the tools, and the ladder, and the chair, and the candle had been brought, he would have another go, the whole family, including the girl and the charwoman, standing round in a semicircle, ready to help. Two persons would have to hold the chair, and a third would help him up on it, and hold him there, and a fourth would hand him a nail, and a fifth would pass him up the hammer, and he would take hold of the nail, and drop it.

"There!" he would say, in an injured tone, "now the nail's gone."

And we would all have to go down on our knees and grovel for it, while he would stand on the chair, and grunt, and want to know whether he was to be kept there all the evening.

The nail would be found at last, and by that time he would have lost the hammer.

" Where's the hammer? What did I do with the hammer? Seven of you, gaping round there, and you don't know what I did with the hammer! "

We would find the hammer for him, and then he would have lost sight of the mark he had made on the wall, where the nail was to go in, and each of us had to get up on a chair, beside him, and see whether we could find it; and we would each discover it in a different place, and he would call us all fools, and tell us to get down. And he would take the rule, and remeasure, and find that he wanted half thirty-one and three-eighths inches from the corner, and would try to do it in his head, and go mad.

And we would all try to do it in our heads, and all arrive at different results, and sneer at one another. And in the general row, the original number would be forgotten, and Uncle Podger would have to measure it over again.

He would use a bit of string this time, and at the critical moment, when he was leaning over the chair at an angle of forty-five degrees, and trying to reach a point three inches beyond what was possible for him to reach, the string would slip, and down he would slide on to the piano, a really fine musical effect being produced by the suddenness with which his head and body struck all the notes at the same time.

And Aunt Maria would say that she would not allow the children to stand round and hear such language.

At last, Uncle Podger would get the spot fixed again, and put the point of the nail on it with his left hand, and take the hammer in his right hand; and, with the first blow, he would smash his thumb, and drop the hammer, with a yell, on somebody's toes.

Aunt Maria would mildly observe that next time Uncle Podger was going to hammer a nail into the wall, she hoped he'd let her know in time, so that she could make arrangements to go and spend a week with her mother while it was being done.

"Oh, you women! you make such a fuss over everything," Uncle Podger would reply, picking himself up. "Why, I *like* doing a little job of this sort."

And then he would have another try, and, at the second blow, the nail would go clear through the plaster, and half the hammer after it, and Uncle Podger would be precipitated against the wall with force nearly sufficient to flatten his nose.

Then we had to find the rule and the string again, and a new hole was made; and, about midnight, the picture would be up — very crooked and insecure, the wall for yards round looking as if it had been smoothed down with a rake, and everybody dead beat and wretched — except Uncle Podger.

"There you are," he would say, stepping heavily off the chair on to the charwoman's corns, and surveying the mess he had made with evident pride. "Why, some persons would have had a man in to do a little thing like that!"

Harris will be just that sort of man when he grows up, I know, and I told him so. I said I could not permit him to take so much labor upon himself. I said : —

" No; *you* get the paper, and the pencil, and the catalogue, and George write down, and I'll do the work."

The first list we made out had to be discarded. It was clear that the upper reaches of the Thames would not allow of the navigation of a boat sufficiently large to take the things we had set down as indispensable ; so we tore the list up, and looked at one another !

George said : —

" You know we are on a wrong track altogether. We must not think of the things we could do with, but only of the things that we can't do without."

George comes out really quite sensible at times. You'd be surprised. I call that downright wisdom, not merely as regards the present case, but with reference to our trip up the river of life, generally. How many people, on that voyage, load up the boat, till it is ever in danger of swamping, with a store of foolish things which they think essential to the pleasure and comfort of the trip, but which are really only useless lumber.

How they pile the poor little craft mast-high with fine clothes and big houses; with useless servants and with a host of swell friends that do not care twopence for them, and that they do not care three ha'pence for; with expensive entertainments that nobody enjoys, with formalities and fashions, with pretence and ostentation, and with — oh, heaviest, maddest lumber of all ! —

the dread of what will my neighbor think; with luxuries that only cloy, with pleasures that bore, with empty show that, like the criminal's iron crown of yore, makes to bleed and swoon the aching head that wears it!

It is lumber, man; all lumber! Throw it overboard. It makes the boat so heavy to pull, you nearly faint at the oars. It makes it so cumbersome and dangerous to manage that you never know a moment's freedom from anxiety and care, never gain a moment's rest for dreamy laziness; no time to watch the windy shadows skimming lightly o'er the shallows, or the glittering sunbeams flitting in and out among the ripples, or the great trees by the margin looking down at their own image, or the woods all green and golden, or the lilies white and yellow, or the somber-waving rushes, or the sedges, or the orchis, or the blue forget-me-nots.

Throw the lumber over, man! Let your boat of life be light, packed with only what you need, — a homely home and simple pleasures, one or two friends worth the name, some one to love and some one to love you, and enough to eat and enough to wear.

You will find the boat easier to pull then. and it will not be so liable to upset, and it will not matter so much if it does upset; good, plain merchandise will stand water. You will have time to think as well as to work; time to drink in life's sunshine; time to listen to the Æolian music that the wind of God draws from the human heartstrings around us.

157

AN ORDER FOR A PICTURE

ALICE CARY

sumac	notched	sovereign
urchins	sassafras	Commodore

O good painter, tell me true,
  Has your hand the cunning to draw
  Shapes of things that you never saw?
Aye? Well, here is an order for you.

Woods and cornfields a little brown, —
  The picture must not be overbright, —
  Yet all in the golden and gracious light
Of a cloud, when the summer sun is down.

Alway and alway, night and morn,
Woods upon woods, with fields of corn
  Lying between them, not quite sere,
And not in the full, thick, leafy bloom,
When the wind can hardly find breathing room
  Under their tassels, — cattle near,
Biting shorter the short green grass,
And a hedge of sumac and sassafras,
With bluebirds twittering all around, —
Ah, good painter, you can't paint sound! —

These and the house where I was born,
  Low and little, and black and old,

With children, many as it can hold,
All at the windows, open wide, —
Heads and shoulders clear outside,
And fair young faces all ablush;
    Perhaps you may have seen, some day,
    Roses crowding the selfsame way,
Out of a wilding, wayside bush.

Listen closer. When you have done
    With woods and cornfields and grazing herds,
A lady, the loveliest ever the sun
Looked down upon, you must paint for me:
Oh, if I only could make you see
    The clear blue eyes, the tender smile,
The sovereign sweetness, the gentle grace,
The woman's soul, and the angel's face
    That are beaming on me all the while, —
I need not speak these foolish words.
Yet one word tells you all I would say, —
    She is my mother: you will agree
That all the rest may be thrown away.

Two little urchins at her knee
You must paint, sir: one like me, —
    The other with a clearer brow,
      And the light of his adventurous eyes
      Flashing with boldest enterprise.
At ten years old he went to sea, —

God knoweth if he be living now, —
He sailed in the good ship *Commodore*.
      Nobody ever crossed her track
      To bring us news, and she never came back.
Ah! it is twenty long years and more,
Since that old ship went out of the bay
   With my great-hearted brother on her deck.
   I watched him till he shrank to a speck,
And his face was toward me all the way.
Bright his hair was, a golden brown,
   The time we stood at our mother's knee;
That beauteous head, if it did go down,
   Carried sunshine into the sea!

Out in the fields one summer night
   We were together, half afraid
   Of the corn leaves' rustling, and of the shade
      Of the high hills, stretching so still and far, —
Loitering till after the low little light
   Of the candle shone through the open door,
And, over the haystack's pointed top,
All of a tremble, and ready to drop,
      The first half-hour the great yellow star,
That we, with staring, ignorant eyes,
   Had often and often watched to see
Propped and held in its place in the skies
   By the fork of a tall, red mulberry tree,

Which close in the edge of our flax field grew, —
  Dead at the top, — just one branch full
  Of leaves, notched round, and lined with wool,
From which it tenderly shook the dew
  Over our heads, when we came to play
  In its handbreadth of shadow, day after day.

  Afraid to go home, sir; for one of us bore
A nest full of speckled and thin-shelled eggs, —
The other, a bird, held fast by the legs,
  Not so big as a straw of wheat:
  The berries we gave her she wouldn't eat,
But cried and cried, till we held her bill,
So slim and shining, to keep her still.

At last we stood at our mother's knee.
  Do you think, sir, if you try,
  You can paint the look of a lie?
    If you can, pray have the grace
    To put it solely in the face
Of the urchin that is likest me:
I think 'twas solely mine, indeed:
  But that's no matter, — paint it so.
The eyes of our mother (take good heed)
  Looking not on the nest full of eggs,
  Nor the fluttering bird, held so fast by the legs,
But straight through our faces down to our lies,
And, oh, with such injured, reproachful surprise!

I felt my heart bleed where that glance went, as though
  A sharp blade struck through it.   You, sir, know
That you on the canvas are to repeat
Things that are fairest, things most sweet, —
  Woods and cornfields and mulberry tree, —
  The mother, — the lads, with their bird, at her knee:
But, oh, that look of reproachful woe!
  High as the heavens your name I'll shout,
  If you paint me the picture, and leave that out.

JOHN HALIFAX, GENTLEMAN

Miss Mulock

Part I

erred	imbibed	thriving	disengage
groat	scanned	stalwart	catechism
propel	Phineas	tolerably	conquered
typhus	Fletcher	Cornwall	involuntary
Norton	Watkins	vagabond	irrepressible

"John Halifax, Gentleman," is the title of Miss Mulock's most popular book.   The following selection is an abridgment of the first four chapters of this book.

"Get out o' Mr. Fletcher's road, ye idle, lounging, little — "

"Vagabond," I think the woman (Sally Watkins, once my nurse) was going to say, but she changed her mind.

My father and I both glanced round, surprised; but when

162

the lad turned, and fixed his eyes on each of us for a moment, and made way for us, we ceased to wonder. Ragged, muddy, and miserable as he was, the poor boy looked anything but a " vagabond."

" Thee need not go into the wet, my lad. Keep close to the wall, and there will be shelter enough both for us and thee," said my father, as he pulled my little hand carriage into the alley, under cover from the pelting rain.

The lad, with a grateful look, put out a hand likewise, and pushed me farther in. A strong hand it was, — roughened and browned with labor, — though he was hardly as old as I. What would I not have given to have been so stalwart and so tall!

Sally called from her house door, " Wouldn't Master Phineas come in and sit by the fire a bit?"

But it was always a trouble to me to move or walk; and I liked staying at the mouth of the alley, watching the autumnal shower come sweeping down the street; besides, I wanted to look again at the stranger lad.

He had hardly stirred, but remained leaning against the wall, either through weariness, or in order to be out of our way. He took little or no notice of us, but kept his eyes fixed on the pavement, watching the eddying raindrops, which, each as it fell, threw up a little mist of spray. It was a serious, haggard face for a boy of only fourteen or so.

From a break in the clouds came a sudden stream of light. The stranger lad lifted up his head to look at it.

" The rain will be over soon," I said, but doubted if he heard me. What could he be thinking of so intently? — a poor working lad, whom few would have given credit for thinking at all.

I do not suppose my father cast a single glance or thought on the boy, whom from a sense of common justice he had made take shelter beside us. In truth, worthy man, he had no lack of matter to occupy his mind, being sole manager of a long, uphill, but now thriving trade. I saw, by the hardening of his features, and the restless way in which he poked his stick into the little water-pools, that he was longing to be in his tanyard close by.

He pulled out his great silver watch — the dread of our house, for it was a watch which seemed to have imbibed something of its master's character; remorseless as justice or fate, it never erred a moment.

"Twenty-three minutes lost by this shower. Phineas, my son, how am I to get thee safe home? unless thee wilt go with me to the tanyard — "

I shook my head. It was very hard for Abel Fletcher to have for his only child such a sickly creature as I, now, at sixteen, — as helpless and useless to him as a baby.

"Well, well, I must find some one to go home with thee." For though my father had got me a sort of carriage in which, with a little external aid, I could propel myself, so as to be his companion occasionally in his walks between our house, the tanyard, and the Friends' meetinghouse — still, he never trusted me anywhere alone. "Here, Sally — Sally Watkins! do any o' thy lads want to earn an honest penny?"

Sally was out of earshot; but I noticed that as the lad near us heard my father's words, the color rushed over his face, and he started forward involuntarily. I had not before perceived how wasted and hungry-looking he was.

"Father!" I whispered. But here the boy had mustered up his courage and voice.

"Sir, I want work; may I earn a penny?"

He spoke in tolerably good English; and taking off his tattered cap, looked right into my father's face. The old man scanned him closely.

"What is thy name lad?"

"John Halifax."

"Where dost thee come from?"

"Cornwall."

"Hast thee any parents living?"

"No."

I wished my father would not question thus; but possibly he had his own motives, which were rarely harsh, though his actions often appeared so.

"How old might thee be, John Halifax?"

"Fourteen, sir."

"Thee art used to work?"

"Yes."

"What sort of work?"

"Anything that I can get to do."

I listened nervously to this catechism, which went on behind my back.

"Well," said my father, after a pause, "thee shalt take my

son home, and I'll give thee a groat. Let me see; art thee a lad to be trusted?" And holding him at arm's length, regarding him meanwhile with eyes that were the terror of all the rogues in Norton Bury, Abel Fletcher jingled temptingly the silver money in the pockets of his long-flapped brown waistcoat. " I say, art thee a lad to be trusted?"

John Halifax neither answered the question nor declined his eyes. He seemed to feel that this was a critical moment, and to gather all his mental forces to meet the attack. He met it, and conquered in silence.

" Lad, shall I give thee the groat now?"

" Not till I've earned it, sir."

So, drawing his hand back, my father slipped the money into mine, and left us.

It still rained slightly, and so we remained under cover. John Halifax leaned in his old place, and did not attempt to talk.

Once only, when the draught through the alley made me shiver, he pulled my coat round me carefully.

" You are not very strong, I'm afraid?"

" No."

As soon as the rain ceased, we took our way home down the High Street toward the Abbey church, he guiding my carriage along in silence. I wished he would talk and let me hear again his pleasant Cornish accent.

" How strong you are!" said I, sighing, when, with a sudden pull, he had saved me from being overturned by a horseman riding past. " So tall and so strong."

JOHN HALIFAX NEITHER ANSWERED THE QUESTION NOR DECLINED HIS EYES.

"Am I? Well, I shall want my strength."

"How?"

"To earn my living."

He drew up his broad shoulders, and planted on the pavement a firmer foot, as if he knew that he had the world before him, would meet it singlehanded, and without fear.

"What have you worked at lately?"

"Anything I could get, for I have never learned a trade."

"Should you like to learn one?"

He hesitated a minute, as if weighing his speech.

"Once I thought I should like to be what my father was."

"What was he?"

"A scholar and a gentleman."

This was news, though it did not much surprise me.

"Then, perhaps," I said, "you would not like to follow a trade?"

"Yes, I should. What would it matter to me? My father was a gentleman."

"And your mother?"

He turned suddenly round; his cheeks hot, his lips quivering. "She is dead. I do not like to hear strangers speak about my mother."

I asked his pardon. It was plain he had loved and mourned her. He had an advantage over me, alas! I did not even remember my mother. Only a few minutes after, I said something about wishing we were not "strangers."

"Do you?" The lad's half-amazed, half-grateful smile went right to my heart.

"Have you been up and down the country much?"

"A great deal, these last three years; doing a hand's turn, as best I could, in hop-picking, apple gathering, harvesting; only this summer I had typhus fever, and could not work."

"What did you do then?"

"I lay in a barn till I got well. I am quite well now; you need not be afraid."

"No, indeed; I never thought of that."

We soon became quite sociable together. He guided me carefully out of the town into the Abbey walk, flecked with sunshine through overhanging trees. Once he stopped to pick up for me the large brown fan of a horse-chestnut leaf.

"It's pretty, isn't it? Only it shows that autumn is come."

"And how shall you live in the winter, when there is no out-of-door work to be had?"

"I don't know."

The lad's countenance fell, and that hungry, weary look which had vanished while we talked returned more painfully than ever. I reproached myself for having, under the influence of his merry talk, temporarily forgotten it.

"Ah!" I cried eagerly, when we left the shade of the Abbey trees, and crossed the street; "here we are, at home!"

"Are you?" The homeless lad just glanced at it, the flight of spotless stone steps, guarded by ponderous railings, which led to my father's respectable and handsome door. "Good day, then, which means good-by."

I started. The word pained me. On my sad, lonely life,—

brief indeed, though ill health seemed to have doubled and trebled my sixteen years, — this lad's face had come like a flash of sunshine; a reflection of the merry boyhood, the youth and strength that never were, never could be, mine. To let it go from me was like going back into the dark.

"Not good-by just yet!" said I, trying painfully to disengage myself from my little carriage and mount the steps. John Halifax came to my aid.

"Suppose you let me carry you. I could — and — and — it would be great fun, you know."

He tried to turn it into jest, so as not to hurt me; but the tremble in his voice was as tender as any woman's — tenderer than any woman's *I* ever was used to hear. I put my arms around his neck; he lifted me safely and carefully, and set me at my own door. Then, with another good-by, he again turned to go.

My heart cried after him with an irrepressible cry. What I said I do not remember, but it caused him to return.

"Is there anything more I can do for you, sir?"

"Don't call me 'sir'; I am only a boy like yourself. I want you; don't go yet. Ah! here comes my father!"

John Halifax stood aside and touched his cap respectfully as the old man passed.

"So here thee be; hast thou taken care of my son? Did he give thee thy groat, my lad?"

We had neither of us once thought of the money.

When I acknowledged this, my father laughed, called John an

honest lad, and began searching in his pocket for some larger coin. I ventured to draw his ear down, and whisper something, but I got no answer; meanwhile John Halifax, for the third time, was going away.

"Stop, lad! I forget thy name; here is thy groat, and a shilling added, for being kind to my son."

"Thank you, but I don't want payment for kindness."

He kept the groat, and put back the shilling into my father's hand.

"Eh!" said the old man, much astonished, "thee 'rt an odd lad; but I can't stay talking with thee. Come in to dinner, Phineas — I say," turning back to John Halifax with a sudden thought, "art thee hungry?"

"Very hungry." Nature gave way at last, and great tears came into the poor lad's eyes; "nearly starving."

"Bless me! then get in and have thy dinner. But first —" and my father held him by the shoulder — "thee art a decent lad, come of decent parents?"

"Yes," almost indignantly.

"Thee works for thy living?"

"I do whenever I can get it."

"Thee hast never been in jail?"

"No!" thundered out the lad, with a furious look. "I don't want your dinner, sir; I would have stayed, because your son asked me, and he was civil to me, and I liked him. Now I think I had better go. Good day, sir."

I caught him by the hand, and would not let him go.

"There, get in, lads, make no more ado," said Abel Fletcher, sharply, as he disappeared.

So, still holding John fast, I brought him into my father's house.

PART II

Jessop	battered	mollified	confounded
witness	ecstasies	compacted	contradicted
Richard	entreaty	impervious	Whittington
clematis	modified	experiment	straightforward

After dinner, when Father had returned to the tanyard, and John and I were left alone, I said, "John, do you know you're uncommonly like a childish hero of mine, Dick Whittington? Did you ever hear of him?"

"No."

"Come into the garden, then. You will hear the Abbey bells chime presently, not unlike Bow bells, I used to fancy sometimes; and we'll lie on the grass, and I will tell you the whole true and particular story of Sir Richard Whittington."

I lifted myself and began looking for my crutches. John found and put them into my hand, with a grave, pitiful look.

"You don't need crutches," I said, making pretense to laugh, for I had not grown used to them, and felt often ashamed.

"I hope you will not need them always."

"Perhaps not; Doctor Jessop isn't sure. But it doesn't matter much; most likely I shan't live long."

John looked at me, surprised, troubled, compassionate, but he

172

did not say a word. I hobbled past him, he following through the long passage to the garden door. There I paused, tired out. John Halifax took gentle hold of my shoulder.

"I think, — if you do not mind, — I'm sure I could carry you. I carried a meal sack once, weighing eight stone."

I burst out laughing, which maybe was what he wanted, and forthwith consented to assume the place of the meal sack. He took me on his back, — what a strong fellow he was! — and fairly trotted with me down the garden walk. We were both very merry, and though I was his senior, I seemed with him, out of my great weakness and infirmity, to feel almost like a child.

"Please take me to that clematis arbor; it looks over the Avon. Now, how do you like our garden?"

"It's a nice place."

He did not go into ecstasies, as I had half expected, but gazed about him observantly, while a quiet, intense satisfaction grew and spread over his whole countenance.

"It's a *very* nice place."

Certainly it was. A large square, chiefly grass, level as a bowling green, with borders around. Beyond, divided by a low hedge, was the kitchen and fruit garden, my father's pride; and above that, the high wall, the yew-hedge, and the river.

John Halifax's comprehensive gaze seemed to take in all.

"Have you lived here long?" he asked me.

"Ever since I was born."

"Ah! — well, it's a nice place," he repeated, somewhat sadly.

" This grass plot is very even — thirty yards square, I should guess. I'd get up and pace it, only I'm rather tired."

" Are you ? Yet you would carry —"

"Oh ! that's nothing. I've often walked farther than to-day. But still it's a good step across the country since morning."

" How far have you come ?"

" From the foot of those hills — I forget what they call them — over there. I have seen bigger ones, — but they are steep enough, — bleak and cold, too, especially when one is lying out among the sheep. At a distance they look pleasant. This is a very pretty view."

He stood gazing at it a good while — a new expression dawning in his eyes. Eyes in which then, for the first time, I watched a thought grow, and grow, till out of them was shining a beauty absolutely divine.

All of a sudden the Abbey chimes burst out, and made the lad start.

" What's that ?"

" Turn again, Whittington, Lord Mayor of London," I sang to the bells ; and then it seemed such a commonplace history, and such a very low degree of honor to arrive at, that I was really glad I had forgotten to tell John the story. I merely showed him where, beyond our garden wall, rose up the grim old Abbey tower.

" Probably this garden belonged to the Abbey in ancient time — our orchard is so fine. The monks may have planted it ; they liked fruit."

"Oh! did they?" He evidently did not quite comprehend, but was trying — without asking — to find out what I referred to. I was almost ashamed, lest he might think I wanted to show off my superior knowledge.

"The monks were parsons, John, you know."

"Oh, indeed. Do you think they planted that yew-hedge?" And he went to examine it.

Now, far and near, our yew-hedge was noted. There was not its like in the whole country. It was about fifteen feet high, and as many thick. Century and century of growth, with careful clipping and training, had compacted it into a massive green barrier, as close and impervious as a wall.

John poked in and about it, peering through every opening, and leaning his breast against the solid depth of branches; but their close shield resisted all his strength.

At length he came back to me, his face glowing with the vain efforts he had made.

"What were you about? Did you want to get through?"

"I wanted just to see if it were possible."

I shook my head. "What would you do, John, if you were shut up here, and had to get over the yew-hedge? You could not climb it!"

"I know that, and therefore should not waste time in trying."

"Would you give up, then?"

He smiled; there was no "giving up" in that smile of his. "I'll tell you what I'd do; I'd begin and break it, twig by twig, till I forced my way through, and got out safe at the other side."

"Well done, lad! but if it's all the same to thee, I would rather thee did not try that experiment upon *my* hedge at present."

My father had come behind, and overheard us, unobserved. We were both somewhat confounded, though a look of grim kindliness showed that he was not displeased, nay, even amused.

"Is that thy usual fashion of getting over a difficulty, friend, — what's thy name?"

I supplied the answer, for the minute Abel Fletcher appeared, John seemed to lose all his boyish fun.

My father sat down beside me on the bench, and leaning on his stick with both hands, eyed John Halifax sharply all over, from top to toe.

"Didn't thee say thee wanted work? It looks rather like it."

His glance upon the shabby clothes made the boy color violently.

"Oh! thee need'st not be ashamed; better men than thee have been in rags. Hast thee any money?"

"The groat you gave me, that is, paid me; I never take what I don't earn," said the lad, sticking a hand in either poor pocket.

"Don't be afraid — I was not going to give thee anything — except, maybe — would thee like some work?"

"Oh, sir!"

"Oh, Father!"

I hardly know which was the more grateful cry.

Abel Fletcher looked surprised, but, on the whole, not ill-pleased. Putting on and pulling down his broad-brimmed hat, he sat meditatively for a minute or so, making circles in the gravel walk with the end of his stick. People said that the wealthy Friend himself had come to Norton Bury without a shilling in his pocket.

"Well, what work canst thee do, lad?"

"Anything," was the eager answer.

"Anything generally means nothing," sharply said my father. "What hast thee been at all this year? The truth, mind!"

John's eyes flashed, but a look from mine seemed to set him right again. He said quietly and respectfully: "Let me think a minute, and I'll tell you. All spring I was at a farmer's, riding the plow-horses, hoeing turnips; then I went up the hills with some sheep; in June I tried hay-making, and caught a fever — you needn't start, sir; I've been well these six weeks, or I shouldn't have come near your son — then —"

"That will do, lad, — I'm satisfied."

"Thank you, sir."

"Thee need not say 'sir' — it is folly. I am Abel Fletcher."

"Very well, I will remember;" answered the boy, fearlessly. "And now, Abel Fletcher, I shall be willing and thankful for any work you can give me."

"We'll see about it."

I looked gratefully and hopefully at my father; but his next words rather modified my pleasure.

"Phineas, one of my men at the tanyard has gone. Dost thee think this lad is fit to take the place?"

"Whose place, Father?"

177

"Bill Watkins'."

I was dumfounded! I had occasionally seen the said Bill Watkins, whose business it was to collect the skins which my father had bought from the farmers round about. The idea of John Halifax in such a position was not agreeable.

"But, Father —"

He read entreaty in my looks — alas! he knew too well how I disliked the tanyard and all belonging to it. "Thee'rt a fool, and the lad's another. He may go about his business for me."

"But, Father, isn't there anything else?"

"I have nothing else, or if I had, I wouldn't give it. 'He that will not work, neither shall he eat.'"

"I will work," said John, sturdily; he had listened, hardly comprehending, to my father and me. "I don't care what it is, if only it's honest work."

Abel Fletcher was mollified. He turned his back on me, — but that I little minded, — and addressed himself solely to John Halifax.

"Canst thee drive?"

"That I can!" and his eyes brightened with boyish delight.

"Tut! it's only a cart; the cart with the skins. Dost thee know anything of tanning?"

"No, but I can learn."

"Hey, not so fast! still, better be fast than slow. In the meantime, thee can drive the cart."

"Thank you, sir, — Abel Fletcher, I mean, — I'll do it well. That is, as well as I can."

"Well, I'll take thee; though it isn't often I take a lad without a character of some sort. I suppose thee hast none."

"None," was the answer, while the straightforward, steady gaze unconsciously contradicted the statement; his own honest face was the lad's best witness — at all events, I thought so.

"'Tis done, then."

Carelessly rising, my father, from some kindly impulse, or else to mark the closing of the bargain, shook the boy's hand, and left in it a shilling.

"What is this for?"

"To show I have hired thee as my servant."

"Servant!" John repeated hastily, and rather proudly. "Oh, yes! I understand; well, I will try to serve you well."

Having settled the question of wages, which John Halifax did not debate at all, my father left us, but turned back when halfway across the green-turfed square.

"Thee said thee had no money; there's a week in advance, my son being witness I pay it to thee; and I can pay thee a shilling less every Saturday till we get straight."

"Very well, sir; good afternoon, and thank you."

John took off his cap as he spoke; Abel Fletcher, involuntarily, almost, touched his hat in return of the salutation. Then he walked away, and we had the garden all to ourselves.

I grasped John's hand for the first time, and looking up at him, as he stood thoughtfully by me, whispered that I was very glad.

"Thank you, so am I;" said he, in a low tone. Then all his

own manner returned; he threw his battered cap high up in the air, and shouted out, "Hurrah!"—a thorough boy.

And I, in my poor, quavering voice, shouted too.

Part III

scoop	required	degrading
abated	avalanche	progressing

Many days came and went before I again saw John Halifax —almost before I again thought of him. For it was one of my seasons of excessive pain, when I found it difficult to think of anything beyond those four gray walls, where morning, noon, and night slipped wearily away, marked by no changes, save from daylight to candlelight, from candlelight to dawn.

Afterwards, as my pain abated, I began to be haunted by occasional memories of something pleasant that had crossed my dreary life; visions of a brave, bright young face, ready alike to battle with and enjoy the world. I could hear the voice, which, speaking to me, was always tender with pity—yet not pity enough to wound.

I wondered whether John had ever asked for me. At length I put the question.

My nurse "thought he had, but wasn't sure. Didn't bother her head about such folk."

"If he asked again, might he come upstairs?"

"No."

I was too weak to combat; so I lay for days and days in my

180

sick room, often thinking, but never speaking, about the lad; never once asking for him to come to me.

At last I broke the bonds of sickness, and plunged into the outer world again. It was on a soft, bright, autumn morning that I came downstairs. A wandering robin came to sing to me. I opened my window to hear him. I then amused myself watching a farmer's cart winding down the rural road. Behind the farmer's cart came another, which at first I hardly noticed. I watched the two carts, the second of which was with difficulty passing the farmer's on the opposite side of the road. At last, it succeeded in getting past, and the driver lifted his hat with a very merry, frank, pleasant smile.

Surely, I knew that smile, and the well-set head with its light curly hair. Also, alas! I knew the cart. It was our cart of skins, and John Halifax was driving it.

"John! John!" I called out, but he did not hear, for his horse had taken fright and required a steady hand. Very steady the boy's hand was, so that the farmer clapped his two great fists, and shouted "Bravo!"

I leaned out, watching him approach our house. The lad looked up. A beaming smile of surprise and pleasure, a friendly nod, then all his manner changed; he took off his cap, and bowed ceremoniously to his master's son. Having made his salutation, he was driving on when I called after him — "John! John!"

"Yes, sir. I am so glad you're better again."

"Stop one minute till I come out to you." And I crawled

181

on my crutches to the front door, forgetting everything but the pleasure of meeting him.

"I had no notion of seeing you," he said. "They told me you were in bed yesterday. Ought you to be standing at the door this cold day?"

"It's quite warm," I said, looking up at the sunshine, and shivering.

"Please, go in."

"If you'll come too."

He nodded, then put his arm around me, and helped me in, as if he had been a big elder brother, and I a little ailing child.

"I'm glad you're better," he said, and said no more. But one look of his expressed as much as half a dozen sympathetic sentences of other people.

"And how have you been, John? How do you like the tanyard? Tell me frankly."

He pulled a wry face, and said, cheerily: "People must like what brings them their daily bread. It's a grand thing for me not to have been hungry for nearly thirty days."

"Poor John!" I put my hand on his wrist, his strong, brawny wrist. "I have so often wanted to see you, John. Couldn't you come in now?"

He shook his head, and pointed to the cart. That minute, through the open hall door, I saw my nurse sauntering leisurely home from market.

Now if I were a coward, it was not for myself this time.

The avalanche of ill words I knew must fall, but it should not fall on him if I could help it.

"Jump up on your cart, John. Let me see how well you can drive. There — good-by, for the present. Are you going to the tanyard?"

"Yes, for the rest of the day." And he made a face as if he did not quite revel in that delightful prospect; no wonder!

"I'll come to see you there this afternoon."

"No?" with a look of delighted surprise. "But you *must* not — you ought not."

"But I *will!*" And I laughed to hear myself actually using that phrase.

When my father came home, he found me waiting in my place at table. He only said, "Thee art better then, my son?" But I knew how glad he was to see me.

"Father," said I, when he ceased talking.

"Well, my son?"

"I should like to go with thee to the tanyard this afternoon."

"So, Phineas, thee art really strong enough to go out?"

"If thou wilt take me, Father."

We set out together; progressing through Norton Bury streets, in our old way, my father marching along in his grave fashion, I steering my little carriage, and keeping as close as I could beside him. I had never been in the town since the day I came through it with John Halifax. In the alleys hundreds of our poor folk were living, huddled together in misery, rags, and dirt. Was John Halifax living there too?

Alice Barber Stephens.

WE SET OUT TOGETHER, IN OUR OLD WAY, MY FATHER MARCHING ALONG IN HIS
GRAVE FASHION.

My father's tanyard was in an alley a little farther on. I already perceived the familiar odor. I wondered how anybody could endure it: yet some did; and among the workingmen, as we entered, I looked for the lad I knew.

He was sitting in a corner of one of the sheds, helping two or three women to split bark, very busy at work; yet he found time to stop now and then to give a wisp of sweet hay to the old blind horse as he went slowly round and round, turning the mill. As we passed, John did not even see us.

I asked my father, in a whisper, how he liked the boy.

"What boy? Eh, him? — Oh, well enough — there's no harm in him that I know of. Dost thee want him to wheel thee about the yard? Here, I say, lad, bless me! I've forgotten thy name."

John Halifax started up at the sharp tone of command, but when he saw me, he smiled. My father walked on.

"John, I want you."

John shook himself free from the heap of bark, and came rather hesitatingly at first.

"Anything I can do for you, sir?"

"Don't call me 'sir'; if I say 'John,' why don't you say 'Phineas'?"

And I held out my hand — his was all grimed with bark dust.

"Are you not ashamed to shake hands with me?"

"Nonsense, John."

So we settled that point entirely.

He guided me carefully among the tan pits until we reached the lower end of the yard. It was bounded by the Avon only, and by a great heap of refuse bark.

"This is not a bad place to rest in; if you wished to get out of the carriage, I'd make you comfortable here in no time."

I was quite willing; so he ran off and fetched an old horse rug which he laid upon the soft, dry mass. Then he helped me thither, and covered me with my cloak. Lying thus, with my hat over my eyes, just distinguishing the shiny glimmer of the Avon running below, and beyond that the green valley, dotted with cows, my position was anything but unpleasant.

"Are you comfortable, Phineas?"

"Very, if you would come and sit down too."

"That I will."

And then we began to talk. "How goes the world with you?" said I. "Have you taken kindly to the tanyard? Answer frankly."

He looked at me hard, put both his hands in his pockets, and began to whistle a tune.

"Don't shirk the question, please, John. I want to know the real truth."

"Well, then, I hate the tanyard."

Having relieved his mind by saying this, and by kicking a small heap of tanbark down into the river, he became composed. "But, Phineas, don't imagine I intend to hate it always; I intend to get used to it, as many a better fellow than I am has got used to many a worse thing. It is wicked to hate what wins one's bread, and is the only thing one is likely to get on in the world with, merely because it is disagreeable."

"You are a wise lad of your age, John."

"Now don't you be laughing at me." But I was not, I was in solemn earnest. "And don't think I'm worse than I am; and especially that I am not thankful to your good father for giving me a lift in the world, the first I have ever really had. If I get one foot on the ladder, perhaps, I may climb."

"I should rather believe so," answered I, very confidently. "But you seem to have thought a good deal about these things."

"Oh, yes! I have plenty of time for thinking, and one's thoughts travel fast enough, lying on this bark-heap, faster than indoors. I often wish I could read; that is, read easily. As it is, I have nothing to do but to think, and nothing to think of but myself, and what I should like to be."

"Suppose, after Dick Whittington's fashion, you succeeded to your master's business, should you like to be a tanner?"

He paused, his truthful face betraying him. Then he said, resolutely, "I should like to be anything that is honest and honorable. It is a notion of mine, that whatever a man may be, his trade does not make him; he makes his trade. That is — but I know I can't put the subject clear, for I have not got it clear in my own head yet — I am only a lad. However, it all comes to this — that whether I like it or not, I'll stick to the tanning as long as I can."

"That's right; I'm so glad. Nevertheless, John, it's my notion that you might be anything you liked."

He laughed. "Whatever I may be, I am just now the lad that drives your father's cart and works in your father's tanyard —John Halifax, and very much at your service, Mr. Phineas Fletcher."

The afternoon had waned during our talk, but I was very loath to part with my friend. Suddenly, I thought of asking where his home was. "How do you mean?"

"Where do you live? where do you take your meals, and where do you sleep?"

"Why, as to that, I have not much time for eating and drinking. Generally, I eat my dinner as I go along the road, where there's lots of blackberries by way of pudding, which is grand! Supper, when I do get it, I like best on this bark heap, after the men are away, and the tanyard is clear. Your father lets me stay."

"And where is your lodging, then? Where do you sleep?"

He hesitated and colored a little. "To tell the truth, anywhere I can. Generally here."

"What, out of doors?"

"Just so."

I was much shocked. To sleep out of doors seemed to me the very lowest ebb of human misery: so degrading, too; like a common tramp or vagabond, instead of a decent lad.

"John — how can you — why do you — do such a thing?"

"I'll tell you," said he, sitting down beside me in a dogged way; as if he had read my thoughts. "Look here. I get three shillings a week, which is about fivepence a day; out of that, I

188

eat threepence; I'm a big, growing lad, and it is hard to be hungry. There's twopence left to pay for lodging. I tried it once — twice — at the best place I could find, but I don't intend to try that again. I was never used to it. Better keep my own company and the open air. Now, you see."

"Oh, John!"

"There's no need to be sorry. You don't know how comfortable it is to sleep out of doors, nor how nice it is to wake in the middle of the night, and see the stars shining over your head."

"But isn't it very cold?"

"No — not often. I scoop out a snug little nest in the bark, and curl up in it like a dormouse, wrapped in this rug, which one of the men gave me. Besides, every morning early I take a plunge and a swim in the stream, and that makes me warm all day."

I shivered; I who feared the touch of cold water. Yet there, with all his hardships, he stood before me, the model of healthy boyhood. Alas! I envied him.

"What shall you do when winter comes?"

John looked grave. "I don't know: I suppose I shall manage somehow — like the sparrows."

My question had evidently made him thoughtful; he remained silent a good while.

At last I said, "John, do you remember the woman who spoke so sharply to you in the alley that day?"

"Yes; I shall never forget anything which happened that day," he answered softly.

"She was my nurse once. She is not such a bad woman, though trouble has sharpened her temper. Her biggest boy, Bill, who has gone off to be a soldier, used to drive your cart, you know.

"Sally is poor, but not so very poor, though. Your twopence a night would help her; and I dare say, if you let me speak to her, you might have Bill's attic room all to yourself. She has but one other lad at home. It's worth trying."

"It is, indeed. You are very kind, Phineas." He said no more, but his tone spoke volumes.

I got into my little carriage again, for I was anxious not to lose a day in this matter. I persuaded John to go at once with me to see Sally Watkins. My father was not to be seen, but I left word for him that I had gone home, and had taken John Halifax with me : it was astonishing how bold I felt myself growing, now that there was another besides myself to think and act for.

Part IV

| chronicle | apprentice | despondency |
| reverence | invariably | transformation |

We reached Widow Watkins' door. It was a poor place, poorer than I had imagined.

Sally sat in her kitchen, tidy and subdued. She consented at once to let John have the room, though she looked up with an odd stare when I said he was " a friend " of mine.

Before we left I wanted to see his room; he carried me up, and we both sat down on the bed. The attic was very low and small, hardly big enough "to whip a cat round," or even a kitten, and yet John gazed about it with an air of proud possession.

"I declare I shall be as happy as a king," said he. "Only look out of the window."

"Do you like your 'castle,' John?" said I, when I had silently watched his beaming face; "will it suit you?"

"I rather think it will!" he cried in hearty delight. And my heart likewise was very glad.

Dear little attic room! Close against the sky; so close that many a time the rain came pattering in, or the sun beating down upon the roof made it like a furnace, or the snow on the leads drifted so high as to obscure the window; yet how merry, how happy we have been there! How often have we both looked back upon it in after days!

Winter came early and suddenly that year.

It was to me a long, dreary season, worse even than my winters inevitably were. I never stirred from my room, and never saw anybody but my father, Dr. Jessop, and my nurse. At last I took courage to say to my father that I wished he would send John Halifax up some day.

"What dost thee want the lad for?"

"Only to see him."

"Pshaw! a lad out of the tanyard is not fit company for thee. Let him alone; he'll do well enough, if thee doesn't try to lift him out of his place."

Lift John Halifax out of his place! I agreed with my father that that was impossible; but then we evidently differed widely in our definition of what his place might be. So, afraid of doing him harm, I did not discuss the matter. Only at every possible opportunity — and they were rare — I managed to send John a little note, written carefully in printed letters, for I knew he could read that; also a book or two, out of which he might teach himself a little more.

Then I waited, eagerly but patiently, until spring came. One February day, when the frost had at last broken up, I crawled down into the parlor, and out of the parlor into the garden. It was delicious to see again the green grass, which had been hidden for weeks; delicious to walk up and down again in the sunshine, under the shelter of the yew-hedge.

" Look at that young gentleman coming down the garden," said my nurse; " and here I am in my dirty gown, and my apron full of cabbages."

And she dropped the vegetables all over the path as the " gentleman " came towards us.

I smiled; for, in spite of his transformation, I, at least, had no difficulty in recognizing John Halifax.

He had on new clothes; let me give the credit due to that wonderful civilizer, the tailor; clothes neat, decent, and plain, such as any apprentice lad might wear. They fitted well his figure, which had increased both in height, compactness, and grace.

" I don't drive the cart now," he said.

Alice Barber Stephens.

I SMILED, FOR I AT LEAST HAD NO DIFFICULTY IN RECOGNIZING JOHN HALIFAX.

"Not drive the cart?" I asked eagerly, for I was afraid some ill chance had happened.

"This winter I have managed to teach myself to read and add up, out of your books; and your father found it out, and he says I shall go round collecting money instead of skins, and it is much better wages, and — I like it better, that's all."

But, little as he said, his whole face beamed with pride and pleasure. It was, in truth, a great step forward.

"He must trust you very much, John," said I, at last, knowing how exceedingly particular my father was in his collectors.

"That's it; that's what pleases me so. He is very good to me, Phineas, and he gave me a special holiday, that I might go out with you. Isn't that grand?"

"Grand, indeed. What fun we shall have! I almost think I could take a walk myself."

For the lad's company invariably gave me new life, and strength, and hope. The very sight of him was as good as the coming of spring.

"Where shall we go?" said he, when we were fairly off, and he was guiding my carriage down Norton Bury streets.

"Now, John, tell me what you have been doing all winter."

It was a brief and simple chronicle — of hard work, all day, and from Monday to Saturday — too hard work to do anything nights, except to drop into the sound, dreamless sleep of youth and labor.

"But how did you teach yourself to read and add up, then?"

"Generally at odd minutes going along the road. It is astonishing what a lot of odd minutes one can catch during the day, if one really sets about it."

"What books have you got through?"

"All you sent, — Pilgrim's Progress, Robinson Crusoe, and the Arabian Nights. That's fine, isn't it?" and his eyes sparkled.

"Any more?"

"Also the one you gave me on Christmas. I have read it a good deal."

I liked the tone of quiet reverence in which he spoke. I liked to hear him own, nor be ashamed to own — that he read "a good deal" in that rare book for a boy to read — the Bible.

But on this subject I did not ask him any more questions; indeed, it seemed to me, and seems still, that no more were needed.

"And you can read quite easily now, John?"

"Pretty well, considering." Then, turning suddenly to me: "You read a great deal, don't you? I overheard your father say you were very clever. How much do you know?"

"Oh, nonsense!" But he pressed me, and I told him. The list was short enough; I almost wished it were shorter, when I saw John's face.

"For me — I can only just read, and I shall be fifteen directly!"

The accent of shame, despondency, even despair, went to my very heart.

"Don't mind," I said, laying my feeble, useless hand upon that which guided me on, so steady and so strong; "how could you have had time, working so hard as you do?"

"But I ought to learn; I must learn."

"You shall. It is little I can teach you; but, if you like, I'll teach you all I know."

"Oh, Phineas!" One flash of those bright, moist eyes, and he walked on beside me in silence.

I was silent, too, but I stole a glance at his mouth, as seen in profile. I could almost always guess at his thoughts by that mouth, so flexible, sensitive, and, at times, so infinitely sweet. It wore that expression now. I was satisfied, for I knew the lad was happy.

NOBILITY

Alice Cary

mete   malice   avenges   beguile

True worth is in *being*, not *seeming*, —
　　In doing each day that goes by
Some little good, — not in the dreaming
　　Of great things to do by and by.
For whatever men say in blindness,
　　And spite of the fancies of youth,
There's nothing so kingly as kindness,
　　And nothing so royal as truth.

We get back our mete as we measure,
  We cannot do wrong and feel right,
Nor can we give pain and gain pleasure,
  For justice avenges each slight.
The air for the wing of the sparrow,
  The bush for the robin and wren,
But always the path that is narrow
  And straight, for the children of men.

'Tis not in the pages of story
  The heart of its ills to beguile,
Though he who makes courtship to glory
  Gives all that he hath for her smile.
For when from her heights he has won her,
  Alas! it is only to prove
That nothing's so sacred as honor,
  And nothing so loyal as love!

We cannot make bargains for blisses,
  Nor catch them like fishes in nets;
And sometimes the thing our life misses,
  Helps more than the thing which it gets.
For good lieth not in pursuing,
  Nor gaining of great nor of small,
But just in the doing, and doing
  As we would be done by, is all.

Through envy, through malice, through hating,
  Against the world, early and late,

No jot of our courage abating —
　　Our part is to work and to wait.
And slight is the sting of his trouble
　　Whose winnings are less than his worth;
For he who is honest is noble,
　　Whatever his fortunes or birth.

Tweed	Melrose	disguise	Abbotsford
similar	chivalry	equipped	introduction
crusade	gorgeous	Locksley	documentary
yeoman	enormous	Sherwood	anonymously

Walter Scott was born in Edinburgh in 1771. He was a boy whom you would have liked to know. He early began to take delight in books, and he read "the usual, or rather ten times the usual, quantity of fairy tales, Eastern tales, and romances," as well as history and poetry.

When his school days came to an end, he decided to try the law, but his father told him that his long rambles through the country, talking with shepherds and farmers, were a far better training for a peddler than for a lawyer. He found the law little to his liking, and little by little he was drawn to the field of literature.

He distinguished himself in both prose and poetry; and though his greatest literary work was to be in prose, he began with poetry. "Why did you quit poetry?" a friend once inquired of Scott. "Because Byron beat me," was the remarkably frank reply.

Scott bought a "mountain farm" at Abbotsford, on the banks of the Tweed, near the picturesque ruins of Melrose Abbey. He lavished care and money upon his estate. The cottage grew to a mansion, the mansion to a castle, and more land was bought and forests were planted.

His novels were all published anonymously, though it was generally believed, even at that time, that Scott was the author. He did not acknowledge

SIR WALTER SCOTT.

the authorship, however, until the failure, in 1826, of the publishing house with which he was secretly connected. He then assumed the vast debt of nearly six hundred thousand dollars which he was not bound in any legal sense to pay. He refused all offers of assistance and asked only for time, time to earn the money by the labor of his brain. Without one word of weak regret or vain repining, he left his splendid home at Abbotsford and shut himself up with his work in humble lodgings at Edinburgh. Book after book came from his pen to delight his eager readers. His romances finally paid the enormous debt he had assumed. He succeeded in his self-imposed task, but it cost him his life. After a voyage in a vain search for health, he returned to Scotland to spend his last days at his beautiful home. There he died in 1832. He has left us a double treasure — the memory of himself and the possession of his works.

Scott wrote "The Lady of the Lake," "Marmion," "The Lay of the Last Minstrel," and other poems; "The Talisman," "Ivanhoe," "Old Mortality," "Kennilworth," and many other novels. He wrote in all twenty-nine romantic novels. The whole series of romances is now known under the name of the "Waverly Novels." "Ivanhoe," from which the following selection about Locksley is taken, is perhaps the chief favorite of young people. With many, it has been the first introduction to the gorgeous world of chivalry; and, above all the rest of his books, it claims the title of romance.

The scene is laid in England at the time when John had wrongfully taken the throne from his brother, King Richard the Lion-Hearted, while the latter was away on a crusade. Richard has returned, however, and, in disguise, is looking on at the entertainments given by John. Locksley is the famous Robin Hood in disguise. On the previous day he had given offense to John, who cannot see through his disguise, but thinks him some blunt and ignorant yeoman.

And who was Robin Hood ? There is no documentary evidence respecting him. Yet a great number of the most popular English ballads make Robin Hood their hero, and recount his lawless pranks and daring deeds. He was said to be an outlaw and robber who lived more than five hundred years ago in the depths of Sherwood Forest in England. He was chief over a company of similar fellows — some say as many as a hundred. He had

ABBOTSFORD — FROM THE RIVER.

many disguises, but was most often clad in green, and equipped with his hunter's horn and his bow and arrows. He was the best archer in the world, for his arrow never missed its aim. Among his constant companions were Little John, so called from his extraordinary height, Will Scarlet, and the rest, — all supposed to have lived in Sherwood Forest, clad in Lincoln green.

THE ARCHERY CONTEST

Sir Walter Scott

cleave	jubilee	braggart	antagonist
sylvan	baldric	scourged	precedence
proffer	archery	Leicester	conclusions
infamy	provost	exhibited	pronounced
Hubert	insolent	medallion	Staffordshire

To the best archer a prize was to be awarded, it being a bugle horn, mounted with silver, and a silken baldric richly ornamented with a medallion of Saint Hubert, the patron of sylvan sport. More than thirty yeomen at first presented themselves as competitors.

Prince John stepped from his royal seat to view more closely the persons of these chosen yeomen, several of whom wore the royal livery. Having satisfied his curiosity, he looked for the object of his resentment, whom he observed standing on the same spot, and with the same composed countenance that he had exhibited upon the preceding day.

" Fellow," said Prince John, " I guessed by thy insolent babble thou wert no true lover of the long bow, and I see thou darest not adventure thy skill among such merrymen as stand yonder."

"Under favor, sir," replied the yeoman, "I have another reason for refraining to shoot, besides the fearing of defeat and disgrace."

"What is thy other reason?" said Prince John, who for some cause which he could not himself have explained, felt a painful curiosity respecting this individual.

"Because," replied the woodsman, "I know not if these yeomen and I are used to shoot at the same marks; and because, moreover, I know not how your Grace might relish the winning of a third prize by one who has unwittingly fallen under your displeasure."

Prince John colored as he put the question, "What is thy name, yeoman?"

"Locksley," answered the yeoman.

"Then, Locksley," said Prince John, "thou shalt shoot in thy turn, when these yeomen have displayed their skill. If thou carriest the prize, I will add to it twenty nobles; but if thou losest it, thou shalt be stripped of thy Lincoln green and scourged out of the lists with bowstrings, for a wordy and insolent braggart."

"And how if I refuse to shoot on such a wager?" said the yeoman. "Your Grace's power, supported as it is by so many men at arms, may indeed easily strip and scourge me, but cannot compel me to bend or draw my bow."

"If thou refusest my fair proffer," said the prince, "the provost of the lists shall cut thy bowstring, break thy bow and arrows, and expel thee from the presence as a faint-hearted craven."

"This is no fair chance you put on me, proud prince," said the yeoman; "to compel me to peril myself against the best archers of Leicester and Staffordshire, under the penalty of infamy if they should overshoot me. Nevertheless, I will obey your pleasure."

A target was placed at the upper end of the southern avenue, which led to the lists. The archers, having previously determined by lot their order of precedence, were each to shoot three shafts in succession.

One by one the archers stepping forward, delivered their shafts yeomanlike and bravely. Of twenty-four arrows, shot in succession, ten were fixed in the target, while the others ranged so near it, that, considering the distance of the mark, it was accounted good archery. Of the ten shafts that hit the target, two within the inner ring were shot by Hubert, a forester, who was accordingly pronounced victorious.

"Now, Locksley," said Prince John to the bold yeoman, with a bitter smile, "wilt thou try conclusions with Hubert, or wilt thou yield up bow, baldric, and quiver to the provost of the sports?"

"Sith it be no better," said Locksley, "I am content to try my fortune, on condition that when I have shot two shafts at yonder mark of Hubert's, he shall be bound to shoot one at that which I shall propose."

"That is but fair," answered Prince John, "and it shall not

be refused thee. If thou dost beat this braggart, Hubert, I will fill the bugle with silver pennies for thee."

"A man can but do his best," answered Hubert; "but my grandsire drew a good long bow at Hastings, and I trust not to dishonor his memory."

The former target was now removed, and a fresh one of the same size was placed in its room. Hubert, who, as victor in the first trial of skill, had the right to shoot first, took his aim with great deliberation, measuring long the distance with his eye, while he held in his hand his bended bow with the arrow placed on the string.

At length he made a step forward, and raising the bow at the full stretch of his left arm, till the center or grasping place was nigh level with his face, he drew his bowstring to his ear. The arrow whistled through the air and lighted within the inner ring of the target, but not exactly in the center.

"You have not allowed for the wind, Hubert," said his antagonist, bending his bow, "or that had been a better shot."

So saying, and without showing the least anxiety to pause upon his aim, Locksley stepped to the appointed station, and shot his arrow as carelessly in appearance as if he had not even looked at the mark. He was speaking almost at the instant that the shaft left the bowstring, and yet it alighted in the target two inches nearer to the white spot which marked the center than that of Hubert.

Hubert resumed his place, and not neglecting the caution that he had received from his adversary, made the necessary allowance for the very light wind that had just arisen, and shot so success-fully that his arrow alighted in the very center of the target.

"A Hubert! A Hubert!" shouted the populace, more interested in a known person than in a stranger.

"Thou canst not mend that shot, Locksley," said the prince, with an insulting smile.

"I will notch his shaft for him, however," replied Locksley.

And letting fly his arrow with a little more precaution than before, it lighted right upon that of his competitor, which it split to shivers. The people who stood around were so aston-ished at his wonderful skill that they could not even *give vent to their surprise in their usual clamor.

"And now," said Locksley, "I will crave your Grace's permission to plant such a mark as is used in the north country, and will welcome every brave yeoman who shall try a shot at it, to win a smile from the bonny lass he loves the best."

He then turned to leave the lists. "Let your guards attend me," he said, "if you please — I go but to cut a rod from the next willow bush."

Prince John made a signal that some attendants should follow him in case of his escape; but the cry of "Shame! shame!" which burst from the multitude induced him to alter his ungenerous purpose.

Locksley returned almost instantly with a willow wand about six feet in length, perfectly straight, and rather thicker than a man's thumb. He began to peel this with great com-posure, observing at the same time that to ask a good woodsman to shoot at a target so broad as had hitherto been used was to put shame upon his skill.

"For his own part," he said, "and in the land where he was bred, men would as soon take for their mark King Arthur's round table, which held sixty knights around it. A child of seven years old," he said, "might hit yonder target with a headless shaft; but," added he, walking deliberately to the other end of the lists, and sticking the willow wand upright in the ground, "he that hits that rod at fivescore yards, I call him an archer fit to bear both bow and quiver before a king, if it were the stout King Richard himself."

"My grandsire," said Hubert, "drew a good bow at the battle of Hastings, and never shot at such a mark in his life, and neither will I. If this yeoman can cleave that rod, I give him the buckler. A man can but do his best, and I will not shoot where I am sure to miss. I might as well shoot at a wheat straw, or at a sunbeam, as at a twinkling white streak which I can hardly see."

"Cowardly dog!" said Prince John. "Sirrah Locksley, do thou shoot; but if thou hittest such a mark, I will say thou art the first man ever did so. Howe'er it be, thou shalt not crow over us with a mere show of superior skill."

"I will do my best, as Hubert says," answered Locksley; "no man can do more."

So saying, he again bent his bow, but on the present occasion looked with attention to his weapon, and changed the string, which he thought was no longer truly round, having been a little frayed by the two former shots. He then took his aim with some deliberation, and the multitude awaited the event in breathless silence.

The archer justified their opinion of his skill : his arrow split the willow rod against which it was aimed. A jubilee of shouts followed ; and even Prince John, in admiration of Locksley's skill, lost for an instant his dislike of his person.

" These twenty nobles," he said, " which, with the bugle, thou hast fairly won, are thine own. We will make them fifty if thou wilt take livery and service with us as a yeoman of our bodyguard, and be near to our person. For never did so strong a hand bend a bow, or so true an eye direct a shaft."

" Pardon me, noble prince," said Locksley ; " but I have vowed that if ever I were to take service, it should be with your royal brother, King Richard. These twenty nobles I leave to Hubert, who has this day drawn as brave a bow as his grandsire did at Hastings. Had his modesty not refused the trial, he would have hit the wand as well as I."

Hubert shook his head as he received with reluctance the bounty of the stranger ; and Locksley, anxious to escape further observation, mixed with the crowd, and was seen no more.

THE LAST LEAF

OLIVER WENDELL HOLMES

prest   Crier   pruning

I saw him once before
As he passed by the door ;

208

LOCKSLEY CLEAVING THE WAND.

H. M. Eaton.

And again,
The pavement stones resound,
As he totters o'er the ground
   With his cane.

They say that in his prime,
Ere the pruning knife of Time
   Cut him down,
Not a better man was found
By the Crier on his round
   Through the town.

But now he walks the streets,
And he looks at all he meets
   Sad and wan;
And he shakes his feeble head,
That it seems as if he said,
   "They are gone."

The mossy marbles rest
On the lips that he has prest
   In their bloom;
And the names he loved to hear
Have been carved for many a year
   On the tomb.

My grandmamma has said —
Poor old lady, she is dead
   Long ago —

That he had a Roman nose,
And his cheek was like a rose
  In the snow.

But now his nose is thin,
And it rests upon his chin
  Like a staff;
And a crook is in his back
And a melancholy crack
  In his laugh.

I know it is a sin
For me to sit and grin
  At him here;
But the old three-cornered hat,
And the breeches, and all that,
  Are so queer!

And if I should live to be
The last leaf upon the tree
  In the spring,
Let them smile as I do now,
At the old forsaken bough
  Where I cling.

NIAGARA FALLS

Anthony Trollope

breach	epithet	caldron	cataracts
revoke	Ontario	tourists	permanent
drought	sublime	Trollope	precipitously
Anthony	Niagara	envelops	comparatively

Anthony Trollope was an English novelist, born in London in 1815. He has published a number of popular works, among which are " The Warden," " Doctor Thorne," and a descriptive work entitled " North America."

Of all the sights on this earth of ours which tourists travel to see, — at least of all those which I have seen, — I am inclined to give the palm to the Falls of Niagara. In the catalogue of such sights, I intend to include all buildings, pictures, statues, and wonders of art made by men's hands, and also all beauties of nature prepared by the Creator for the delight of his creatures.

This is a long word, but as far as my taste and judgment go, it is justified. I know no other one thing so beautiful, so glorious, so powerful.

I came across an artist at Niagara who was attempting to draw the spray of the waters. " You have a difficult subject," said I.

" All subjects are difficult," he replied, " to a man who desires to do well."

" But yours, I fear, is impossible," I said.

" You have no right to say so till I have finished my picture," he replied.

I acknowledged the justice of his rebuke, regretted that I could not remain till the completion of his work should enable me to revoke my words, and passed on. Then I began to reflect whether I did not intend to try a task as difficult in describing the falls.

I will not say that it is as difficult to describe aright that

NIAGARA FALLS FROM THE CANADIAN SHORE.

rush of waters as it is to paint it well; but I doubt whether it is not quite as difficult to write a description of it that shall interest the reader as it is to paint a picture of it that shall be pleasant to the beholder.

213

That the waters of Lake Erie have come down in their courses from the broad basins of Lake Michigan, Lake Superior, and Lake Huron; that these waters fall into Lake Ontario by the short and rapid river of Niagara, and that the falls of Niagara are made by a sudden break in the level of this rapid river, are probably known to all who will read this book.

All the waters of these huge northern inland seas run over that breach in the rocky bottom of the stream, and thence it comes that the flow is unceasing in its grandeur, and that no one can perceive a difference in the weight, or sound, or violence of the fall, whether it be visited in the drought of autumn, amidst the storms of winter, or after the melting of the upper worlds of ice in the days of the early summer.

How many cataracts does the habitual tourist visit at which the waters fail him! But at Niagara the waters never fail. There it thunders over its ledge in a volume that never ceases and is never diminished — as it has done from times previous to the life of man, and as it will do till tens of thousands of years shall see the rocky bed of the river worn away back to the upper lake.

This stream divides Canada from the States, the western or farthermost bank belonging to the British Crown, and the eastern or nearer bank being in the State of New York.

The falls are, as I have said, made by a sudden breach in the level of the river. All cataracts are, I presume, made by such breaches, but generally the waters do not fall precipitously as they do at Niagara; and never elsewhere, so far as the world yet knows, has a breach so sudden been made in a river carrying in its channel such, or any approach to such, a body of water.

Up above the falls for more than a mile, the waters leap and burst over the rapids as though conscious of the destiny that awaits them. Here the river is very broad and comparatively shallow, but from shore to shore, it frets itself into little torrents and begins to assume the majesty of its power.

Looking at it even here in the expanse which forms itself over the greater fall, one feels sure that not the strongest swimmer could have a chance of saving himself if fate had cast him in among even those petty whirlpools. The waters, though so broken in their descent, are deliciously green. This color, as seen early in the morning, or just as the sun has set, is so bright as to give to the place one of its chief charms.

This will be best seen from the farther end of the island, Goat Island, as it is called, which, as the reader will understand, divides the river immediately above the falls. Indeed, the island is a part of that precipitously broken ledge over which the river tumbles, and no doubt in the process of time will be worn away and covered with water. The time, however, will be very long. In the meanwhile it is perhaps a mile round, and is covered thickly with timber.

At the upper end of the island the waters are divided, and, coming down in two courses, each over its own rapids, form two separate falls. The bridge by which the island is reached is a hundred yards or more above the smaller fall.

We will go at once on to the glory, and the thunder, and

215

the majesty, and the wrath of the larger fall. Advancing beyond the path leading down to the lesser fall, we come to that point of the island at which the waters of the main river begin to descend. Hence, across to the Canadian side, the cataract continues itself in one unabated line; but the line is very far from being direct or straight.

After stretching for some little way from the shore to a point in the river which is reached by a wooden bridge, and at the end of which stands a tower upon the rock,—after stretching to this, the line of the ledge bends inward against the floods — in, and in, and in, till one is led to think that the depth of that horseshoe is immeasurable.

Go down to the end of that wooden bridge, seat yourself on the rail, and there sit till all the outer world is lost to you. There is no grander spot about Niagara than this. The waters are absolutely around you. If you have that power of eye, — control, — which is so necessary to the full enjoyment of scenery, you will see nothing but the water.

You will certainly hear nothing else; and the sound, I beg you to remember, is not an ear-cracking, agonizing crash and clang of noises, but is melodious and soft withal, though loud as thunder. It fills your ears, and, as it were, envelops them; but at the same time you can speak to your neighbor without an effort. But, at this place and in these moments, the less of speaking, I should say, the better.

There is no grander spot than this. Here, seated on the rail of the bridge, you will not see the whole depth of the fall.

012135, AMERICAN FALLS FROM GOAT ISLAND.

COPR. DETROIT PHOTOGRAPHIC CO.

AMERICAN FALLS FROM GOAT ISLAND.

In looking at the grandest works of nature, and of art, too, I fancy it is never well to see all. There should be something left to the imagination, and much should be half concealed in mystery.

It is glorious to watch the waters in their first curve over the rocks. They come green as a bank of emeralds, but with a fitful flying color, as though conscious that in one moment they would be dashed into spray and would rise into the air, pale as driven snow.

The vapor rises high into the air, and is gathered there, visible always as a permanent white cloud over the cataract; but the bulk of the spray which fills the lower hollow of that horseshoe is like a tumult of snow. This you will not fully see from your seat on the rail. The head of it rises ever and anon out of the caldron below, but the caldron itself will be invisible. It is ever so far down — far as your own imagination can sink it.

But your eyes will rest full upon the curve of the waters. The shape at which you will be looking is that of a horseshoe, but of a horseshoe miraculously deep from toe to heel; and this depth becomes greater as you sit there. That which was at first only great and beautiful becomes gigantic and sublime, till the mind is at a loss to find an epithet for its own use.

To realize Niagara, you must sit there till you see nothing else than that which you have come to see. You will hear nothing else, and think of nothing else. At length you will be at one with the tumbling water before you. You will find yourself among the waters, as though you belonged to them.

The cool, liquid green will run through your veins, and the voice of the cataract will be the expression of your own heart. You will fall as the bright waters fall, with no dismay; and you will rise again as the spray rises, bright, beautiful, and pure. Then you will flow away in your own course to the unbounded, distant, and eternal ocean.

THE REPUBLIC

Henry Wadsworth Longfellow

Union   anvils   anchors

Thou, too, sail on, O Ship of State!
Sail on, O Union, strong and great!
Humanity, with all its fears,
With all the hopes of future years,
Is hanging breathless on thy fate!
We know what Master laid thy keel,
What Workman wrought thy ribs of steel,
Who made each mast and sail and rope,
    What anvils rang, what hammers beat,
    In what a forge and what a heat
Were shaped the anchors of thy hope!
Fear not each sudden sound and shock,
'Tis of the wave, and not the rock;
'Tis but the flapping of the sail,
And not a rent made by the gale!
In spite of rock and tempest's roar,

219

In spite of false lights on the shore,
Sail on, nor fear to breast the sea!
Our hearts, our hopes, are all with thee,
　Our hearts, our hopes, our prayers, our tears,
　Our faith triumphant o'er our fears,
Are all with thee, — are all with thee!

— From "The Building of the Ship."

THE FLAG OF OUR COUNTRY

ROBERT C. WINTHROP

proclaim　　　　　officially　　　　　Declaration
cherished　　　　　symbolizes　　　　　constellation

There is the national flag. He must be cold indeed who can look upon its folds, rippling in the breeze, without pride of country. If he be in a foreign land, the flag is companionship and country itself, with all its endearments. Its highest beauty is in what it symbolizes. It is because it represents all, that all gaze at it with delight and reverence.

It is a piece of bunting lifted in the air; but it speaks sublimely, and every part has a voice. Its stripes of alternate red and white proclaim the original union of thirteen states to maintain the Declaration of Independence. Its stars of white on a field of blue proclaim that union of states constituting our national constellation, which receives a new star with every new state. The two together signify union past and present.

The very colors have a language which was officially recognized by our fathers. White is for purity, red for valor, blue for justice; and all together, — bunting, stripes, stars, and colors, — blazing in the sky, make the flag of our country to be cherished by all our hearts, to be upheld by all our hands.

THE NAME OF OLD GLORY

James Whitcomb Riley

humor   blended   audible   sanctified

When, why, and by whom, was our flag, the Stars and Stripes, first called " Old Glory " ? — (1898) — Daily Query to Press.

I

Old Glory ! say, who,
By the ships and the crew,
And the long, blended ranks of the gray and the blue, —
Who gave you, Old Glory, the name that you bear
With such pride everywhere
As you cast yourself free to the rapturous air
And leap out full-length, as we're wanting you to ? —
Who gave you that name, with the ring of the same,
And the honor and fame so becoming to you ? —
Your stripes stroked in ripples of white and of red,
With your stars at their glittering best overhead —
By day or by night
Their delightfulest light
Laughing down from their little square heaven of blue ! —

221

Who gave you the name of Old Glory? — say, who —
    Who gave you the name of Old Glory?

The old banner lifted, and faltering then
In vague lisps and whispers fell silent again.

II

Old Glory, — speak out! — we are asking about
How you happened to "favor" a name, so to say,
That sounds so familiar and careless and gay
As we cheer it and shout in our wild breezy way —
We — the *crowd*, every man of us, calling you that —
We — Tom, Dick, and Harry — each swinging his hat
And hurrahing "Old Glory!" like you were our kin,
When — *Lord!* — we all know we're as common as sin!
And yet it just seems like you *humor* us all
And waft us your thanks, as we hail you and fall
Into line, with you over us, waving us on
Where our glorified, sanctified betters have gone. —
And this is the reason we're wanting to know —
(And we're wanting it *so!* —
Where our own fathers went we are willing to go) —
Who gave you the name of Old Glory — Oh-ho! —
    Who gave you the name of Old Glory?

The old flag unfurled with a billowy thrill
For an instant, then wistfully sighed and was still.

III

Old Glory: the story we're wanting to hear
Is what the plain facts of your christening were, —
For your name — just to hear it,
Repeat it, and cheer it, 's a tang to the spirit
As salt as a tear; —
And seeing you fly, and the boys marching by,
There's a shout in the throat and a blur in the eye
And an aching to live for you always — or die,
If, dying, we still keep you waving on high.
And so, by our love
For you, floating above,
And the scars of all wars and the sorrows thereof,
Who gave you the name of Old Glory, and why
    Are we thrilled at the name of Old Glory?

Then the old banner leaped, like a sail in the blast,
And fluttered an audible answer at last. —

IV

And it spake, with a shake of the voice, and it said:

By the driven snow-white and the living blood-red
Of my bars, and their heaven of stars overhead —
By the symbol conjoined of them all, skyward cast,
As I float from the steeple, or flap at the mast,
Or droop o'er the sod where the long grasses nod, —

My name is as old as the glory of God.
. . . So I came by the name of Old Glory.

-– From "Home Folks," by James Whitcomb Riley. Copyright, 1897. Used by special permission of the publishers, The Bobbs-Merrill Company.

ADDRESS AT GETTYSBURG

Abraham Lincoln

orator	dedicated	Gettysburg
Everett	continent	proposition
conceived	consecrate	congratulated

Fourscore and seven years ago our fathers brought forth upon this continent a new nation, conceived in liberty and dedicated to the proposition that all men are created equal.

Now we are engaged in a great civil war, testing whether that nation — or any nation so conceived and so dedicated — can long endure. We are met on a great battlefield of that war. We have come to dedicate a portion of that field as the final resting-place of those who here gave their lives that that nation might live. It is altogether fitting and proper that we should do this.

But, in a larger sense, we cannot dedicate, we cannot consecrate, we cannot hallow this ground. The brave men, living and dead, who struggled here, have consecrated it far above our poor power to add or detract. The world will little note, nor long remember, what we say here ; but it can never forget what they did here. It is for us, the living, rather to be dedicated here to the unfinished work which they who fought here have thus far so nobly advanced. It is rather for us to be here dedicated to the

224

great task remaining before us; that from these honored dead we take increased devotion to that cause for which they gave the last full measure of devotion; that we here highly resolve that these dead shall not have died in vain; that this nation, under God, shall have a new birth of freedom; and that government of the people, by the people, for the people, shall not perish from the earth.

This short address was delivered at the dedication of the National Cemetery at Gettysburg, November 19, 1863. It has become a classic. At the close of the ceremonies, when Lincoln congratulated Edward Everett, the orator of the day, upon his address, Mr. Everett replied, "Ah! Mr. President, how gladly would I exchange all my hundred pages, to have been the author of your twenty lines!"

THE LAND OF LIBERTY

(AUTHOR UNKNOWN)

hoary   fantastic

I love my country's pine-clad hills,
Her thousand bright and gushing rills,
  Her sunshine and her storms;
Her rough and rugged rocks, that rear
Their hoary heads high in the air
  In wild, fantastic forms.

I love her rivers, deep and wide,
Those mighty streams that seaward glide
  To seek the ocean's breast;
Her smiling fields, her pleasant vales,
Her shady dells, her flow'ry dales,
  The haunts of peaceful rest.

I love her forests, dark and lone,
For there the wild bird's merry tone
    I hear from morn till night;
And there are lovelier flowers, I ween,
Than e'er in Eastern lands were seen,
    In varied colors bright.

Her forests and her valleys fair,
Her flowers that scent the morning air,
    All have their charms for me;
But more I love my country's name,
Those words that echo deathless fame,
    "The Land of Liberty."

LAND OF THE SOUTH

Alexander B. Meek

verdure   imperial

Land of the South! — imperial land!
    How proud thy mountains rise!
How sweet thy scenes on every hand!
    How fair thy covering skies!
But not for this, — oh! not for these,
    I love thy fields to roam, —
Thou hast a dearer spell to me;
    Thou art my native home!

Thy rivers roll their liquid wealth,
    Unequaled to the sea;

226

Thy hills and valleys bloom with health,
  And green with verdure be!
But not for thy proud ocean streams,
  Not for thine azure dome, —
Sweet, sunny South! I cling to thee;
  Thou art my native home!

OLIVER GOLDSMITH

William Makepeace Thackeray

succor	designed	reconcile	fictitious
vagrant	response	unanimous	pensioners
deplored	substance	promissory	benevolent

Who of the millions that he has amused, does not love him? To be the most beloved of English writers, what a title that is for a man! "He was a friend to virtue," says Sir Walter Scott, "and in his most playful pages never forgets what is due to it."

A wild youth, wayward, but full of tenderness and affection, in fond longing to see the great world out of doors and to achieve name and fortune; quits the country village where his boyhood has been passed in happy musing, in idle shelter. And, after years of dire struggle and neglect and poverty, his heart turning back as fondly to his native place as it had longed eagerly for a change when sheltered there, he writes a book and a poem, full of the recollections and feelings of home.

Who could harm the kind vagrant harper? Whom did he ever hurt? He carries no weapon save the harp on which he plays to you, and with which he delights great and humble, young and old, the captains in the tents or the soldiers round the fire, the women and children in the villages, at whose porches he stops and sings his simple songs of love and beauty. With that sweet story of "The Vicar of Wakefield," he has found entry into every castle and every hamlet in Europe.

"We read it," says the gentle Sir Walter, "in youth and in age; we return to it again and again, and bless the memory of an author who contrives so well to reconcile us to human nature. The admirable ease and grace of the narrative, as well as the pleasing truth with which the characters are designed, make ‘The Vicar of Wakefield’ one of the most delicious morsels of fictitious composition on which the human mind has ever been employed.”

Goldsmith’s sweet and friendly nature bloomed kindly always in the midst of life’s storm and rain and bitter weather. The poor fellow was never so friendless but he could befriend some one; never so pinched and wretched but he could give of his crust, and speak a word of compassion. If he had but his flute left, he could give that and make the children happy in the dreary London Court. While he was an under-teacher in a school, he spent all his earnings in treats for the boys. His purse and his heart were everybody’s, — his friends’ as much as his own.

As has been the case with many another good fellow of his nation, his life was tracked and his substance wasted by hungry beggars and lazy dependents. If they came at a lucky time, — and be sure they knew his affairs better than he did himself, and watched his pay day, — he gave them of his money; if they begged on empty-purse days, he gave them his promissory bills, or took them to a house where he had credit.

Staggering under a load of debt and labor, tracked by reproachful creditors, running from a hundred poor dependents, whose appealing looks, perhaps, were the hardest of all pains for him to bear, devising fevered plans for the morrow, new histories, new comedies, all sorts of new literary schemes, flying from all these into seclusion, and out of seclusion into pleasure, — at last, at five-and-forty, death closed his career.

Ah! it was a different lot from that for which the poor fellow sighed, when he wrote, with heart yearning for home, those most charming of all fond verses, in which he fancies he revisits Auburn: —

“In all my wanderings round this world of care,
    In all my griefs — and God has given my share —
I still had hopes my latest hours to crown,
    Amid these humble bowers to lay me down;
To husband out life’s taper at the close,

And keep the flame from wasting, by repose;
I still had hopes — for pride attends us still —
Amidst the swains to show my book-learned skill;
Around my fire an evening group to draw,
And tell of all I felt, and all I saw;
And, as a hare, whom hounds and horns pursue,
Pants to the place from whence at first she flew, —
I still had hopes — my long vexations past —
Here to return, and die at home at last."

Think of him, reckless, thriftless, vain, if you like, but merciful, gentle, generous, full of love and pity. He passes out of our life, and goes to render his account beyond it. Think of the poor pensioners weeping at his grave! think of the noble spirits that admired and deplored him! and of the wonderful and unanimous response of affection with which the world has paid back the love he gave it.

His humor delighting us still; his song as fresh and beautiful as when he first charmed with it; his words in every mouth; his very weaknesses beloved and familiar; his benevolent spirit seems still to shine upon us; to do gentle kindness; to succor with sweet charity; to soothe, caress, and forgive; to plead with the fortunate for the unhappy and the poor.

SELECTIONS FROM "THE DESERTED VILLAGE"

OLIVER GOLDSMITH

furze	remote	bashful	fluctuate
copse	allured	welfare	doctrines
gauge	reprove	sleights	venerable
cipher	presage	mirthful	vanquished
gambol	gabbled	remitting	counterfeited

Sweet Auburn! loveliest village of the plain,
Where health and plenty cheered the laboring swain,

Where smiling spring its earliest visit paid,
And parting summer's lingering blooms delayed.
Dear lovely bowers of innocence and ease,
Seats of my youth, when every sport could please,
How often have I loitered o'er thy green,
Where humble happiness endeared each scene,
How often have I paused on every charm,
The sheltered cot, the cultivated farm,
The never-failing brook, the busy mill,
The decent church that topped the neighboring hill,
The hawthorn bush with seats beneath the shade,
For talking age and whispering lovers made!
How often have I blest the coming day
When toil remitting lent its turn to play,
And all the village train, from labor free,
Led up their sports beneath the spreading tree;
While many a pastime circled in the shade,
The young contending as the old surveyed,
And many a gambol frolicked o'er the ground,
And sleights of art and feats of strength went round!
And still, as each repeated pleasure tired,
Succeeding sports the mirthful band inspired;
The dancing pair that simply sought renown
By holding out to tire each other down,
The swain mistrustless of his smutted face
While secret laughter tittered round the place,
The bashful virgin's sidelong looks of love,

The matron's glance that would those looks reprove.
These were thy charms, sweet village! sports like these,
With sweet succession, taught even toil to please;
These round thy bowers their cheerful influence shed;
These were thy charms — but all these charms are fled.

    *   *   *   *   *   *   *   *

Sweet was the sound, when oft at evening's close
Up yonder hill the village murmur rose.
There, as I passed with careless steps and slow,
The mingling notes came softened from below;
The swain responsive as the milkmaid sung,
The sober herd that lowed to meet their young,
The noisy geese that gabbled o'er the pool,
The playful children just let loose from school,
The watchdog's voice that bayed the whispering wind,
And the loud laugh that spoke the vacant mind, —
These all in sweet confusion sought the shade,
And filled each pause the nightingale had made.
But now the sounds of population fail,
No cheerful murmurs fluctuate in the gale,
No busy steps the grass-grown footway tread,
For all the bloomy flush of life is fled.

    *   *   *   *   *   *   *   *

Near yonder copse, where once the garden smiled,
And still where many a garden flower grows wild,
There, where a few torn shrubs the place disclose,
The village preacher's modest mansion rose.

A man he was to all the country dear,
And passing rich with forty pounds a year.
Remote from towns he ran his godly race,
Nor e'er had changed, nor wished to change, his place;
Unpracticed he to fawn, or seek for power
By doctrines fashioned to the varying hour;
Far other aims his heart had learned to prize —
More skilled to raise the wretched than to rise.
His house was known to all the vagrant train;
He chid their wanderings, but relieved their pain;
The long-remembered beggar was his guest,
Whose beard descending swept his aged breast;
The ruined spendthrift, now no longer proud,
Claimed kindred there, and had his claims allowed;
The broken soldier, kindly bade to stay,
Sat by his fire, and talked the night away, —
Wept o'er his wounds, or tales of sorrow done,
Shouldered his crutch and showed how fields were won.
Pleased with his guests, the good man learned to glow,
And quite forgot their vices in their woe;
Careless their merits or their faults to scan,
His pity gave ere charity began.
   Thus to relieve the wretched was his pride,
And e'en his failings leaned to virtue's side;
But in his duty prompt at every call,
He watched and wept, he prayed and felt for all;
And, as a bird each fond endearment tries

To tempt its new-fledged offspring to the skies,
He tried each art, reproved each dull delay,
Allured to brighter worlds, and led the way.

    Beside the bed, where parting life was laid,
And sorrow, guilt, and pain, by turns dismayed,
The reverend champion stood: at his control
Despair and anguish fled the struggling soul;
Comfort came down the trembling wretch to raise,
And his last faltering accents whispered praise.

    At church with meek and unaffected grace
His looks adorned the venerable place;
Truth from his lips prevailed with double sway,
And fools who came to scoff remained to pray.
The service passed, around the pious man,
With steady zeal, each honest rustic ran;
Even children followed, with endearing wile,
And plucked his gown, to share the good man's smile;
His ready smile a parent's warmth expressed,
Their welfare pleased him and their cares distressed.
To them his heart, his love, his griefs were given,
But all his serious thought had rest in heaven:
As some tall cliff, that lifts its awful form,
Swells from the vale, and midway leaves the storm,
Though round its breast the rolling clouds are spread,
Eternal sunshine settles on its head.

    Beside yon straggling fence that skirts the way,
With blossomed furze unprofitably gay,

W. *Lee Hankey.*

EVEN CHILDREN FOLLOWED, WITH ENDEARING WILE,
AND PLUCKED HIS GOWN, TO SHARE THE GOOD MAN'S SMILE.

There in his noisy mansion, skilled to rule,
The village master taught his little school.
A man severe he was, and stern to view;
I knew him well, and every truant knew:
Well had the boding tremblers learned to trace
The day's disasters in his morning face;
Full well they laughed with counterfeited glee
At all his jokes, for many a joke had he;
Full well the busy whisper, circling round,
Conveyed the dismal tidings when he frowned:
Yet he was kind, or if severe in aught,
The love he bore to learning was in fault.
The village all declared how much he knew;
'Twas certain he could write, and cipher too,
Lands he could measure, terms and tides presage,
And e'en the story ran that he could gauge.
In arguing, too, the parson owned his skill,
For e'en though vanquished he could argue still:
While words of learned length and thundering sound
Amazed the gazing rustics ranged around, —
And still they gazed, and still the wonder grew
That one small head could carry all he knew.

But past is all his fame: the very spot,
Where many a time he triumphed, is forgot.

SELECTIONS FROM "THE VICAR OF WAKEFIELD"

Oliver Goldsmith

Mrs. Primrose's Schemes

latent	pillion	Burchell	conference
serene	vicious	trudging	expedition
smock	exalted	genteelly	mortification

Toward the end of the week we received a card from the town ladies, in which, with their compliments, they hoped to see all our family at church the Sunday following.

All Saturday morning I could perceive, in consequence of this, my wife and daughters in close conference together, and now and then glancing at me with looks that betrayed a latent plot. To be sincere, I had strong suspicions that some absurd proposal was preparing for their appearing with splendor the next day.

In the evening they began their operations in a very regular manner, and my wife undertook to conduct the siege.

After tea, when I seemed in spirits, she began thus: "I fancy, Charles, my dear, we shall have a great deal of good company at our church to-morrow."

"Perhaps we may, my dear," returned I, "though you need be under no uneasiness about that; you shall have a sermon whether there be or not."

"That is what I expect," returned she; "but I think, my dear, we ought to appear there as decently as possible, for who knows what may happen?"

"Your precautions," replied I, "are highly commendable. A decent behavior and appearance in church is what charms me. We should be devout and humble, cheerful and serene."

"Yes;" cried she, "I know that; but I mean we should go there in as proper a manner as possible, not altogether like the scrubs about us."

"You are quite right, my dear," returned I, "and I was going to make the very same proposal. The proper manner of going is to go there as early as possible, to have time for meditation before the service begins."

"Pooh! Charles," interrupted she, "all that is very true; but not what I would be at. I mean, we should go there genteelly. You know the church is two miles off, and I protest I don't like to see my daughters trudging up to their pew all blowzed and red with walking, and looking for all the world as if they had been winners at a smock-race.

"Now, my dear, my proposal is this: there are our two plow-horses, — the colt that has been in our family these nine years, and his companion Blackberry, that has scarcely done an earthly thing for this month past; they are both grown fat and lazy. Why should they not do something as well as we? And let me tell you, when Moses has trimmed them a little, they will cut a very tolerable figure."

To this proposal I objected that walking would be twenty times more genteel than such a paltry conveyance, as Blackberry was wall-eyed and the colt wanted a tail; that they had never been broken to the rein, and had a hundred vicious tricks; and that we had but one saddle and pillion in the whole house. All these objections, however, were overruled ; so that I was obliged to comply.

The next morning I perceived them not a little busy in collecting such materials as might be necessary for the expedition ; but as I found it would be a business of time, I walked on to the church, and they promised speedily to follow. I waited nearly an hour in the reading-room for their arrival; but not finding them come as expected, I was obliged to begin, and went through the service, not without some uneasiness at finding them absent. This was increased when all was finished, and no appearance of the family.

I therefore walked back by the horseway, which was five miles round, though the footway was but two, and when I got halfway home perceived the procession marching slowly forward towards the church, — my son, my wife and the two little ones exalted on one horse, and my two daughters upon the other. I demanded the cause of their delay ; but I soon found by their looks that they had met with a thousand misfortunes on the road.

The horses had at first refused to move from the door, till Mr. Burchell was kind enough to beat them forward for about two hundred yards, with his cudgel. Next, the straps of my wife's pillion had broken down, and that they had been obliged to stop to repair them before they could proceed.

After that, one of the horses, they informed me, had taken it into his head to stand still, and neither blows nor entreaties could prevail with him to proceed. He was just recovering from this dismal situation when I found them : but perceiving everything safe, I own their present mortification did not much displease me, as it would give me many opportunities of future triumph, and would teach my daughters more humility.

MOSES SELLS THE COLT

higgles	discreet	shagreen
varnish	warrant	prowling
murrain	prophecy	Flamborough

When we were returned home, the night was dedicated to schemes of future conquest. My wife could talk of nothing else. "Well, faith, my dear Charles, between ourselves, I think we have made an excellent day's work of it." — "Pretty well," cried I, not knowing what to say. — "What, only pretty well?" returned she; "I think it is very well. Suppose the girls should come to make acquaintances of taste in town! When they came to talk of places in town you saw at once how I nailed them. Tell me, my dear, don't you think I did for my children there?" — "Aye," returned I, not knowing well what to think of the matter, "Heaven grant that they may both be the better for it this day three months!" This was one of those observations I usually made to impress my wife with an opinion of my sagacity; for if the girls succeeded, then it was a pious wish fulfilled; but if anything unfortunate ensued, then it might be looked upon as a prophecy.

All this conversation, however, was only preparatory to another scheme, which indeed I dreaded as much. This was nothing less than, that, as we were now to hold up our heads a little higher in the world, it would be proper to sell the colt, which was grown old, at a neighboring fair, and buy us a horse that would carry single or double upon occasion, and make a pretty appearance at church or upon a visit. This at first I opposed stoutly; but it was as stoutly defended. However, as I weakened, my antagonists gained strength, till at last it was resolved to part with him.

As the fair happened on the following day, I had intentions of going myself; but my wife persuaded me that I had a cold, and nothing could prevail upon her to permit me from home.

"No, my dear," said she, "our son Moses is a discreet boy, and can buy and sell to very good advantage; you know all our great bargains are of his purchasing. He always stands out and higgles, and actually tires them till he gets a bargain."

As I had some opinion of my son's prudence, I was willing enough to intrust him with this commission; and the next morning I perceived his sisters mighty busy in fitting out Moses for the fair; trimming his hair, brushing his buckles, and cocking his hat with pins.

The business of the toilet being over, we had at last the satisfaction of seeing him mounted upon the colt, with a deal-box before him to bring home groceries in. He had on a coat made of that cloth they call thunder and lightning, which, though grown too short, was much too good to be thrown away. His waistcoat was of gosling green, and his sisters had tied his hair with a broad black ribbon. We all followed him

C. E. Brock.

WE ALL FOLLOWED HIM SEVERAL PACES FROM THE DOOR, BAWLING AFTER HIM,
"GOOD LUCK, GOOD LUCK!"

several paces from the door, bawling after him, "Good luck, good luck!" till we could see him no longer.

As night came on, I began to wonder what could keep our son so long at the fair.

"Never mind our son," cried my wife, "depend upon it, he knows what he is about. I'll warrant we'll never see him sell his hen on a rainy day. I have seen him buy such bargains as would amaze one. I'll tell you a good story about that, that will make you split your sides with laughing. But as I live, yonder comes Moses, without a horse, and the box at his back."

As she spoke, Moses came slowly on foot, and sweating under the deal-box, which he had strapped round his shoulders like a peddler.

"Welcome, welcome, Moses! Well, my boy, what have you brought us from the fair?"

"I have brought you myself," cried Moses, with a sly look, and resting the box on the dresser.

"Ah, Moses," cried my wife, "that we know, but where is the horse?"

"I have sold him," cried Moses, "for three pounds, five shillings, and twopence."

"Well done, my good boy," returned she, "I knew you would touch them off. Between ourselves, three pounds, five shillings, and twopence is no bad day's work. Come, let us have it then."

"I have brought back no money," cried Moses again. "I

242

have laid it all out in a bargain, and here it is," pulling out a bundle from his breast: "here they are, a gross of green spectacles, with silver rims and shagreen cases."

"A gross of green spectacles!" repeated my wife in a faint voice. "And you have parted with the colt, and brought us back nothing but a gross of paltry green spectacles!"

"Dear mother," cried the boy, "why won't you listen to reason? I had them a dead bargain, or I should not have bought them. The silver rims will sell for double the money."

"A fig for the silver rims!" cried my wife, in a passion, "I dare swear they won't sell for above half the money at the rate of broken silver, five shillings an ounce."

"You need be under no uneasiness," cried I, "about selling the rims; for they are not worth sixpence, for I perceive they are only copper varnished over."

"What," cried my wife, "not silver, the rims not silver!"

"No," cried I, "no more silver than your saucepan."

"And so," returned she, "we have parted with the colt, and have only got a gross of green spectacles, with copper rims and shagreen cases! A murrain take such trumpery! The blockhead has been imposed upon, and should have known his company better."

"There, my dear," cried I, "you are wrong; he should not have known them at all."

"Marry, hang the idiot," returned she, "to bring me such stuff; if I had them I would throw them into the fire."

"There again you are wrong, my dear," cried I; "for

though they be copper, we will keep them by us, as copper spectacles, you know, are better than nothing."

By this time the unfortunate Moses was undeceived. He now saw that he had indeed been imposed upon by a prowling sharper, who, observing his figure, had marked him for an easy prey. I therefore asked the circumstances of his deception. He sold the horse, it seems, and walked the fair in search of another. A reverend-looking man brought him to a tent, under pretense of having one to sell.

"Here," continued Moses, "we met another man, very well dressed, who desired to borrow twenty pounds upon these, saying that he wanted money and would dispose of them for a third of the value. The first gentleman, who pretended to be my friend, whispered me to buy them and cautioned me not to let so good an offer pass. I sent for Mr. Flamborough, and they talked him up as finely as they did me, and so at last we were persuaded to buy the two gross between us."

Dr. Primrose sells the Horse

spavin	pathetic	challenge	mercantile
esteem	preacher	sentiment	controversy
Solomon	harangue	Jenkinson	transactions
Ephraim	squeezing	clergyman	presumption

The journey of my daughters to town was now resolved upon, and it was thought necessary that their appearance should equal the greatness of their expectations, which could not be done with-

244

out expense. We debated, therefore, in full council what were the easiest methods of raising money, or more properly speaking, what we could most conveniently sell. The deliberation was soon finished; it was found that our remaining horse was utterly useless for the plow without his companion, and equally unfit for the road with only one eye. It was therefore determined that we should dispose of him, for the purposes above mentioned, at the neighboring fair, and to prevent imposition, that I should go with him myself.

Though this was one of the first mercantile transactions of my life, yet I had no doubt about acquitting myself with reputation. The opinion a man forms of his own prudence is measured by that of the company he keeps; and as mine was mostly that of my own family, I had conceived no unfavorable sentiments of my worldly wisdom. My wife, however, next morning at parting, after I had got some paces from the door, called me back to advise me in a whisper to have all my eyes about me.

When I came to the fair, I put my horse through all of his paces, but for some time had no bidders. At last a man approached, and after he had examined the horse for a good while, finding him blind of one eye, he would have nothing to say; a second came up, but observing he had a spavin, declared he would not take him for the driving home; a third perceived that he had a windgall, and would bid no money; a fourth knew by his eye that he had the bots; a fifth wondered what I could do at the fair with a blind, spavined, and galled hack. By this time I began to have a most hearty contempt for the poor animal my-

C. E. Brock.

THE VICAR AT THE FAIR.

self, and was almost ashamed at the approach of every customer; for though I did not entirely believe all the fellows told me, yet I reflected that the number of witnesses was a strong presumption that they were right.

I was in this mortifying situation when a brother clergyman, an old acquaintance, who had also business at the fair, came up, and shaking me by the hand proposed adjourning to a public house. I readily closed with the offer and we were shown into a little room where there was only a venerable old man, who sat wholly intent over a large book which he was reading.

I never in my life saw a figure that prepossessed me more favorably. His locks of silver gray venerably shaded his temples, and his green old age seemed to be the result of health and benevolence. However, his presence did not interrupt our conversation. My friend and I discoursed on the various turns of fortune we had met.

But our attention was in a short time taken off by the appearance of a youth, who, entering the room, respectfully said something softly to the old stranger. "Make no apologies, my child," said the old man, "to do good is a duty we owe to all our fellow-creatures: take this, I wish it were more; but five pounds will relieve your distress, and you are welcome." The modest youth shed tears of gratitude, and yet his gratitude was scarce equal to mine. I could have hugged the good old man in my arms, his benevolence pleased me so. He continued to read, and we resumed our conversation, until my companion, after some time, recollecting that he had business to transact in the fair, promised to be back soon, adding that he always desired to have as much of Dr. Primrose's company as possible.

The old gentleman, hearing my name mentioned, seemed to look at me with attention for some time, and when my friend was gone, most respectfully demanded if I were in any way related to the great Primrose, who had been the bulwark of the church. Never did my heart feel sincerer rapture than at that moment. "Sir," cried I, "the applause of so good a man, as I am sure you are, adds to that happiness in my breast which your benevolence has already excited. You behold before you, Sir, that Dr. Primrose, whom you have been pleased to call great." — "Sir," cried the stranger, struck with awe, "I fear I have been too familiar, but you will forgive my curiosity, Sir; I beg your pardon." — "Sir," cried I, grasping his hand, "you are so far from displeasing me by your familiarity that I must beg you to accept my friendship, as you already have my esteem." — "Then with gratitude I accept the offer," cried he, squeezing me by the hand. I here interrupted what he was going to say; for though I could digest no small share of flattery, yet now, my modesty would permit no more.

We talked upon several subjects. Whenever I made any observation that looked like a challenge to controversy, he would smile, shake his head, and say nothing, by which I understood he could say much, if he thought proper. The subject, therefore, insensibly changed to that which brought us both to the fair; my errand I told him was to sell a horse, and, very luckily indeed, his was to buy one for one of his tenants.

My horse was soon produced, and, in fine, we struck a bargain. Nothing now remained but to pay me, and he accordingly pulled out a thirty-pound note, and asked me to change it. Not being in a capacity to comply with his demand, he ordered his footman to be called up, who made his appearance in a very genteel livery. "Here, Abraham," said he, " go and get gold for this; you will get it at neighbor Jackson's or anywhere." While the fellow was gone, he entertained me with a pathetic harangue on the great scarcity of silver, which I undertook to improve, by deploring also the great scarcity of gold; so that by the time Abraham returned, we had both agreed that money was never so hard to be come at as now.

Abraham returned to inform us that he had been over the whole fair, and could get no change, though he had offered half a crown for it. This was a very great disappointment for us all; but the old gentleman having paused a little, asked me if I knew one Solomon Flamborough, in my part of the country. I replied that he was my next-door neighbor. "If that be the case, then," replied he, "I believe we shall deal. You shall have a draft upon him, payable at sight, and let me tell you he is as warm a man as any within five miles around him. Honest Solomon and I have been acquainted for many years. I remember I always beat him at three jumps; but he could hop upon one leg farther than I could." A draft upon my neighbor was the same to me as money, for I was sufficiently convinced of his ability to pay. The draft was signed and put into my hands, and Mr. Jenkinson, the old gentleman, his man

Abraham, and my horse, old Blackberry, trotted off very well pleased with one another.

After a short interval, being left to reflection, I began to recollect that I had done wrong in taking a draft from a stranger; and so I prudently resolved upon following the purchaser, and getting back my horse; but this was now too late; I therefore made directly homeward, resolving to get the draft changed into money at my friend's as fast as possible. I found my honest neighbor smoking his pipe at his own door, and informing him that I had a small bill upon him, he read it twice over. "You can read the name, I suppose," said I, "Ephraim Jenkinson." — "Yes," returned he, "the name is written plain enough, and I know the gentleman, too, the greatest rascal under the canopy of heaven. This is the very same rogue who sold us the spectacles. Was he not a venerable looking man, with gray hair?" To this I replied with a groan. "Aye," continued he, "I know the rogue and will catch him yet."

Though I was already sufficiently mortified, my greatest struggle was to come in facing my wife and daughters. No truant was ever more afraid of returning to school, there to behold the master's visage, than I was of going home.

Nearly all of Goldsmith's characters are portraits from real life. It is interesting to know that his father, Dr. Charles Goldsmith, was the original of Dr. Primrose in "The Vicar of Wakefield," and also of the preacher in "The Deserted Village."

SELECTIONS FROM "THE TRAVELER"

Oliver Goldsmith

tepid	alpine	felicity	dissemble
frigid	estimate	impelled	consigned
extols	Damien's	domestic	philosophic

Where'er I roam, whatever realms to see,
My heart, untraveled, fondly turns to thee;
Still to my brother turns, with ceaseless pain,
And drags at each remove a lengthening chain.

Eternal blessings crown my earliest friend,
And round his dwelling guardian saints attend:
Blest be that spot, where cheerful guests retire
To pause from toil, and trim their evening fire;
Blest that abode, where want and pain repair,
And every stranger finds a ready chair;
Blest be those feasts with simple plenty crowned,
Where all the ruddy family around
Laugh at the jests or pranks that never fail,
Or sigh with pity at some mournful tale,
Or press the bashful stranger to his food,
And learn the luxury of doing good.

But me, not destined such delights to share,
My prime of life in wandering spent and care —
Impelled with steps unceasing to pursue
Some fleeting good that mocks me with the view,

That, like the circle bounding earth and skies,
Allures from far, yet, as I follow, flies —
My fortune leads to traverse realms alone,
And find no spot of all the world my own.

Even now, where Alpine solitudes ascend,
I sit me down a pensive hour to spend;
And placed on high, above the storm's career,
Look downward where an hundred realms appear —
Lakes, forests, cities, plains extending wide,
The pomp of kings, the shepherd's humbler pride.

When thus creation's charms around combine,
Amidst the store should thankless pride repine?
Say, should the philosophic mind disdain
That good which makes each humble bosom vain?
Let school-taught pride dissemble all it can,
These little things are great to little man;
And wiser he whose sympathetic mind
Exults in all the good of all mankind.
Ye glittering towns, with wealth and splendor crowned,
Ye fields, where summer spreads profusion round,
Ye lakes, whose vessels catch the busy gale,
Ye bending swains, that dress the flowery vale —
For me your tributary stores combine;
Creation's heir, the world, the world is mine!

As some lone miser, visiting his store,
Bends at his treasure, counts, recounts it o'er —
Hoards after hoards his rising raptures fill,

Yet still he sighs, for hoards are wanting still —
Thus to my breast alternate passions rise,
Pleased with each good that Heaven to man supplies,
Yet oft a sigh prevails, and sorrows fall,
To see the hoard of human bliss so small;
And oft I wish, amidst the scene, to find
Some spot to real happiness consigned,
Where my worn soul, each wandering hope at rest,
May gather bliss to see my fellows blest.

But where to find that happiest spot below,
Who can direct, when all pretend to know?
The shuddering tenant of the frigid zone
Boldly proclaims that happiest spot his own,
Extols the treasures of his stormy seas,
And his long nights of revelry and ease;
The naked negro, panting at the line,
Boasts of his golden sands and palmy wine,
Basks in the glare, or stems the tepid wave,
And thanks his gods for all the good they gave.
Such is the patriot's boast, where'er we roam;
His first, best country ever is at home.
And yet, perhaps, if countries we compare,
And estimate the blessings which they share,
Though patriot's flatter, still shall wisdom find,
An equal portion dealt to all mankind;
As different good, by art or nature given,
To different nations makes their blessings even.

Vain, very vain, my weary search to find
That bliss which only centers in the mind:
Why have I strayed from pleasure and repose,
To seek a good each government bestows?
In every government, though terrors reign,
Though tyrant kings or tyrant laws restrain,
How small, of all that human hearts endure,
That part which laws or kings can cause or cure!
Still to ourselves in every place consigned,
Our own felicity we make or find:
With secret course, which no loud storms annoy,
Glides the smooth current of domestic joy.
The lifted ax, the agonizing wheel,
Luke's iron crown, and Damien's bed of steel,
To men remote from power but rarely known,
Leave reason, faith, and conscience, all our own.

THE NIGHT SCHOOL AND THE SCHOOLMASTER

GEORGE ELIOT

fiber	element	irregular	discomfited
Bartle	aquiline	specimen	Treddleston
bristly	perverse	arabesque	exasperating
Hazelow	Massey's	formidable	discriminated

Bartle Massey's was one of a few scattered houses on the edge
of a common, which was divided by the road to Treddleston.

254

Adam reached it in a quarter of an hour after leaving the Hall Farm; and when he had his hand on the door-latch, he could see, through the curtainless window, that there were eight or nine heads bending over the desks, lighted by thin dips.

When he entered, a reading lesson was going forward, and Bartle Massey merely nodded, leaving him to take his place where he pleased. It was a scene which Adam had beheld almost weekly for years; he knew by heart every arabesque flourish in the framed specimen of Bartle Massey's handwriting which hung over the schoolmaster's head, by way of keeping a lofty ideal before the minds of his pupils; he knew the backs of all the books on the shelf running along the whitewashed wall above the pegs for the slates; he knew exactly how many grains were gone out of the ear of Indian corn that hung from one of the rafters; he had long ago exhausted the resources of his imagination in trying to think how the bunch of feathery seaweed had looked and grown in its native element; and from the place where he sat, he could make nothing of the old map of England that hung against the opposite wall, for age had turned it of a fine yellow-brown. The drama that was going on was almost as familiar as the scene; nevertheless, habit had not made him indifferent to it, and even in his present, self-absorbed mood, Adam felt a momentary stirring of the old fellow-feeling, as he looked at the rough men painfully holding pen or pencil with their cramped hands, or humbly laboring through their reading lesson.

The reading class now seated on the form in front of the schoolmaster's desk consisted of the three most backward pupils.

255

Adam would have known it, only by seeing Bartle Massey's face as he looked over his spectacles, which he had shifted to the ridge of his nose, not requiring them for present purposes. The face wore its mildest expression; the grizzled bushy eyebrows had taken their more acute angle of compassionate kindness, and the mouth was relaxed so as to be ready to speak a helpful word or syllable in a moment. This gentle expression was the more interesting because the schoolmaster's nose, an irregular aquiline twisted a little on one side, had rather a formidable character; and his brow, moreover, had that peculiar tension which always impresses one as a sign of a keen, impatient temperament; the blue veins stood out like cords under the transparent skin, and this brow was softened by no tendency to baldness, for the gray bristly hair, cut down to about an inch in length, stood round it in as close ranks as ever.

"Nay, Bill, nay," Bartle was saying, in a kind tone, as he nodded to Adam, "begin that again, and then perhaps it'll come to you what d, r, y, spells. It's the same lesson you read last week, you know."

"Bill" was a sturdy fellow, aged four-and-twenty, an excellent stone sawyer, who could get as good wages as any man in the trade of his years; but he found a reading lesson in words of one syllable a harder matter to deal with than the hardest stone he had ever had to saw. The letters, he complained, were so "uncommon alike, there was no tellin' 'em one from another," the sawyer's business not being concerned with minute differences such as exist between a letter with its tail turned up and a letter with its tail turned down. But Bill had a firm determination that he would learn to read, founded chiefly on two reasons: first, that Tom Hazelow, his cousin, could read anything " right off," whether it was print or writing, and Tom had sent him a letter from twenty miles off, saying how he was prospering in the world, and had an overlooker's place; secondly, that Sam Phillips, who sawed with him, had learned to read when he was turned twenty; and that what could be done by a little fellow like Sam Phillips, Bill considered, could be done by himself. So here he was, pointing his big finger toward three words at once, and turning his head on one side that he might keep better hold with his eye of the one word which was to be discriminated out of the group. The amount of knowledge Bartle Massey must possess was something so dim and vast that Bill's imagination recoiled before it; he would hardly have ventured to deny that the schoolmaster might have something to do in bringing about the regular return of daylight and the changes in the weather.

The man seated next to Bill was of a very different type: he was a brickmaker, who, after spending thirty years of his life in perfect satisfaction with his ignorance, had lately been seized with the desire to read the Bible. But with him, too, learning was a heavy business; and on his way out to-night he had offered as usual a special prayer for help, seeing that he had undertaken this hard task with a single eye to the nourishment of his soul.

The third beginner was a much more promising pupil. He

was a tall but thin and wiry man, with a very pale face, and hands stained a deep blue. He was a dyer, who, in the course of dipping homespun wool, was fired with the ambition to learn a great deal more about the strange secrets of color. He had already a high reputation in the district for his dyes, and he was bent on discovering some method by which he could reduce the expense of crimsons and scarlets. The druggist at Treddleston had given him a notion that he might save himself a great deal of labor and expense if he could learn to read, and so he had begun to give his spare hours to the night school, resolving that his "little chap" should lose no time in coming to Mr. Massey's day school as soon as he was old enough.

It was touching to see these three big men, with the marks of their hard labor about them, anxiously bending over the worn books, and painfully making out, "The grass is green," "The sticks are dry," "The corn is ripe," — a very hard lesson to pass to after columns of single words all alike except in the first letter. It was almost as if three rough animals were making humble efforts to learn how they might become human. And it touched the tenderest fiber in Bartle Massey's nature, for such full-grown children as these were the only pupils for whom he had no severe epithets, and no impatient tones. He was not gifted with an amiable temper, but this evening, as he glances over his spectacles at Bill Downes, the sawyer, turning his head on one side with a desperate sense of blankness before the letters d, r, y, his eyes shed their mildest and most encouraging light.

After the reading class, two youths, between the ages of sixteen and nineteen, came up with imaginary bills of parcels, which they had been writing out on their slates, and which they were now required to calculate "off-hand," — a test which they stood with such imperfect success, that Bartle Massey, whose eyes had been glaring at them through his spectacles for some minutes, at length burst out in a bitter, high-pitched tone, pausing between every sentence to rap the floor with a knobbed stick which rested between his legs.

"Now, you see, you don't do this thing a bit better than you did a fortnight ago; and I'll tell you what's the reason. You want to learn accounts; that's well and good. But you think all you need do to learn accounts is to come to me and do sums for an hour or so, two or three times a week; and no sooner do you get your caps on and turn out of doors again, than you sweep the whole thing clean out of your mind. You go whistling about, and take no more care what you're thinking of than if your heads were gutters for any rubbish that happened to be in the way; and if you get a good notion in 'em, it's pretty soon washed out again. You think knowledge is to be had cheap; you'll come and pay Bartle Massey sixpence a week, and he'll make you clever at figures without your taking any trouble. But knowledge isn't to be had with paying sixpence, let me tell you; if you're to know figures, you must turn 'em in your own heads, and keep your thoughts fixed on 'em. There's nothing you can't turn into a sum, for there's nothing but what has number in it — even a fool. You may say to yourselves,

'I'm one fool and Jack's another; if my fool's head weighed four pound, and Jack's three pound three ounces and three quarters, how much heavier would my head be than Jack's?' A man that has his heart in learning figures would make sums for himself, and work 'em in his head; when he sat at his shoe-making, he'd count his stitches by fives, and then put a price on his stitches, say half a farthing, and then see how much money he could get in one hour, and then ask himself how much money he'd get in a day at that rate; and then how much ten workmen would get working three, or twenty, or a hundred years at that rate — and all the while his needle would be going just as fast as if he left his head empty. But the long and the short of it is, I'll have nobody in my night school that doesn't strive to learn what he comes to learn, as hard as if he were striving to get out of a dark hole into broad daylight. I'll send no man away because he is stupid; if Billy, the idiot, wanted to learn anything, I'd not refuse to teach him. But I'll not throw away good knowledge on people who think they can get it by the six-pennyworth, and carry it away with them as they would an ounce of snuff. So never come to me again, if you can't show that you have been working with your own heads, instead of thinking you can pay mine to work for you. That's the last word I've got to say to you."

With this final sentence, Bartle Massey gave a sharper rap than ever with his knobbed stick, and the discomfited lads got up to go with a sulky look. The other pupils had happily only their writing-books to show, in various stages of progress from pothooks to round text; and mere pen-strokes, however perverse, were less exasperating to Bartle than false arithmetic. He was a little more severe than usual on Jacob Storey's *Z*'s, of which poor Jacob had written a page full, all with their tops turned the wrong way, with a puzzled sense that they were not right "some-how." But he observed in apology, that it was a letter you never wanted hardly, and he thought it had been put there only "to finish off the alphabet like, though & would have done as well, for what he could see."

— This sketch is taken from the novel "Adam Bede."

TO-DAY

THOMAS CARLYLE

Lo! here hath been dawning
    Another blue day:
Think, wilt thou let it
    Slip useless away?

Out of Eternity
    This new day is born;
Into Eternity,
    At night, will return.

Behold it aforetime
    No eye ever did;
So soon it forever
    From all eyes is hid.

Here hath been dawning
Another blue day;
Think, wilt thou let it
Slip useless away?

THE RUNAWAY CANNON

Victor Hugo

pigmy	billiard	gladiator	frantically
impede	sinister	projectile	inaccessible
cyclone	fractures	assaulting	complicated
cordage	mastodon	lieutenant	perspiration
larboard	impassive	stupendous	biographical
opponent	animation	destruction	extinguished

This selection is taken from a book entitled "Ninety-three." It is well to keep in mind that all the works of Victor Hugo were written in the French language, and afterwards translated into English. See a brief biographical sketch of Victor Hugo and his portrait on pages fifty-two and fifty-three of the Fourth Reader of this series.

On the first day of June, 1793, about an hour before sunset, a vessel set sail from a little lonely British Bay, in that kind of foggy weather which is favorable to flight, because pursuit is rendered dangerous. The crew of this vessel was French, but it belonged to the English fleet stationed on the lookout at the eastern point of the island.

This vessel was, to all appearances, a merchant ship, but in reality it was a sloop of war. It had the clumsy, peaceful look of a merchantman; but this was a mere blind. It had been built for a double purpose, deception and strength; to deceive if possible; to fight if necessary.

It was evident that this vessel had some extraordinary service before her. Indeed, a man had just gone on board who had every appearance of starting on an adventure. He was a tall, old man, straight and sturdy, with a stern face, whose age it would have been difficult to tell exactly, because he seemed at once old and young; one of those men, full of years and strength, with white locks on their brow and fire in their eye; forty years in point of vigor, and eighty in point of authority.

This great man had boarded the vessel disguised as a peasant. The peasant costume which he wore was threadbare at the elbows and knees, and appeared to have been in use a long time, and his cloak, made of coarse material, resembled that of a fisherman. He had on the round hat of the day, with high crown and broad brim, which when turned down has a rustic appearance, and when caught up with a cord has a military air. He wore this hat after the peasant fashion, with the rim flattened out.

" The peasant " was the name by which the crew began at once to designate their passenger, in the short conversations seamen have together; but without knowing more about him, they understood that this peasant was no more a peasant than the man-of-war was a merchantman.

The vessel headed north, then turned to the west. The sun had set, the night was dark, more so than is usual in summer; there was a moon, but heavy clouds more like autumn than summer covered the sky like a ceiling, and to judge from all appearances, the moon would not be visible till she touched the horizon just before setting. Clouds hung low over the sea, and covered it with fog. All this darkness was favorable.

All was going well; about nine o'clock the weather began to grow sulky, as the sailors say, and there was some wind and sea; but the wind was favorable, and the sea strong without being violent. However, occasionally a heavy sea swept over the bow of the vessel. About ten o'clock the sea grew rougher. The officers were discussing the state of affairs in France when the last speaker's words were suddenly cut short by a cry of despair, and at the same time a noise was heard wholly unlike any other sound. This cry and this sound came from within the vessel. The officers rushed towards the gun deck, but could not get down. All the gunners were hurrying frantically up. Something terrible had just happened.

One of the short cannons of the battery, a twenty-four pounder, had broken loose.

This is perhaps the most dangerous accident that can possibly take place on shipboard. Nothing more terrible can happen to a ship of war in open sea and under full sail.

A cannon that breaks its moorings suddenly becomes some strange, supernatural beast. It is a machine transformed into a monster. This short mass on wheels moves like a billiard ball, rolls with the rolling of the ship, plunges with the pitching, goes, comes, pauses, seems to meditate, starts on its course again, shoots like an arrow, from one end of the vessel to the other, whirls around, slips away, rears, breaks, kills. It is a battering ram assaulting a wall. Add to this, the fact that the ram is of metal, the wall of wood.

This mad mass leaps like a panther, it has the clumsiness of an elephant, the nimbleness of a mouse, the uncertainty of the billows, the zigzag of the lightning, the deafness of the grave. It weighs ten thousand pounds, and it rebounds like a child's ball.

And what is to be done? How to end this? A tempest ceases, a cyclone passes over, a wind dies down, a broken mast can be replaced, a leak can be stopped, a fire extinguished, but what will become of this enormous brute of bronze? How can it be captured? You can reason with a bulldog, astonish a bull, frighten a tiger, tame a lion; but you have no resource against this monster, a loose cannon. You cannot kill it, it is dead; and at the same time it lives. It lives with a sinister life which comes to it from the infinite. The deck beneath it gives it full swing. It is moved by the ship, which is moved by the sea, which is moved by the wind. This destroyer is a toy. The ship, the waves, the winds all play with it; hence, its frightful animation.

What is to be done with it? How fetter this stupendous engine of destruction? How anticipate its comings and goings, its returns, its shocks? Any one of its blows on the side of the ship may stave it in. How foretell its frightful meanderings? It is dealing with a projectile which alters its mind, which seems to have ideas, and changes its direction every instant. How check the course of what must be avoided? The horrible cannon struggles, advances, recoils, strikes to the right, strikes to the left, retreats, passes by, grinds up obstacles, crushes men like flies.

265

In an instant the whole crew was on foot. It was the fault of the gun-captain, who had neglected to fasten the mooring-chain, and had insecurely clogged the four wheels of the gun carriage. A heavy sea struck the port, and the cannon, insecurely fastened, had recoiled and broken its chain, and had begun its terrible course over the deck.

To form an idea of this strange sliding, let one imagine a drop of water running over a glass.

At the moment when the fastenings gave way, the gunners were in the battery. Some in groups, others scattered about, busied with the customary work among sailors getting ready for a signal for action. The cannon, hurled forward by the pitching of the vessel, dashed into this crowd of men and crushed four at the first blow ; then sliding back and shooting out again as the ship rolled, it cut in two a fifth unfortunate, and knocked a piece of the battery against the larboard side with such force as to unship it. This caused the cry of distress which had just been heard. All the men rushed to the ladder. The gun deck was vacated in the twinkling of an eye.

The enormous cannon was left alone. It was given up to itself. It was its own master, and master of the ship. It could do what it pleased. The whole crew, accustomed to laugh in time of battle, trembled now. To describe the terror is impossible.

The captain and the lieutenant, although both brave men, stopped at the head of the stairs, and dumb, pale, and hesitating, looked down on the deck below. Some one elbowed past and went down. It was their passenger, the peasant, the man of whom they had just been speaking a moment before. When he reached the foot of the ladder, he stood still.

The cannon was rushing back and forth on the deck. The marine lantern swinging overhead added a dizzy shifting of light and shade to the picture. The shape of the cannon could not be distinguished so rapid was its course. It looked now black in the light, now mysteriously white in the darkness. The whole ship was filled with the awful tumult.

The captain promptly recovered his presence of mind and ordered everything that could check and impede the cannon's mad course to be thrown through the hatchway down on the gun deck, — mattresses, hammocks, spare sails, rolls of cordage, and bales of paper, of which the ship carried a full cargo.

But what could these rags do? No one dared to go below to arrange them properly, and they were reduced to lint in a few minutes.

There was just sea enough to make the accident as bad as possible. A tempest would have been desirable, for it might have upset the cannon, and with its four wheels once in the air there would be some hope of getting it under control.

Meanwhile, the havoc increased. There were splits and fractures in the masts. The battery was being ruined. Ten pieces out of thirty were disabled ; the breeches in the side of the vessel were increasing and the ship was beginning to take in water.

The old passenger, having gone down to the gun deck, stood like a man of stone at the foot of the steps. He cast a stern glance over this scene of devastation. He did not move. It seemed impossible to take a step forward. Every movement of the loose cannon threatened the ship's destruction. A few moments more and shipwreck would be inevitable.

They must perish or put a speedy end to the disaster; some course must be decided on; but what? What an opponent was this cannon! Something must be done to stop this terrible madness, to capture this flash of lightning, to overthrow this thunderbolt.

"Do you believe in God?" said the captain to the lieutenant.

"Yes; no; sometimes;" was the reply.

"During a tempest?"

"Yes; and in moments like this."

"God alone can save us from this," said the captain.

Everybody was silent; but the cannon kept up its horrible din.

Outside, the waves beating against the ship responded with their blows to the shocks of the cannon. It was like two hammers alternating.

Suddenly, in the midst of this inaccessible ring, where the escaped cannon was leaping, a man was seen to appear, with an iron bar in his hand. He was the gun-captain, whose criminal carelessness had caused the accident. Having been the means of bringing about the misfortune, he was anxious to repair it. He had seized the iron bar in one hand, a rope with a slip-noose in the other hand, and had jumped down the hatchway to the gun deck.

Then began an awful sight; the contest between a gun and a

gunner; a battle between matter and intelligence; a duel between man and the inanimate.

The man stationed himself in a corner, and with bar and rope in his hands, he waited for the cannon to pass him. The gunner knew his gun, and it seemed to him as if the gun ought to know him. He had lived long with it. How many times he had thrust his hand into its mouth! It was his own tame monster. He began to speak to it as if it were his dog.

"Come!" he said. Perhaps he loved it. He seemed to wish it to come to him. But to come to him was to come upon him. And then he would be lost. How could he avoid being crushed? That was the question. All looked on in terror.

No one breathed freely except perhaps the old man who stood in his place at the foot of the ladder. He might be crushed himself by the cannon. He did not stir. Beneath them the sea blindly directed the contest.

At the moment when the gunner came near to challenge the cannon, some chance movement of the waves caused the cannon to remain for an instant motionless, as if stupefied.

"Come on!" the man said to it. It seemed to listen. Suddenly it leaped towards him. The man dodged the blow. The battle began, an unheard of battle. The gladiator of flesh attacking the beast of brass. On one side blind force; on the other a human soul.

All this was taking place in semi-darkness. It was like the shadowy vision of a miracle.

A soul — strange to say; one would have thought the cannon

also had a soul; but a soul full of hatred and rage. This sightless thing seemed to have eyes. The monster appeared to lie in wait for the man. One would have at least believed that there was craft in this mass. It also chose its time. It was a strange, gigantic insect of metal, having or seeming to have the will of a demon. For a moment it would beat against the low ceiling overhead, then it would come down on its four wheels like a tiger on its four paws, and begin to run at the man. He, supple, nimble, expert, glided away like a snake from all these lightning movements. He avoided the blows, but they fell upon the vessel, and continued their work of destruction.

A piece of broken chain had been left hanging to the cannon. One end of the chain was fastened to the carriage. The other end, left loose, whirled desperately about the cannon, making all its blows more dangerous. An iron lash in a fist of brass. This chain complicated the contest.

However, the man went on fighting. Occasionally, it was the man who attacked the cannon. He would creep along the side of the vessel, bar and rope in hand; and the cannon, as if it understood, and as though suspecting some snare, would flee away. The man, bent on victory, pursued it. Such a duel could not last long. The cannon seemed to say to itself all of a sudden, "Come now! Make an end of it!" and it paused. One felt that the crisis was at hand.

The cannon made a sudden, quick dash at the gunner. The gunner sprang out of the way, let it pass by, and cried out to it with a laugh, "Try it again!" The cannon, as if enraged, smashed another cannon on the port side ; then, again seized by the invisible sling which controlled it, it was hurled at the man, who made his escape. Three other cannons gave way under the blows of this one ; then, as if blind and not knowing what more to do, it turned its back on the man, rolled from stern to bow, injured the stern, and made a breech in the planking of the prow.

The gunner took refuge at the foot of the steps, not far from the old man who was looking on. The gunner held his iron bar in rest. The cannon seemed to notice it, and without taking the trouble to turn around, slid back on the man, swift as the blow of an ax. The gunner, if driven back against the side of the ship, was lost. The whole crew cried out with horror.

But the old passenger, till this minute motionless, darted forth more quickly than any of this wildly swift rapidity. He seized a bale of paper, and, at the risk of being crushed, succeeded in throwing it between the wheels of the cannon.

The bale of paper had the effect of a clog. A pebble may stop a log, the branch of a tree turn aside an avalanche. The cannon stumbled. The gunner, taking advantage of this critical opportunity, plunged his iron bar between the spokes of one of the hind wheels.

The cannon stopped. It leaned forward. The man using the bar as a lever, rocked it to and fro. The heavy mass was overthrown, with the crash of a falling bell, and the man, rushing with all his might, dripping with perspiration, passed the slip noose around the bronze neck of the subdued monster.

It was ended. The man had conquered. The ant had con-

271

trol over the mastodon ; the pygmy had taken the thunderbolt prisoner. The marines and the sailors clapped their hands. The whole crew rushed forward with cables and chains, and in an instant the cannon was secured.

The gunner saluted the passenger.

"Sir," he said, "you have saved my life."

The old man, who had resumed his impassive attitude, made no reply.

THE PRISONER OF CHILLON

GEORGE GORDON, LORD BYRON

lineal	tenets	athwart	accursed
solace	inured	suppress	enthralls
Byron	crevice	stagnant	cankering
Gothic	meteor	abhorred	perchance
Gordon	Chillon	profaned	admonished
Geneva	assuage	martyred	Persecution's

George Gordon Byron was born in London in 1788. At the age of ten, by the death of his great uncle, he became Lord Byron. The next morning when the roll was called at school and he heard "Lord Byron," he was so startled that he burst into tears.

He traveled extensively through Europe, spending much time in Italy and Switzerland. The "Prisoner of Chillon" was written in 1816 on the shores of Lake Geneva, at a time when Byron was living with the poet Shelley. Thirty-six short stormy years make up the life of George Gordon Byron. He died in 1824. Hearing the news of his death, the boy Tennyson, dreaming at Somersby on poetic greatness, crept away to weep and carve upon sandstone the words, "Byron is dead."

272

George Gordon, Lord Byron.

I

My hair is gray, but not with years;
  Nor grew it white
  In a single night,
As men's have grown from sudden fears.
My limbs are bowed, though not with toil,
  But rusted with the vile repose,
For they have been a dungeon's spoil,
  And mine has been the fate of those
To whom the goodly earth and air
Are banned and barred, — forbidden fare.
But this was for my father's faith
I suffered chains and courted death;
That father perished at the stake
For tenets he would not forsake;
And for the same his lineal race
In darkness found a dwelling place.
We were seven, who now are one,
  Six in youth and one in age,
Finished as they had begun,
  Proud of Persecution's rage;
One in fire, and two in field,
Their belief with blood have sealed,
Dying as their father died
For the God their foes denied;
Three were in a dungeon cast,
Of whom this wreck is left the last.

II

There are seven pillars of Gothic mold,
In Chillon's dungeons deep and old;
There are seven columns, massy and gray,
Dim with a dull imprisoned ray, —
A sunbeam which hath lost its way,
And through the crevice and the cleft
Of the thick wall is fallen and left,
Creeping o'er the floor so damp,
Like a marsh's meteor lamp;
And in each pillar there is a ring,
  And in each ring there is a chain.
That iron is a cankering thing,
  For in these limbs its teeth remain,
With marks that will not wear away,
Till I have done with this new day,
Which now is painful to these eyes,
Which have not seen the sun to rise
For years, — I cannot count them o'er;
I lost their long and heavy score
When my last brother drooped and died,
And I lay living by his side.

III

They chained us each to a column stone,
And we were three, — yet, each alone.
We could not move a single pace,

We could not see each other's face,
But with that pale and livid light
That made us strangers in our sight:
And thus together, yet apart,
Fettered in hand, but joined in heart;
'Twas still some solace, in the dearth
Of the pure elements of earth,
 To hearken to each other's speech,
And each turn comforter to each
With some new hope, or legend old,
Or song heroically bold;
But even these at length grew cold.
Our voices took a dreary tone,
·An echo of the dungeon stone,
    A grating sound, not full and free
    As they of yore were wont to be;
    It might be fancy, but to me
They never sounded like our own.

IV

I was the eldest of the three,
    And to uphold and cheer the rest
    I ought to do, and did, my best,
And each did well in his degree.
    The youngest, whom my father loved,
Because our mother's brow was given

To him, — with eyes as blue as Heaven, —
    For him my soul was sorely moved:
And truly might it be distrest
To see such bird in such a nest;
For he was beautiful as day, —
    (When day was beautiful to me
    As to young eagles, being free), —
    A polar day which will not see
A sunset till its summer's gone,
    Its sleepless summer of long light,
The snow-clad offspring of the sun;
    And thus he was as pure and bright,
And in his natural spirit gay,
With tears for naught but others' ills,
And then they flowed like mountain rills
Unless he could assuage the woe
Which he abhorred to view below.

V

The other was as pure of, mind,
But formed to combat with his kind;
Strong in his frame, and of a mood
Which 'gainst the world in war had stood,
And perished in the foremost rank
With joy, — but not in chains to pine.
His spirit withered with their clank,
I saw it silently decline,

And so perchance in sooth did mine;
But yet I forced it on to cheer
Those relics of a home so dear.
He was a hunter of the hills,
　　Had followed there the deer and wolf;
　　To him this dungeon was a gulf,
And fettered feet the worst of ills.

VI

　Lake Leman lies by Chillon's walls;
A thousand feet in depth below
Its massy waters meet and flow;
Thus much the fathom line was sent
From Chillon's snow-white battlement,
　　Which round about the wave enthralls:
A double dungeon wall and wave
Have made, — and like a living grave,
Below the surface of the lake
The dark vault lies wherein we lay.
We heard it ripple night and day;
　　Sounding o'er our heads it knocked.
And I have felt the winter's spray
Wash through the bars when winds were high
And wanton in the happy sky;
　　And then the very rock hath rocked,
　　And I have felt it shake unshocked,

PRISON OF CHILLON.

Because I could have smiled to see
The death that would have set me free.

VII

I said my nearer brother pined,
I said his mighty heart declined.
He loathed and put away his food:
It was not that 'twas coarse and rude,
For we were used to hunter's fare,
And for the like had little care.
The milk drawn from the mountain goat
Was changed for water from the moat;
Our bread was such as captives' tears
Have moistened many a thousand years,
Since man first pent his fellow-men
Like brutes within an iron den;
But what were these to us or him?
These wasted not his heart or limb.
My brother's soul was of that mold
Which in a palace had grown cold,
Had his free breathing been denied
The range of the steep mountain's side;
But why delay the truth? — he died.
I saw, and could not hold his head,
Nor reach his dying hand, — nor dead, —
Though hard I strove, but strove in vain,
To rend and gnash my bonds in twain.

280

He died, — and they unlocked his chain,
And scooped for him a shallow grave
Even from the cold earth of our cave.
I begged them, as a boon, to lay
His corse in dust whereon the day
Might shine; it was a foolish thought,
But then within my brain it wrought,
That even in death his free-born breast
In such a dungeon could not rest.
I might have spared my idle prayer;
They coldly laughed, and laid him there:
The flat and turfless earth above
The being we so much did love;
His empty chain above it leant,
Such murder's fitting monument!

VIII

But he, the favorite and the flower,
Most cherished since his natal hour,
His mother's image in fair face,
The infant love of all his race,
His martyred father's dearest thought,
My latest care, for whom I sought
To hoard my life, that his might be
Less wretched now, and one day free;
He, too, who yet had held untired
A spirit natural or inspired, —

He, too, was struck, and day by day
Was withered on the stalk away.
He faded, and so calm and meek,
So softly worn, so sweetly weak,
So tearless, yet so tender, — kind,
And grieved for those he left behind;
With all the while a cheek whose bloom
Was as a mockery of the tomb,
Whose tints as gently sunk away
As a departing rainbow's ray;
An eye of most transparent light,
That almost made the dungeon bright,
And not a word of murmur, — not
A groan o'er his untimely lot;
A little talk of better days,
A little hope my own to raise,
For I was sunk in silence, — lost
In this last loss, of all the most;
And then the sighs he would suppress
Of fainting nature's feebleness,
More slowly drawn, grew less and less.
I listened, but I could not hear;
I called, for I was wild with fear;
I knew 'twas hopeless, but my dread
Would not be thus admonishèd;
I called, and thought I heard a sound, —
I burst my chain with one strong bound,

And rushed to him: I found him not,
I only stirred in this black spot,
I only lived, *I* only drew
The accursèd breath of dungeon dew.
The last, — the sole — the dearest link
Between me and the eternal brink,
Which bound me to my failing race,
Was broken in this fatal place.
One on the earth, and one beneath, —
My brothers, — both had ceased to breathe:
I took that hand which lay so still,
Alas! my own was full as chill;
I had not strength to stir or strive,
But felt that I was still alive, —
A frantic feeling when we know
That what we love shall ne'er be so.
   I know not why
   I could not die,
I had no earthly hope but faith,
And that forbade a selfish death.

IX

What next befell me then and there
   I know not well — I never knew: —
First came the loss of light, and air,
   And then of darkness too:
I had no thought, no feeling — none —

Among the stones I stood a stone,
And was, scarce conscious what I wist,
As shrubless crags within the mist;
For all was blank, and bleak, and gray;
It was not night — it was not day;
It was not even the dungeon light,
So hateful to my heavy sight,
But vacancy absorbing space,
And fixedness — without a place:
There were no stars, — no earth, — no time, —
No check, — no change, — no good, — no crime, —
But silence, and a stirless breath
Which neither was of life nor death;
A sea of stagnant idleness,
Blind, boundless, mute. and motionless!

X

A light broke in upon my brain,
  It was the carol of a bird;
It ceased, and then it came again,
  The sweetest song ear ever heard,
And mine was thankful till mine eyes
Ran over with the glad surprise,
And they that moment could not see
I was the mate of misery;
But then by dull degrees came back
My senses to their wonted track.

I saw the dungeon walls and floor
Close slowly round me as before;
I saw the glimmer of the sun
Creeping as it before had done,
But through the crevice where it came
That bird was perched, as fond and tame,
   And tamer than upon the tree;
A lovely bird, with azure wings,
And song that said a thousand things,
   And seemed to say them all for me!
I never saw its like before,
I ne'er shall see its likeness more.
It seemed like me to want a mate,
But was not half so desolate,
And it was come to love me when
None lived to love me so again,
And cheering from my dungeon's brink,
Had brought me back to feel and think.
I know not if it late were free,
   Or broke its cage to perch on mine,
But knowing well captivity,
   Sweet bird! I could not wish for thine,
Or if it were, in wingèd guise,
A visitant from Paradise;
For — Heaven forgive that thought! the while
Which made me both to weep and smile —
I sometimes deemed that it might be

My brother's soul come down to me;
But then at last away it flew,
And then 'twas mortal, well I knew,
For he would never thus have flown,
And left me twice so doubly lone, —
Lone, — as the corse within its shroud,
Lone, — as a solitary cloud,
　A single cloud on a sunny day,
While all the rest of Heaven is clear,
A frown upon the atmosphere,
That hath no business to appear
　When skies are blue and earth is gay.

XI

A kind of change came in my fate,
My keepers grew compassionate;
I know not what had made them so,
They were inured to sights of woe,
But so it was: my broken chain
With links unfastened did remain,
And it was liberty to stride
Along my cell from side to side,
And up and down, and then athwart,
And tread it over every part;
And round the pillars one by one,
Returning where my walk begun,
Avoiding only, as I trod,

My brothers' graves without a sod;
For if I thought with heedless tread
My step profaned their lowly bed,
My breath came gaspingly and thick,
And my crushed heart felt blind and sick.

XII

I made a footing in the wall;
  It was not therefrom to escape,
For I had buried one and all
  Who loved me in a human shape;
And the whole earth would henceforth be
A wider prison unto me.
No child, no sire, no kin had I,
No partner in my misery;
I thought of this, and I was glad,
For thought of them had made me mad;
But I was curious to ascend
To my barred windows, and to bend
Once more upon the mountains high,
The quiet of a loving eye.

XIII

I saw them — and they were the same,
They were not changed like me in frame;
I saw their thousand years of snow
On high, — their wide long lake below,

And the blue Rhone in fullest flow;
I heard the torrents leap and gush
O'er channeled rock and broken bush;
I saw the white-walled distant town,
And whiter sails go skimming down;
And then there was a little isle,
Which in my very face did smile,
   The only one in view;
A small green isle, it seemed no more,
Scarce broader than my dungeon floor,
But in it there were three tall trees,
And o'er it blew the mountain breeze,
And by it there were waters flowing,
And on it there were young flowers growing,
   Of gentle breath and hue.
The fish swam by the castle wall,
And they seemed joyous, each and all;
The eagle rode the rising blast;
Methought he never flew so fast
As then to me he seemed to fly,
And then new tears came in my eye,
And I felt troubled, and would fain
I had not left my recent chain;
And when I did descend again,
The darkness of my dim abode
Fell on me as a heavy load;
It was as is a new-dug grave

Closing o'er one we sought to save, —
And yet my glance, too much opprest,
Had almost need of such a rest.

XIV

It might be months, or years, or days,
  I kept no count, I took no note,
I had no hope my eyes to raise,
  And clear them of their dreary mote;
At last men came to set me free,
  I asked not why, and recked not where,
It was at length the same to me,
  Fettered or fetterless to be, —
  I learned to love despair.
And thus when they appeared at last,
And all my bonds aside were cast,
These heavy walls to me had grown
A hermitage, — and all my own!
And half I felt as they were come
To tear me from a second home:
With spiders I had friendship made,
And watched them in their sullen trade,
Had seen the mice by moonlight play,
And why should I feel less than they?
We were all inmates of one place,
And I, the monarch of each race,
Had power to kill, — yet, strange to tell!

In quiet we had learned to dwell.
My very chains and I grew friends, —
So much a long communion tends
To make us what we are : even I
Regained my freedom with a sigh.

CHISWICK MALL

WILLIAM MAKEPEACE THACKERAY

adieu	austere	filigree	inscription
depict	dubious	guileless	Pinkerton's
Saltire	scullery	hysterics	undeviating
somber	Sedley's	demurely	disconsolate
Esquire	epitaphs	audacious	orthography
Jemima	Amelia's	receptacle	correspondent
Chapone	Thackeray	embroidery	Lexicographer

William Makepeace Thackeray, a distinguished English novelist, was born in India in 1811, but at the age of five was taken to England. It was not, however, until 1848, when Thackeray was thirty-seven years old and when Dickens, a year younger, was already famous, that Thackeray made an enduring name for himself by the publication of "Vanity Fair," still counted as one of the greatest of English novels. The rest of his short life was occupied with novel writing and with lecturing. He died in 1863.

The following selection is the first chapter of his famous novel, "Vanity Fair," with a few additional lines from Chapter II.

While the present century was in its teens, and on one sunshiny morning in June, there drove up to the great iron gate of Miss Pinkerton's academy for young ladies, on Chiswick Mall, a

WILLIAM MAKEPEACE THACKERAY.

large family coach, with two fat horses in blazing harness, driven by a fat coachman in a three-cornered hat and wig, at the rate of four miles an hour. A black servant, who reposed on the box beside the fat coachman, uncurled his bandy legs as soon as the equipage drew up opposite Miss Pinkerton's shining brass plate, and as he pulled the bell, at least a score of young heads were seen peering out of the narrow windows of the stately, old brick house. Nay, the acute observer might have recognized the little red nose of good-natured Miss Jemima Pinkerton herself, rising over some geranium-pots in the window of that lady's own drawing-room.

"It is Mrs. Sedley's coach, Sister," said Miss Jemima. "Sambo, the black servant, has just rung the bell; and the coachman has a new red waistcoat."

"Have you completed all the necessary preparations incident to Miss Sedley's departure, Miss Jemima?" asked Miss Pinkerton herself, a majestic lady, the friend of Dr. Johnson, and the correspondent of Mrs. Chapone herself.

"The girls were up at four this morning, packing her trunks, Sister," replied Miss Jemima; "we have made her a bowpot."

"Say a bouquet, sister Jemima, 'tis more genteel."

"Well, a booky as big almost as a haystack; I have put up two bottles of the gillyflower-water for Mrs. Sedley, and the receipt for making it, in Amelia's box."

"And I trust, Miss Jemima, you have made a copy of Miss Sedley's account. This is it, is it? Very good — ninety-three pounds four shilling. Be kind enough to address it to John

Sedley, Esquire, and to seal this billet which I have written to his lady."

In Miss Jemima's eyes an autograph letter of her sister, Miss Pinkerton, was an object of as deep veneration as would have been a letter from a sovereign. Only when her pupils quitted the establishment, or when they were about to be married, and once, when poor Miss Birch died of the scarlet fever, was Miss Pinkerton known to write personally to the parents of her pupils; and it was Jemima's opinion that if anything *could* console Mrs. Birch for her daughter's loss, it would be that pious and eloquent composition in which Miss Pinkerton announced the event.

In the present instance Miss Pinkerton's "billet" was to the following effect: —

THE MALL, CHISWICK, June 15, 18 —.

" MADAM, — After her six years' residence at the Mall, I have the honor and happiness of presenting Miss Amelia Sedley to her parents, as a young lady not unworthy to occupy a fitting position in their polished and refined circle. Those virtues which charac- terize the young English gentlewoman, those accomplishments which become her birth and station, will not be found wanting in the amiable Miss Sedley, whose *industry* and *obedience* have en- deared her to her instructors, and whose delightful sweetness of temper has charmed her *aged* and her *youthful* companions.

" In music, in dancing, in orthography, in every variety of embroidery and needlework, she will be found to have realized her friends' *fondest wishes*. In geography there is still much to be desired; and a careful and undeviating use of the backboard, for four hours daily during the next three years, is recommended as necessary to the acquirement of that dignified *deportment and carriage,* so requisite for every young lady of *fashion.*

"In the principles of religion and morality, Miss Sedley will be found worthy of an establishment which has been honored by the presence of *The Great Lexicographer,* and the patronage of the admirable Mrs. Chapone. In leaving the Mall, Miss Amelia carries with her the hearts of her companions, and the affectionate regard of her mistress, who has the honor to subscribe herself,

"Madam, your most obliged humble servant,

"BARBARA PINKERTON."

"P. S. — Miss Sharp accompanies Miss Sedley. It is particularly requested that Miss Sharp's stay in Russel Square may not exceed ten days. The family of distinction with whom she is engaged desire to avail themselves of her services as soon as possible."

This letter completed, Miss Pinkerton proceeded to write her own name and Miss Sedley's in the flyleaf of a Johnson's Dictionary — the interesting work which she invariably presented to her scholars on their departure from the Mall. On the cover was inserted a copy of "Lines addressed to a young lady on quitting Miss Pinkerton's school, at the Mall; by the late revered Doctor Samuel Johnson." In fact, the Lexicographer's name was always on the lips of this majestic woman, and a visit he had paid to her was the cause of her reputation and her fortune.

Being commanded by her elder sister to get "the Dictionary" from the cupboard, Miss Jemima had extracted two copies of the

294

book from the receptacle in question. When Miss Pinkerton had finished the inscription in the first, Jemima, with rather a dubious and timid air, handed her the second.

" For whom is this, Miss Jemima ? " said Miss Pinkerton, with awful coldness.

" For Becky Sharp," answered Jemima, trembling very much, and blushing over her withered face and neck, as she turned her back on her sister. " For Becky Sharp: she's going too."

" *Miss Jemima!* " exclaimed Miss Pinkerton, in the largest capitals. " Are you in your senses ? Replace the Dictionary in the closet, and never venture to take such a liberty in future."

" Well, Sister, it's only two-and-ninepence, and poor Becky will be miserable if she don't get one."

" Send Miss Sedley instantly to me," said Miss Pinkerton. And so venturing not to say another word, poor Jemima trotted off, exceedingly flurried and nervous.

Miss Sedley's papa was a merchant in London and a man of some wealth ; whereas Miss Sharp was an articled pupil, for whom Miss Pinkerton had done, as she thought, quite enough, without conferring upon her at parting the high honor of the Dictionary.

Although schoolmistress's letters are to be trusted no more nor less than churchyard epitaphs ; yet, as it sometimes happens that a person departs this life who is really deserving of all the praises the stonecutter carves over his bones ; who *is* a good Christian, a good parent, child, wife, or husband ; who actually *does* leave a disconsolate family to mourn his loss ; so in academies of the male and female sex it occurs every now and then that the pupil is fully worthy of the praises bestowed by the disinterested instructor. Now, Miss Amelia Sedley was a young lady of this singular species; and not only deserved all that Miss Pinkerton had said in her praise, but had many charming qualities which that pompous old Minerva of a woman could not see, because of the differences of rank and age between her pupil and herself.

For she could not only sing like a lark, and embroider beautifully, and spell as well as a Dictionary itself, but she had such a kindly, smiling, tender, gentle, generous heart of her own, as won the love of everybody who came near her, from Minerva herself down to the poor girl in the scullery, and the one-eyed tartwoman's daughter, who was permitted to vend her wares once a week to the young ladies in the Mall. She had twelve intimate and bosom friends out of the twenty-four young ladies. Even envious Miss Briggs never spoke ill of her, and high and mighty Miss Saltire (Lord Dexter's granddaughter) allowed that her figure was genteel. Miss Pinkerton's attachment was, as may be supposed, from the high position and eminent virtues of that lady, calm and dignified; but Miss Jemima had already whimpered several times at the idea of Amelia's departure; and, but for fear of her sister, would have gone off into downright hysterics. Such luxury of grief, however, is allowed only to parlor boarders. Honest Jemima had all the bills, and the washing, and the mending, and the puddings, and the plate and crockery, and the servants to superintend. But why speak about her? It is probable that we shall not hear of her again from this moment to the end of time, and that when the great filigree iron gates are once closed on her, she and her awful sister will never issue therefrom into this little world of history.

But as we are to see a great deal of Amelia, there is no harm in saying, at the outset of our acquaintance, that she was a dear little creature; and a great mercy it is, both in life and in novels, which (and the latter especially) abound in villains of the most somber sort, that we are to have for a constant companion, so guileless and good-natured a person. As she is not a heroine, there is no need to describe her person; indeed I am afraid that her nose was rather short than otherwise, and her cheeks a great deal too round and red for a heroine; but her face blushed with rosy health, and her lips with the freshest of smiles, and she had a pair of eyes which sparkled with the brightest and honestest good humor, except indeed when they filled with tears, and that was a great deal too often; for the silly thing would cry over a dead canary bird, or over a mouse which the cat haply had seized upon, or over the end of a novel, were it ever so stupid; and as for saying an unkind word to her, were any persons hard-hearted enough to do so, why, so much the worse for them. Even Miss Pinkerton, that austere and godlike woman, ceased scolding her after the first time; and though she no more comprehended sensibility than she did Algebra, had given all masters and teachers particular orders to treat Miss Sedley with the utmost gentleness, as harsh treatment was injurious to her.

So that when the day of departure came, between her two customs of laughing and crying, Miss Sedley was greatly puzzled how to act. She was glad to go home, and yet most woefully sad at leaving school. For three days before, little Laura Martin, the orphan, followed her about like a little dog. She had to make and receive at least fourteen presents, and to make fourteen solemn promises of writing every week. "Send my letters under cover to my grandpapa, the Earl of Dexter," said Miss Saltire (who, by the way, was rather shabby): and the orphan, little Laura Martin, took her friend's hand and said, looking up in her face wistfully, "Amelia, when I write to you I shall call you Mamma." All which details, I have no doubt, *Jones*, who reads this book at his Club, will pronounce to be excessively foolish, trivial, and twaddling. Yes; I can see Jones at this minute, taking out his pencil and scoring under the words "foolish, twaddling," etc., and adding to them his own remark of "*quite true.*" Well, he is a lofty man of genius, and admires the great and heroic in life and novels; and so had better take warning and go elsewhere.

Well, then. The flowers, and the presents, and the trunks, and the bonnet-boxes of Miss Sedley having been arranged by Mr. Sambo in the carriage, together with a very small and weather-beaten old cow's skin trunk with Miss Sharp's card neatly nailed upon it, which was delivered by Sambo with a grin, and packed by the coachman with a corresponding sneer, the hour for parting came; and the grief of that moment was considerably lessened by the admirable discourse which Miss Pinkerton addressed to her pupil.

"You'll go in and say good-by to Miss Pinkerton, Becky!" said Miss Jemima to a young lady of whom nobody took any notice, and who was coming downstairs with her own band-box.

"I suppose I must," said Miss Sharp, calmly, and much to the wonder of Miss Jemima; and the latter having knocked at the door, and receiving permission to come in, Miss Sharp advanced in a very unconcerned manner, and said in French, and with perfect accent, " Miss, I come to say good-by to you."

Miss Pinkerton did not understand French; she only directed those who did: but biting her lips and throwing up her venerable and Roman-nosed head, on the top of which figured a large and solemn turban, she said, "Miss Sharp, I wish you a good morning." As she spoke, she waved one hand, both by way of adieu and by way of giving Miss Sharp an opportunity to shake one of the fingers of the hand which was left out for that purpose.

Miss Sharp only folded her own hands with a very frigid smile and bow, and quite declined to accept the proffered honor, on which Miss Pinkerton tossed up her turban more indignantly than ever. In fact, it was a little battle between the young lady and the old one, and the latter was worsted. "Heaven bless you, my child," said she, embracing Amelia, and scowling the while over the girl's shoulder at Miss Sharp. "Come away, Becky," said Miss Jemima, pulling the young woman away in great alarm, and the drawing-room door closed upon them forever.

Then came the struggle and parting below. Words refuse to tell it. All the servants were there in the hall, all the dear friends, all the young ladies, the dancing master who had just arrived;

and there was such a scuffling, and hugging, and kissing, and crying, as no pen can depict, and as the tender heart would fain pass over. The embracing was over; they parted; that is, Miss Sedley parted from her friends. Miss Sharp had demurely entered the carriage some minutes before. Nobody cried for leaving *her*. She said that all the world used her ill, and we may be pretty certain that persons whom all the world treats ill deserve entirely the treatment that they get. The world is a looking-glass, and gives back to every man the reflection of his own face. Frown at it, and it will in turn look sourly upon you; laugh at it and with it, and it is a jolly kind companion; and so let all young persons take their choice. This is certain, that if the world neglected Miss Sharp, she never had been known to do a good action in behalf of anybody; nor can it be expected that twenty-four young ladies should all be as amiable as the heroine of this work, — Miss Sedley, whom we have selected for the very reason that she was the best-natured of all, otherwise what on earth was to prevent us from putting Miss Crump, or Miss Hopkins, as heroine in her place?

Sambo of the bandy legs slammed the carriage door on his young weeping mistress. He sprang up behind the carriage. "Stop!" cried Miss Jemima, rushing to the gate with a parcel.

"It's some sandwiches, my dear," said she to Amelia. "You may be hungry, you know; and Becky, Becky Sharp, here's a book for you that my sister — that is, I — Johnson's Dictionary, you know; you mustn't leave us without that. Good-by. Drive on, coachman. God bless you!"

And the kind creature retreated into the garden, overcome with emotion.

But, lo! and just as the coach drove off, Miss Sharp put her pale face out of the window, and actually flung the book back into the garden.

This almost caused Jemima to faint with terror. "Well, I never!" said she. "What an audacious"—emotion prevented her from completing either sentence. The carriage rolled away; the great gates were closed; the bell rang for the dancing lesson. The world is before the two young ladies; and so, farewell to Chiswick Mall.

SOLITUDE

ELLA WHEELER WILCOX

nectared

Laugh, and the world laughs with you;
    Weep, and you weep alone,
For the sad old earth must borrow its mirth,
    But has trouble enough of its own.
Sing, and the hills will answer;
    Sigh, it is lost on the air.
The echoes bound to a joyful sound,
    But shrink from voicing care.

Rejoice, and men will seek you;
    Grieve, and they turn and go.
They want full measure of all your pleasure,
    But they do not need your woe.

Be glad, and your friends are many;
　　Be sad, and you lose them all.
There are none to decline your nectared wine,
　　But alone you must drink life's gall.

Feast, and your halls are crowded;
　　Fast, and the world goes by.
Succeed and give, and it helps you live,
　　But no man can help you die.
There is room in the halls of pleasure
　　For a long and lordly train,
But one by one we must all file on
　　Through the narrow aisles of pain.

THE HOMES OF THE PEOPLE

HENRY WOODFIN GRADY

lien　　　　　　resonant　　　　　covenant　　　　tremendous
requiem　　　　Congress　　　　mortgage　　　　regeneration

I went to Washington the other day, and I stood on the
Capitol Hill; my heart beat quick as I looked at the towering
marble of my country's Capitol, and a mist gathered in my eyes
as I thought of its tremendous significance; the armies and the
treasury; the judges and the President; the Congress and the
courts, and all that was gathered there. And I felt that the sun
in all its course could not look down on a better sight than that
majestic home of a republic, which had taught the world its best
lessons of liberty. And I felt that if honor and wisdom and
justice abided therein, the world would at last owe that great

house in which the ark of the covenant of our country is lodged, its final uplifting and its regeneration.

But a few days later, I visited a quiet country home. It was just a simple, modest house, sheltered by big trees and encircled by meadow and field, rich with the promise of harvest. The fragrance of the pink and of the hollyhock in the front yard was mingled with the aroma of the orchard and of the garden, and the resonant clucking of poultry and the hum of bees.

Inside the house were thrift, comfort, and that cleanliness which is next to godliness. There was the old clock that had held its steadfast pace amid the frolic of weddings, that had welcomed in steady measure every newcomer to the family, that had kept company with the watches at the bedside, and that had ticked the solemn requiem of the dead. There were the big, restful beds and the open fireplace, and the old family Bible, thumbed with the fingers of hands long since still, and blurred with the tears of eyes long since closed, holding the simple annals of the family and the heart and the conscience of the home.

Outside the house stood the master, a simple, upright man, with no mortgage on his roof, and no lien on his growing crops; master of his lands and master of himself. Near by stood his aged father, happy in the heart and home of his son. And as they started to the house, the old man's hand rested on the young man's shoulder, laying there the unspeakable blessing of the honored and grateful father and ennobling it with the knighthood of the fifth commandment.

And as they reached the door, the old mother came with the

sunset falling fair on her face, and lighting up her deep, patient eyes, while her lips, trembling with the rich music of her heart, bade her husband and her son welcome to their home. Beyond was the good wife, happy amid her household cares, clean of heart and conscience, the buckler and the helpmeet of her husband. Down the lane came the children, trooping home after the cows, seeking as truant birds do the quiet of their home nest.

And I saw the night descend on that home, falling gently as from the wings of the unseen dove. And the old man, while a startled bird called from the forest, and the trees thrilled with the cricket's cry, and the stars were swarming in the bending sky, called the family around him and took the Bible from the table and read the old, old story of love and faith. He then called them to their knees in prayer, and the little baby hid in the folds of its mother's dress while he closed the record of that simple day by calling down God's blessing on their simple home.

And while I gazed, the vision of the great marble Capitol faded from my brain. Forgotten were its treasure and its splendor. And I said, "Oh, surely here in the homes of the people are lodged at last the strength and the responsibility of this government, the hope and the promise of this Republic."

THE USE OF FLOWERS

MARY HOWITT

lotus

God might have made the earth bring forth
Enough for great and small,

304

The oak tree and the cedar tree,
  Without a flower at all.
He might have made enough, enough
  For every want of ours,
For luxury, medicine, and toil,
  And yet have made no flowers.

The ore within the mountain mine
  Requireth none to grow;
Nor does it need the lotus flower
  To make the river flow.
The clouds might give abundant rain,
  The nightly dews might fall,
And the herb that keepeth life in man
  Might yet have drunk them all.

Then wherefore, wherefore were they made,
  All dyed with rainbow light,
All fashioned with supremest grace,
  Upspringing day and night,—
Springing in valleys green and low,
  And on the mountain high,
And in the silent wilderness,
  Where no man passes by?

Our outward life requires them not,
  Then wherefore had they birth?—
To minister delight to man,
  To beautify the earth;

To comfort man, to whisper hope
Whene'er his faith is dim;
For Whoso careth for the flowers
Will much more care for him.

CHARLES DICKENS

William Makepeace Thackeray

peruse   brewing   contact   hospitality
myriads   endowed   slaughter   preachments

As for the charities of Mr. Dickens, multiplied kindnesses which he has conferred upon us all, — upon our children, upon people educated and uneducated, upon the myriads here and at home, who speak our common tongue, — have not you, have not I, all of us, reason to be thankful to this kind friend who has soothed and charmed so many, many homes, made such multitudes of children happy, endowed us with such a sweet store of gracious thoughts, fair fancies, soft sympathies, hearty enjoyments? There are creations of Mr. Dickens which seem to me to rank as personal benefits, — figures so delightful that one feels happier and better for knowing them, as one does for being brought into the society of very good men and women. That atmosphere in which these people live is wholesome to breathe in; you feel that to be allowed to speak to them is a personal kindness; you come away better for your contact with them; your hands seem cleaner for having had the privilege of shaking theirs. Has there ever been a better charity sermon preached in the world than Dickens'

"Christmas Carol"? I believe it has occasioned immense hospitality throughout England; has been the means of lighting up hundreds of kind fires at Christmas time; has caused a wonderful outpouring of Christmas good feeling, of Christmas punch brewing; and awful slaughter of Christmas turkeys and roasting and basting of Christmas beef. As for this man's love of children, that amiable organ at the back of his honest head must be perfectly monstrous. All children ought to love him. I know two that do, and that read his books ten times for once that they peruse the dismal preachments of their father. I know one who, when she is happy, reads "Nicholas Nickleby"; when she is unhappy, reads "Nicholas Nickleby"; when she is tired, reads "Nicholas Nickleby"; when she is in bed, reads "Nicholas Nickleby"; when she has nothing to do, reads "Nicholas Nickleby"; when she has something to do, reads "Nicholas Nickleby"; and when she has finished the book, reads "Nicholas Nickleby" over again. This candid young critic, at ten years of age, said, "I like Mr. Dickens' books much better than your books, Papa;" and frequently expressed her desire that I should write a book like one of Mr. Dickens' books. Who can? Every man must say his own thoughts in his own voice, in his own way; lucky is he who has such a charming gift of nature as this, which brings all the children in the world trooping to him, and makes them fond of him.

A CHRISTMAS CAROL

CHARLES DICKENS

Dickens' "Christmas Carol" is a story of good will to men. It was originally written in fifty thousand words; but when Dickens began his series of public readings in America, he was obliged to condense it to a quarter of its original length, in order to bring it within the limits of an evening's entertainment. In so doing, he made a far better story of it. No more popular short story was ever written. The following is an abridgment of the condensed form used by the author in his public readings.

PART I

MARLEY'S GHOST

cravat	tacitly	register	originally
Marley	lobster	calendar	veneration
surplus	specter	deceased	undigested
ghostly	decrease	ferocious	susceptible
amends	scraping	predicted	Parliament
homage	condense	balancing	inexplicable
Scrooge	Ebenezer	apparition	administrator

Marley was dead, to begin with. There is no doubt whatever about that. The register of his burial was signed by the clergyman, the clerk, the undertaker, and the chief mourner. Scrooge signed it. And Scrooge's name was good upon 'Change for anything he chose to put his hand to.

Old Marley was as dead as a doornail.

Scrooge knew he was dead? Of course he did. How could it be otherwise? Scrooge and he were partners for — I don't

308

know how many years. Scrooge was his sole executor, his sole administrator, his sole friend, his sole mourner.

Scrooge never painted out old Marley's name, however. There it stood, years afterwards, above the warehouse door, — Scrooge and Marley. The firm was known as Scrooge and Marley. Sometimes people new to the business called Scrooge Scrooge, and sometimes Marley. He answered to both names, it was all the same to him.

Oh! But he was a tight-fisted hand at the grindstone, was Scrooge! a squeezing, wrenching, grasping, scraping, clutching, covetous old sinner! External heat and cold had little influence on him. No warmth could warm, no cold could chill him. No wind that blew was bitterer than he, no falling snow was more intent upon its purpose, no pelting rain less open to entreaty. The heaviest rain and snow and hail and sleet could boast of the advantage over him in only one respect, — they often " came down " handsomely, and Scrooge never did.

Nobody ever stopped him in the street to say, with gladsome looks, " My dear Scrooge, how are you? When will you come to see me?" No beggars implored him to bestow a trifle, no children asked him what it was o'clock, no man or woman ever once in all his life inquired the way to such and such a place, of Scrooge. Even the blind men's dogs appeared to know him; and when they saw him coming, would tug their owners into doorways and up courts; and then would wag their tails as though they said, " No eye at all is better than an evil eye, dark master !"

But what did Scrooge care! It was the very thing he liked.

To edge his way along the crowded paths of life, warning all human sympathy to keep its distance, was what the knowing ones called "nuts" to Scrooge.

Once upon a time, — of all the good days in the year, upon a Christmas eve, — old Scrooge sat busy in his countinghouse. It was cold, bleak, biting, foggy weather; the city clocks had only just gone three, but it was quite dark already.

The door of Scrooge's countinghouse was open, that he might keep his eye upon his clerk, who, in a dismal little cell beyond, a sort of tank, was copying letters. Scrooge had a very small fire, but the clerk's fire was so very much smaller that it looked like one coal. But he couldn't replenish it, for Scrooge kept the coal-box in his own room; and so surely as the clerk came in with the shovel, the master predicted that it would be necessary for them to part. Wherefore, the clerk put on his white comforter, and tried to warm himself at the candle; in which effort, not being a man of a strong imagination, he failed.

"A merry Christmas, Uncle! God save you!" cried a cheerful voice. It was the voice of Scrooge's nephew, who came upon him so quickly that this was the first intimation Scrooge had of his approach.

"Bah!" said Scrooge; "humbug!"

"Christmas a humbug, Uncle! You don't mean that, I am sure?"

"I do. Out upon merry Christmas! What's Christmas time to you but a time for paying bills without money; a time for finding yourself a year older, and not an hour richer; a time for balancing your books and having every item in 'em through a round dozen of months presented dead against you? If I had my will, every idiot who goes about with ' Merry Christmas' on his lips should be boiled with his own pudding! He should!"

" Uncle!"

" Nephew, keep Christmas in your own way, and let me keep it in mine."

" Keep it! But you don't keep it."

" Let me leave it alone, then. Much good may it do you! Much good it has ever done you!"

" There are many things from which I might have derived good, by which I have not profited, I dare say, Christmas among the rest. But I am sure I have always thought of Christmas time, when it has come round, — apart from the veneration due to its sacred origin, if anything belonging to it *can* be apart from that, — as a good time; a kind, forgiving, charitable, pleasant time; the only time I know of, in the long calendar of the year, when men and women seem by one consent to open their shut-up hearts freely, and to think of people below them as if they really were fellow-travelers to the grave, and not another race of creatures bound on other journeys. And, therefore, Uncle, though it has never put a scrap of gold or silver in my pocket, I believe that it *has* done me good, and *will* do me good; and I say, God bless it!"

The clerk in the Tank involuntarily applauded.

" Let me hear another sound from *you*," said Scrooge, " and you'll keep your Christmas by losing your situation! You're quite a powerful speaker, sir," he added, turning to his nephew. "I wonder you don't go into Parliament."

"Don't be angry, Uncle. Come! Dine with us to-morrow."

Scrooge said that he would see him — yes, indeed he did. He went the whole length of the expression, and said that he would see him in that extremity first.

"But why?" cried Scrooge's nephew. "Why?"

"Why did you get married?"

"Because I fell in love."

"Because you fell in love!" growled Scrooge, as if that were the only one thing in the world more ridiculous than a merry Christmas. "Good afternoon!"

"Nay, Uncle, but you never came to see me before that happened. Why give it as a reason for not coming now?"

"Good afternoon!"

"I want nothing from you; I ask nothing of you; why cannot we be friends?"

"Good afternoon!"

"I am sorry, with all my heart, to find you so resolute. We have never had any quarrel, to which I have been a party. But I have made the trial in homage to Christmas, and I'll keep my Christmas humor to the last. So, a Merry Christmas, Uncle!"

"Good afternoon!"

"And a Happy New Year!"

"Good afternoon!"

His nephew left the room without an angry word, notwithstanding. The clerk, in letting Scrooge's nephew out, had let two other persons in. They were portly gentlemen, pleasant to behold, and now stood, with their hats off, in Scrooge's office. They had books and papers in their hands, and bowed to him.

"Scrooge and Marley's, I believe," said one of the gentlemen, referring to his list. "Have I the pleasure of addressing Mr. Scrooge or Mr. Marley?"

"Mr. Marley has been dead these seven years. He died seven years ago this very night."

"At this festive season of the year, Mr. Scrooge," said the gentleman, taking up a pen, "it is more than usually desirable that we should make some slight provision for the poor and destitute, who suffer greatly at the present time. Many thousands are in want of common necessaries; hundreds of thousands are in want of common comforts, sir."

C. E. Brock.

"ARE THERE NO PRISONS?" ASKED SCROOGE.

"Are there no prisons?" asked Scrooge.

"Plenty of prisons. But under the impression that they hardly furnish Christian cheer of mind or body to the unoffending multitude, a few of us are endeavoring to raise a fund to buy

313

the poor some meat and drink, and means of warmth. We choose this time, because it is a time of all others when Want is keenly felt and Abundance rejoices. What shall I put you down for?"

"Nothing!"

"You wish to be anonymous?"

"I wish to be left alone. Since you ask me what I wish, gentlemen, that is my answer. I don't make merry myself at Christmas, and I can't afford to make idle people merry. I help to support the prisons and the workhouses, — they cost enough, — and those who are badly off must go there."

"Many can't go there; and many would rather die."

"If they would rather die, they had better do it, and decrease the surplus population."

At length the hour of shutting up the countinghouse arrived. With an ill-will, Scrooge, dismounting from his stool, tacitly admitted the fact to the expectant clerk in the Tank, who instantly snuffed his candle out, and put on his hat.

"You'll want all day to-morrow, I suppose?"

"If quite convenient, sir."

"It's not convenient, and it's not fair. If I were to stop half a crown for it, you'd think yourself mightily ill-used, I'll be bound?"

"Yes, sir."

"And yet you don't think *me* ill-used, when I pay a day's wages for no work."

"It's only once a year, sir."

"A poor excuse for picking a man's pocket every twenty-fifth of December! But I suppose you must have the whole day. Be here all the earlier *next* morning."

The clerk promised that he would, and Scrooge walked out with a growl. The office was closed in a twinkling, and the clerk, with the long ends of his white comforter dangling below his waist (for he boasted no great-coat), went down a slide, at the end of a lane of boys, twenty times, in honor of its being Christmas eve, and then ran home as hard as he could pelt, to play at blind-man's-buff.

Scrooge took his melancholy dinner in his usual melancholy tavern; and having read all the newspapers, and beguiled the rest of the evening with his banker's book, went home to bed. He lived in chambers which had once belonged to his deceased partner. They were a gloomy suite of rooms, in a lowering pile of building up a yard. The building was old enough now, and dreary enough; for nobody lived in it but Scrooge, the other rooms being all let out as offices.

Now it is a fact, that there was nothing at all particular about the knocker on the door of this house, except that it was very large; also, that Scrooge had seen it, night and morning, during his whole residence in that place; also, that Scrooge had as little of what is called fancy about him as any man in the city of London. And yet Scrooge, having his key in the lock of the door, saw in the knocker, without its undergoing any inter-mediate process of change, not a knocker, but Marley's face; — Marley's face, with a dismal light about it, like a bad lobster in a dark cellar! It was not angry or ferocious, but it looked at

Scrooge as Marley used to look, with ghostly spectacles turned up upon its ghostly forehead.

As Scrooge looked fixedly at this phenomenon, it was a knocker again. He said, " Pooh, pooh ! " and closed the door with a bang.

The sound resounded through the house like thunder. Every room above, and every cask in the wine-merchant's cellars below, appeared to have a separate peal of echoes of its own. Scrooge was not a man to be frightened by echoes. He fastened the door, and walked across the hall, and up the stairs; slowly, too, trimming his candle as he went.

Up Scrooge went, not caring a button for its being very dark. Darkness is cheap, and Scrooge liked it. But before he shut his heavy door, he walked through his rooms to see that all was right. He had just enough recollection of the face to desire to do that.

Sitting room, bedroom, all were as they should be : nobody under the table, nobody under the sofa; a small fire in the grate; nobody under the bed; nobody in the closet; nobody in his dressing gown, which was hanging up in a suspicious attitude against the wall; old fire-guard, old shoes, two fish baskets, washing stand on three legs, and a poker.

Quite satisfied, he closed his door, and locked himself in; double-locked himself in, which was not his custom. Thus secured against surprise, he took off his cravat, put on his dressing gown and slippers and his night cap, and sat down before the very low fire.

As he threw his head back in the chair, his glance happened to rest upon a bell, a disused bell, that hung in the room, and that communicated, for some purpose now forgotten, with a chamber in the highest story of the building. It was with great astonishment, and with a strange, inexplicable dread, that, as he looked, he saw this bell begin to swing. Soon it rang out loudly, and so did every bell in the house.

This was succeeded by a clanking noise, deep down below, as if some person were dragging a heavy chain over the casks in the wine-merchant's cellar.

Then he heard the noise grow much louder on the floors below; then coming up the stairs; then coming straight towards his door.

It came on through the heavy door, and a specter passed into the room before his eyes. And upon its coming in, the dying flame leaped up, as though it cried, "I know him! Marley's ghost!"

The same face, the very same! — Marley in his pigtail, usual waistcoat, tights, and boots. The chain he drew was clasped about his middle. It was made (for Scrooge observed it closely) of cash-boxes, keys, padlocks, ledgers, deeds, and heavy purses wrought in steel.

"How now!" said Scrooge, caustic and cold as ever. "What do you want with me?"

"Much!" — Marley's voice, no doubt about it.

"Who are you?"

"Ask me who I *was*."

"Who *were* you, then?"

"In life I was your partner, Jacob Marley."

"Can you — can you sit down?"

C. E. Brock.

THE GHOST SAT DOWN ON THE OPPOSITE SIDE
OF THE FIREPLACE.

"I can."

"Do it, then."

The ghost sat down on the opposite side of the fireplace, as if he were quite used to it.

"You don't believe in me."

"I don't."

"What evidence would you have of my reality beyond that of your senses?"

"I don't know."

"Why do you doubt your senses?"

"Because a little thing affects them. A slight disorder of the stomach makes them cheats. You may be an undigested bit of beef, a blot of mustard, a crumb of cheese, a fragment of an underdone potato. Mercy! Dreadful apparition, why do you trouble me? Why do spirits walk the earth, and why do they come to me?"

"It is required of every man that the spirit within him

318

should walk abroad among his fellow-men, and travel far and wide; and if that spirit goes not forth in life, it is condemned to do so after death. I cannot tell you all I would. A very little more is permitted to me. I cannot rest, I cannot stay, I cannot linger anywhere. My spirit never walked beyond our counting-house, — mark me! — in life my spirit never roved beyond the narrow limits of our money-changing hole; and weary journeys lie before me!"

"Seven years dead. And traveling all the time? You travel fast?"

"On the wings of the wind."

"You might have got over a great deal of ground in seven years."

"O blind man, blind man! not to know that ages of incessant labor by immortal creatures for this earth must pass into eternity before the good of which it is susceptible is all developed. Not to know that any Christian spirit working kindly in its little sphere, whatever it may be, will find its mortal life too short for its vast means of usefulness. Not to know that no space of regret can make amends for one life's opportunities misused! Yet I was like this man; I once was like this man!"

"But you were always a good man of business, Jacob," faltered Scrooge, who now began to apply this to himself.

"Business!" cried the ghost, wringing its hands again. "Mankind was my business. The common welfare was my business; charity, mercy, forbearance, benevolence, were all my business. The dealings of my trade were but a drop of water in the comprehensive ocean of my business."

Scrooge was very much dismayed to hear the specter going on at this rate, and began to quake exceedingly.

"Hear me! My time is nearly gone."

"I will. But don't be hard upon me!"

"I am here to-night to warn you that you have yet a chance and hope of escaping my fate. A chance and hope of my procuring, Ebenezer."

"You were always a good friend to me. Thank-ee!"

"You will be haunted by Three Spirits."

"Is that the chance and hope you mentioned, Jacob? I — I think I'd rather not."

"Without their visits, you cannot hope to shun the path I tread. Expect the first to-morrow night, when the bell tolls One. Expect the second on the next night at the same hour. The third, upon the next night, when the last stroke of twelve has ceased to vibrate. Look to see me no more; and look that, for your own sake, you remember what has passed between us!"

It walked backward from him; and at every step it took, the window raised itself a little, so that, when the apparition reached it, it was wide open.

Scrooge closed the window, and examined the door by which the Ghost had entered. It was double-locked, as he had locked it with his own hands, and the bolts were undisturbed. Scrooge tried to say, "Humbug!" but stopped at the first syllable. And being, from the emotion he had undergone, or the fatigues of the day, or his glimpse of the invisible world, or the dull conversation of the Ghost, or the lateness of the hour, much in need of repose, he went straight to bed, without undressing, and fell asleep on the instant.

PART II

THE FIRST OF THE THREE SPIRITS

Welsh	fiddler	adjusted	irresistible
opaque	receded	Fezziwig	proportions
medium	Wilkins	thermometer	supplication

When Scrooge awoke, it was so dark, that, looking out of bed, he could scarcely distinguish the transparent window from the opaque walls of his chamber, until suddenly the church clock tolled a deep, dull, hollow, melancholy ONE.

Light flashed up in the room upon the instant, and the curtains of his bed were drawn aside by a strange figure, — like a child: yet not so like a child as like an old man, viewed through some supernatural medium, which gave him the appearance of having receded from the view, and being diminished to a child's proportions. Its hair, which hung about its neck and down its back, was white as if with age; and yet the face had not a wrinkle in it, and the tenderest bloom was on the skin. It held a branch of fresh green holly in its hand; and, in singular contradiction of that wintry emblem, had its dress trimmed with summer flowers. But the strangest thing about it was, that from the crown of its head there sprang a bright clear jet of light, by which all this was visible; and which was doubtless the occasion of its using, in its duller moments, a great extinguisher for a cap, which it now held under its arm.

"Are you the Spirit, sir, whose coming was foretold to me?"

THE CURTAINS WERE DRAWN ASIDE BY A STRANGE FIGURE.

"I am!"

"Who and what are you?"

"I am the Ghost of Christmas Past."

"Long past?"

"No. Your past. The things that you will see with me are shadows of the things that have been; they will have no consciousness of us."

Scrooge then made bold to inquire what business brought him there.

"Your welfare. Rise, and walk with me!"

It would have been in vain for Scrooge to plead that the weather and the hour were not adapted to pedestrian purposes; that the bed was warm, and the thermometer a long way below freezing; that he was clad but lightly in his slippers, dressing gown, and nightcap; and that he had a cold upon him at that time. The grasp, though gentle as a woman's hand, was not to be resisted. He arose; but, finding that the spirit made towards the window, he clasped its robe in supplication.

" I am a mortal, and liable to fall."

" Bear but a touch of my hand *there*," said the Spirit, laying it upon his heart, " and you shall be upheld in more than this ! "

As the words were spoken, they passed through the wall, and stood in the busy thoroughfares of a city. It was made plain enough by the dressing of the shops that here, too, it was Christmas time.

The Ghost stopped at a certain warehouse door, and asked Scrooge whether he knew it.

" Know it ! Was I apprenticed here ! "

They went in. At sight of an old gentleman in a Welsh wig, sitting behind such a high desk that, if he had been two inches taller, he must have knocked his head against the ceiling, Scrooge cried in great excitement, " Why, it's old Fezziwig ! Bless his heart, it's Fezziwig, alive again ! "

Old Fezziwig laid down his pen, and looked up at the clock, which pointed to the hour of seven. He rubbed his hands, adjusted his capacious waistcoat, laughed all over himself, from his shoes to his organ of benevolence, and called out in a comfortable, oily, rich, fat, jovial voice, " Yo ho, there ! Ebenezer ! Dick ! "

A living and moving picture of Scrooge's former self, a young man, came briskly in, accompanied by his fellow 'prentice.

" Dick Wilkins, to be sure ! " said Scrooge to the Ghost. " My old fellow 'prentice ! Bless me, yes. There he is. He was very much attached to me, was Dick. Poor Dick! Dear, dear!"

"Yo ho, my boys!" said Fezziwig. "No more work to-night. Christmas eve, Dick! Christmas, Ebenezer! Let's have the shutters up, before a man can say Jack Robinson! Clear away, my lads, and let's have lots of room here!"

Clear away! There was nothing they wouldn't have cleared away, or couldn't have cleared away, with old Fezziwig looking on. It was done in a minute. Every movable was packed off, as if it were dismissed from public life forevermore; the floor was swept and watered, the lamps were trimmed, fuel was heaped upon the fire; and the warehouse became as snug and warm and dry and bright a ballroom as you would desire to see upon a winter's night.

In came a fiddler with a music-book, and went up to the lofty desk, and made an orchestra of it. In came Mrs. Fezziwig, one vast, substantial smile. In came the three Miss Fezziwigs, beaming and lovable. In came the six young followers whose hearts they had broken. In came all the young men and women employed in the business. In came the housemaid, with her cousin the baker. In came the cook, with her brother's particular friend the milkman. In they all came, one after another; some shyly, some boldly, some gracefully, some awkwardly, some pushing, some pulling; in they all came, anyhow and everyhow. Away they all went, twenty couples at once; hands half round and back again the other way; down the middle and up again; round and round in various stages of affectionate grouping; old top couple always turning up in the wrong place; new top couple starting off again, as soon as they got there; all top couples at last, and not a bottom one to help them. When this result was brought about, old Fezziwig, clapping his hands to stop the dance, cried out, " Well done ! "

There were more dances, and there were forfeits, and then more dances; and there was cake, and there was a great piece of Cold Roast, and there was a great piece of Cold Boiled, and there were mince pies. But the great effect of the evening came after the Roast and Boiled, when the fiddler struck up " Sir Roger de Coverley." Then old Fezziwig stood out to dance with Mrs. Fezziwig. Top couple, too; with a good stiff piece of work cut out for them; three or four and twenty

C. E. Brock.

THEN OLD FEZZIWIG STOOD OUT TO DANCE WITH MRS. FEZZIWIG.

pair of partners; people who were not to be trifled with; people who *would* dance, and who had no notion of walking.

But if they had been twice as many, — four times, — old Fezziwig would have been a match for them, and so would Mrs.

Fezziwig. As to *her*, she was worthy to be his partner in every sense of the term. A positive light appeared to issue from Fezziwig's calves. They shone in every part of the dance. You couldn't have predicted, at any given time, what would become of 'em next. And when old Fezziwig and Mrs. Fezziwig had gone all through the dance, — advance and retire, turn your partner, bow and courtesy, corkscrew, thread the needle, and back again to your place, — Fezziwig "cut," — cut so deftly, that he appeared to wink with his legs.

When the clock struck eleven, this domestic ball broke up. Mr. and Mrs. Fezziwig took their stations, one on each side the door; and, shaking hands with every person individually as he or she went out, wished him or her a Merry Christmas. When everybody had retired but the two 'prentices, they did the same to them; and thus the cheerful voices died away, and the lads were left to their beds, which were under a counter in the back shop.

"A small matter," said the Ghost, "to make these silly folks so full of gratitude. He has spent but a few pounds of your mortal money, — three or four perhaps. Is that so much that he deserves this praise?"

"It isn't that," said Scrooge, heated by the remark, and speaking unconsciously like his former, not his latter, self, — "it isn't that, Spirit. He has the power to render us happy or unhappy; to make our service light or burdensome, a pleasure or a toil. Say that his power lies in words and looks; in things so slight and insignificant that it is impossible to add and count 'em up; what then? The happiness he gives is quite as great as if it cost a fortune."

He felt the Spirit's glance, and stopped.

"What is the matter?"

"Nothing particular."

"Something, I think?"

"No, no. I should like to be able to say a word or two to my clerk just now. That's all."

"My time grows short," observed the Spirit. "Quick!"

"Spirit! remove me from this place."

"I told you these were shadows of the things that have been," said the Ghost. "That they are what they are, do not blame me!"

"Remove me!" Scrooge exclaimed. "I cannot bear it! Leave me! Take me back. Haunt me no longer!"

As he struggled with the Spirit, he was conscious of being exhausted and overcome by an irresistible drowsiness; and, further, of being in his own bedroom. He had barely time to reel to bed before he sank into a heavy sleep.

PART III

THE SECOND OF THE THREE SPIRITS

Martha	elicited	infection	almshouse
Topper	shuffled	credulity	laundress's
exposed	escorted	incredible	custard-cup
Belinda	precepts	Cratchit's	investments
bedight	dispelled	declension	prematurely
rampant	gallantly	ubiquitous	pawnbroker's
Phantom	shovelful	compulsion	imperceptibly

Scrooge awoke in his own bedroom. There was no doubt about that. But it and his own adjoining sitting room, into which he shuffled in his slippers, attracted by a great light there, had undergone a surprising transformation. The walls and ceiling were so hung with living green that it looked a perfect grove. The leaves of holly, mistletoe, and ivy reflected back the light, as if so many little mirrors had been scattered there; and such a mighty blaze went roaring up the chimney as that hearth had never known in Scrooge's time, or Marley's or for many and many a winter season gone. Heaped upon the floor, to form a kind of throne, were turkeys, geese, game, great joints of meat, mince pies, plum puddings, barrels of oysters, red-hot chestnuts, cherry-cheeked apples, juicy oranges, luscious pears, and immense twelfth-cakes. In easy state upon this couch, there sat a Giant glorious to see, who bore a glowing torch, in shape not unlike Plenty's horn, and who raised it high to shed its light on Scrooge, as he came peeping round the door.

"Come in, — come in! and know me better, man! I am the Ghost of Christmas Present. Look upon me! You have never seen the like of me before!"

"Never."

"Have you never walked forth with the younger members of my family; meaning (for I am very young) my elder brothers born in these later years?" pursued the Phantom.

"I don't think I have; I am afraid I have not. Have you had many brothers, Spirit?"

"More than eighteen hundred."

"A tremendous family to provide for! Spirit, conduct me where you will. I went forth last night on compulsion, and I learnt a lesson which is working now. To-night, if you have aught to teach me, let me profit by it."

"Touch my robe!"

Scrooge did as he was told, and held it fast.

The room and its contents all vanished instantly, and they stood in the city streets upon a snowy Christmas morning.

Scrooge and the Ghost passed on, invisible, straight to Scrooge's clerk's; and on the threshold of the door the Spirit smiled, and stopped to bless Bob Cratchit's dwelling with the sprinklings of his torch. Think of that! Bob had but fifteen "Bob" a week himself; he pocketed on Saturdays but fifteen copies of his Christian name; and yet the Ghost of Christmas Present blessed his four-roomed house!

Then up rose Mrs. Cratchit, Cratchit's wife, dressed out but poorly in a twice-turned gown, but brave in ribbons, which though cheap make a goodly show for sixpence; and she laid the cloth, assisted by Belinda Cratchit, second of her daughters, also brave in ribbons; while Master Peter Cratchit plunged a fork into the saucepan of potatoes, and, getting the corners of his monstrous shirt-collar (Bob's private property, conferred upon his son and heir in honor of the day) into his mouth, rejoiced to find himself so gallantly attired, and yearned to show his linen in the fashionable Parks. And now two smaller Cratchits, boy and girl, came tearing in, screaming that outside the baker's they had smelt the goose, and had known it for their own. Basking in luxurious

329

thoughts of sage and onion, these young Cratchits danced about the table, and exalted Master Peter Cratchit to the skies, while he (not proud, although his collars nearly choked him) blew the fire, until the slow potatoes, bubbling up, knocked loudly at the saucepan lid to be let out and peeled.

"What has ever got your precious father, then?" said Mrs. Cratchit. "And your brother Tiny Tim! And Martha wasn't so late last Christmas day by half an hour!"

"Here's Martha, Mother!" said a girl, appearing as she spoke.

"Here's Martha, Mother!" cried the two young Cratchits. "Hurrah! There's *such* a goose, Martha!"

"Why, bless your heart alive, my dear, how late you are!" said Mrs. Cratchit, kissing her a dozen times, and taking off her shawl and bonnet for her.

"We'd a deal of work to finish up last night," replied the girl, "and I had to clear away this morning, Mother!"

"Well! Never mind so long as you are come," said Mrs. Cratchit. "Sit ye down before the fire, my dear, and have a warm, Lord bless ye!"

"No, no! There's Father coming," cried the two young Cratchits, who were everywhere at once. "Hide, Martha, hide!"

So Martha hid herself, and in came little Bob, the father, with at least three feet of comforter, exclusive of the fringe, hanging down before him; and his threadbare clothes darned up and brushed, to look seasonable; and Tiny Tim upon his shoulder.

Alas for Tiny Tim, he bore a little crutch, and had his limbs supported by an iron frame!

"Why, where's our Martha?" cried Bob Cratchit, looking round.

"Not coming," said Mrs. Cratchit.

"Not coming!" said Bob, with a sudden declension of his high spirits; for he had been Tim's bloodhorse all the way from church, and had come home rampant, — "not coming upon Christmas day!"

Martha didn't like to see him disappointed, even if it were only in a joke; so she came out prematurely from behind the closet door, and ran into his arms, while the two young Cratchits hustled Tiny Tim, and bore him off into the washhouse that he might hear the pudding singing in the copper.

"And how did little Tim behave?" asked Mrs. Cratchit, when she had rallied Bob on his credulity, and Bob had hugged his daughter to his heart's content.

"As good as gold," said Bob, "and better. Somehow he gets thoughtful, sitting by himself so much, and thinks the strangest things you ever heard. He told me, coming home, that he hoped the people saw him in the church, because he was a cripple, and it might be pleasant to them to remember, upon Christmas day, who made lame beggars walk and blind men see."

Bob's voice was tremulous when he told them this, and it trembled more when he said that Tiny Tim was growing strong and hearty.

His active little crutch was heard upon the floor, and back

came Tiny Tim before another word was spoken, escorted by his brother and sister to his stool beside the fire; and while Bob, turning up his cuffs, — as if, poor fellow, they were capable of being made more shabby, — compounded some hot mixture in a jug, and stirred it round and round and put it on the hob to simmer, Master Peter and the two ubiquitous young Cratchits went to fetch the goose, with which they soon returned in high procession.

Mrs. Cratchit made the gravy (ready beforehand in a little saucepan) hissing hot; Master Peter mashed the potatoes with incredible vigor; Miss Belinda sweetened up the apple sauce; Martha dusted the hot plates; Bob took Tiny Tim beside him in a tiny corner at the table; the two young Cratchits set chairs for everybody, not forgetting themselves, and mounting guard upon their posts, crammed spoons into their mouths, lest they should shriek for goose before their turn came to be helped. At last the dishes were set on, and grace was said. It was succeeded by a breathless pause, as Mrs. Cratchit, looking slowly all along the carving-knife, prepared to plunge it in the breast; but when she did, and when the long-expected gush of stuffing issued forth, one murmur of delight arose all round the board, and even Tiny Tim, excited by the two young Cratchits, beat on the table with the handle of his knife, and feebly cried, "Hurrah!"

There never was such a goose. Bob said he didn't believe there ever was such a goose cooked. Its tenderness and flavor, size and cheapness, were the themes of universal admiration. Eked out by apple sauce and mashed potatoes, it was a sufficient dinner for the whole family; indeed, as Mrs. Cratchit said with great delight (surveying one small atom of a bone upon the dish), " they hadn't ate it all at last!" Yet every one had had enough, and the youngest Cratchits in particular were steeped in sage and onion to the eyebrows! But now, the plates being changed by Miss Belinda, Mrs. Cratchit left the room alone, — too nervous to bear witnesses, — to take the pudding up, and bring it in.

Suppose it should not be done enough! Suppose it should break in turning out! Suppose somebody should have got over the wall of the back yard, and stolen it, while they were merry with the goose, — a supposition at which the two young Cratchits became livid! All sorts of horrors were supposed.

Hallo! A great deal of steam! The pudding was out of the copper. A smell like a washing-day! That was the cloth. A smell like an eating house and a pastry cook's next door to each other, with the laundress's next door to that! That was the pudding! In half a minute Mrs. Cratchit entered, — flushed but smiling proudly, — with the pudding, like a speckled cannon ball, so hard and firm, and bedight with Christmas holly stuck into the top.

Oh, a wonderful pudding! Bob Cratchit said, and calmly, too, that he regarded it as the greatest success achieved by Mrs. Cratchit since their marriage. Mrs. Cratchit said that now the weight was off her mind, she would confess she had had her doubts about the quantity of flour. Everybody had something to say about it, but nobody said or thought it was at all a small pudding for a large family. Any Cratchit would have blushed to hint at such a thing.

At last the dinner was all done, the cloth was cleared, the hearth swept, and the fire made up. The compound in the jug being tasted and considered perfect, apples and oranges were put upon the table, and a shovelful of chestnuts on the fire.

Then all the Cratchit family drew round the hearth, in what Bob Cratchit called a circle, and at Bob Cratchit's elbow stood the family display of glass, — two tumblers, and a custard-cup without a handle.

These held the hot stuff from the jug, however, as well as golden goblets would have done; and Bob served it out with beaming looks, while the chestnuts on the fire sputtered and crackled noisily. Then Bob proposed: "A Merry Christmas to us all, my dears. God bless us!"

Which all the family reëchoed.

"God bless us every one!" said Tiny Tim, the last of all.

He sat very close to his father's side, upon his little stool. Bob held his withered little hand in his, as if he loved the child, and wished to keep him by his side, and dreaded that he might be taken from him.

Scrooge raised his head speedily, on hearing his own name.

"Mr Scrooge!" said Bob; "I'll give you Mr. Scrooge, the Founder of the Feast!"

"The Founder of the Feast, indeed!" cried Mrs. Cratchit, reddening. "I wish I had him here. I'd give him a piece of my mind to feast upon, and I hope he'd have a good appetite for it."

"My dear," said Bob, "the children! Christmas day."

"It should be Christmas day, I am sure," said she, "on

which one drinks the health of such an odious, stingy, hard, unfeeling man as Mr. Scrooge. You know he is, Robert! Nobody knows it better than you do, poor fellow!"

" My dear," was Bob's mild answer, " Christmas day."

" I'll drink his health for your sake and the day's," said Mrs. Cratchit, " not for his. Long life to him. A merry Christmas and a happy New Year! He'll be very merry and very happy, I have no doubt!"

The children drank the toast after her. It was the first of their proceedings which had no heartiness in it. Tiny Tim drank it last of all, but he didn't care twopence for it. Scrooge was the Ogre of the family. The mention of his name cast a dark shadow on the party, which was not dispelled for full five minutes.

After it had passed away, they were ten times merrier than before, from the mere relief of Scrooge the Baleful being done with. Bob Cratchit told them how he had a situation in his eye for Master Peter, which would bring in, if obtained, full five and sixpence weekly. The two young Cratchits laughed tremendously at the idea of Peter's being a man of business; and Peter himself looked thoughtfully at the fire from between his collars, as if he were deliberating what particular investments he should favor when he came into the receipt of that bewildering income. Martha, who was a poor apprentice at a milliner's, then told them what kind of work she had to do, and how many hours she worked at a stretch, and how she meant to lie abed to-morrow morning for a good long rest; to-morrow being a holiday she could pass it at home. Also how she had seen a countess and a lord some days before, and how the lord "was much about as tall as Peter"; at which Peter pulled up his collars so high that you couldn't have seen his head if you had been there. All this time the chestnuts and the jug went round and round; and by and by they had a song, about a lost child traveling in the snow, from Tiny Tim, who had a plaintive little voice, and who sang it very well indeed.

There was nothing of high mark in this. They were not a handsome family; they were not well dressed; their shoes were far from being waterproof; their clothes were scanty; and Peter might have known, and very likely did, the inside of a pawnbroker's. But they were happy, grateful, pleased with one another, and contented with the time; and when they faded, and looked happier yet in the bright sprinklings of the Spirit's torch at parting, Scrooge had his eye upon them, and especially on Tiny Tim, until the last.

It was a great surprise to Scrooge, as this scene vanished, to hear a hearty laugh. It was a much greater surprise to Scrooge to recognize it as his own nephew's, and to find himself in a bright, dry, gleaming room, with the Spirit standing smiling by his side, and looking at that same nephew.

It is a fair, even-handed, noble adjustment of things, that while there is infection in disease and sorrow, there is nothing in the world so irresistibly contagious as laughter and good humor. When Scrooge's nephew laughed, Scrooge's niece by marriage laughed as heartily as he. And their assembled friends, being not a bit behindhand, laughed out lustily.

"He said that Christmas was a humbug, as I live!" cried Scrooge's nephew. "He believed it, too!"

"More shame for him, Fred!" said Scrooge's niece, indignantly. Bless those women! they never do anything by halves. They are always in earnest.

She was very pretty, exceedingly pretty. With a dimpled, surprised-looking, capital face; all kinds of good little dots about her chin, that melted into one another when she laughed; and the sunniest pair of eyes that you ever saw in any little creature's head. Altogether she was what you would have called provoking, but satisfactory, too. Oh, perfectly satisfactory!

"He's a comical old fellow," said Scrooge's nephew, "that's the truth; and not so pleasant as he might be. However, his offenses carry their own punishment, and I have nothing to say against him. Who suffers by his ill whims? Himself, always. Here he takes it into his head to dislike us, and he won't come and dine with us. What's the consequence? He don't lose much of a dinner."

"Indeed, I think he loses a very good dinner," interrupted Scrooge's niece. Everybody else said the same, and they must be allowed to have been competent judges, because they had just had dinner; and, with the dessert upon the table, were clustered round the fire, by lamplight.

"Well, I am very glad to hear it," said Scrooge's nephew, "because I haven't any great faith in these young housekeepers. What do *you* say, Topper?"

Topper clearly had his eye on one of Scrooge's niece's sisters, for he answered that a bachelor was a wretched outcast, who had no right to express an opinion on the subject. Whereat Scrooge's niece's sister, the plump one, with the lace tucker, not the one with the roses, blushed.

After tea they had some music; for they were a musical family, and they knew what they were about when they sang a Glee or Catch, I can assure you, — especially Topper, who could growl away in the bass like a good one, and never swell the large veins in his forehead, or get red in the face over it.

But they didn't devote the whole evening to music. After a while they played at forfeits; for it is good to be children sometimes, and never better than at Christmas, when its mighty Founder was a child himself. There was first a game at blindman's-buff, though. And I no more believe Topper was really blinded than I believe he had his eyes in his boots. Because the way in which he went after that plump sister in the lace tucker was an outrage on the credulity of human nature. Knocking down the fire irons, tumbling over the chairs, bumping up against the piano, smothering himself among the curtains, wherever she went, there went he! He always knew where the plump sister was. He wouldn't catch anybody else. If you had fallen up against him, as some of them did, and stood there, he would have made a feint of endeavoring to seize you, which would have been an affront to your understanding, and would instantly have sidled off in the direction of the plump sister.

"Here is a new game," said Scrooge. "One half hour, Spirit, only one!"

It was a game called Yes and No, where Scrooge's nephew had to think of something, and the rest must find out what; he answering only to their questions yes or no, as the case was. The fire of questioning to which he was exposed elicited from him that he was thinking of an animal, a live animal, rather a disagreeable animal, a savage animal, an animal that growled and grunted sometimes, and talked sometimes, and lived in London, and walked about the streets, and wasn't made a show of, and wasn't led by anybody, and didn't live in a menagerie, and was never killed in the market, and was not a horse, or a donkey, or a cow, or a tiger, or a dog, or a pig, or a cat, or a bear. At every new question put to him, this nephew burst into a fresh roar of laughter, and was so inexpressibly tickled that he was obliged to get up off the sofa and stamp. At last the plump sister cried out,—

"I have found it out! I know what it is, Fred! I know what it is!"

"What is it?" cried Fred.

"It's your uncle, Scro-o-o-o-oge!"

Which it certainly was. Admiration was the universal sentiment, though some objected that the reply to "Is it a bear?" ought to have been "Yes."

Uncle Scrooge had imperceptibly become so gay and light of heart that he would have drunk to the unconscious company in an inaudible speech. But the whole scene passed off in the breath of the last word spoken by his nephew; and he and the Spirit were again upon their travels.

Much they saw, and far they went, and many homes they

visited, but always with a happy end. The Spirit stood beside sick beds, and they were cheerful; on foreign lands, and they were close at home; by struggling men, and they were patient in their greater hope; by poverty, and it was rich. In almshouse, hospital, and jail, in misery's every refuge, where vain man in his little brief authority had not made fast the door, and barred the Spirit out, he left his blessing, and taught Scrooge his precepts. Suddenly, as they stood together in an open place, the bell struck twelve.

Scrooge looked about him for the Ghost, and saw it no more. As the last stroke ceased to vibrate, he remembered the prediction of old Jacob Marley, and, lifting up his eyes, beheld a solemn Phantom, draped and hooded, coming like a mist along the ground towards him.

PART IV

THE LAST OF THE SPIRITS

feign	unanimity	intercourse
salary	immovable	Poulterer's

The Phantom slowly, gravely, silently approached. When it came near him, Scrooge bent down upon his knee; for in the air through which this Spirit moved, it seemed to scatter gloom and mystery.

It was shrouded in a deep black garment, which concealed its head, its face, its form, and left nothing of it visible save one outstretched hand. He knew no more, for the Spirit neither spoke nor moved.

" I am in the presence of the Ghost of Christmas yet to come ? Ghost of the Future ! I fear you more than any specter I have seen. But as I know your purpose is to do me good, and as I hope to live to be another man from what I was, I am prepared to bear you company, and do it with a thankful heart. Will you not speak to me ? "

It gave him no reply. The hand was pointed straight before them.

" Lead on ! Lead on ! The night is waning fast, and it is precious time to me, I know. Lead on, Spirit ! "

They hardly seemed to enter the city; for the city rather seemed to spring up about them. But there they were in the heart of it; on 'Change, amongst the merchants.

The Spirit stopped beside one little knot of business men. Observing that the hand was pointed to them, Scrooge advanced to listen to their talk.

" No," said a great fat man with a monstrous chin, " I don't know much about it either way. I only know he's dead."

" When did he die ? " inquired another.

" Last night, I believe."

" Why, what was the matter with him ? I thought he'd never die."

" What has he done with his money ? " asked a red-faced gentleman.

" I haven't heard," said the man with the large chin. " Company, perhaps. He hasn't left it to me. That's all I know. By, by ! "

The scene had changed, and now he almost touched a bare, uncurtained bed. A pale light, rising in the outer air, fell straight upon this bed; and on it, unwatched, unwept, uncared for, was the body of an unknown man.

"Specter," said Scrooge, "something informs me that our parting moment is at hand. I know it, but I know not how. Tell me what man that was, with the covered face, whom we saw lying dead?"

The Ghost of Christmas Yet to Come conveyed him to a dismal, wretched, ruinous churchyard.

The Spirit stood among the graves, and pointed down to one.

"Before I draw nearer to that stone to which you point, answer me one question. Are these the shadows of the things that *will* be, or are they shadows of the things that *may* be only?"

Still the Ghost pointed downward to the grave by which it stood.

"Men's courses will foreshadow certain ends, to which, if persevered in, they must lead. But if the courses be departed from, the ends will change. Say it is thus with what you show me!"

The Spirit was immovable as ever.

Scrooge crept towards it, trembling as he went; and, following the finger, read upon the stone of the neglected grave his own name, — Ebenezer Scrooge.

"Am *I* that man who lay upon the bed? No, Spirit! Oh no, no! Spirit! hear me! I am not the man I was. I will not be the man I must have been but for this. Why show me this, if

I am past all hope? Assure me that I yet may change these shadows you have shown me by an altered life."

For the first time the kind hand faltered.

"I will honor Christmas in my heart, and try to keep it all the year. I will live in the Past, the Present, and the Future. The Spirits of all three shall strive within me. I will not shut out the lessons that they teach. Oh, tell me I may sponge away the writing on this stone!"

Holding up his hands in one last prayer to have his fate reversed, he saw an alteration in the Phantom's hood and dress. It shrank, collapsed, and dwindled down into a bedpost.

C. E. Brock.

SCROOGE CREPT TOWARDS IT, TREMBLING AS HE WENT.

Yes, and the bedpost was his own. The bed was his own, and the room was his own. Best and happiest of all, the Time before him was his own, to make amends in!

He was checked in his transports by the churches ringing out the lustiest peals he had ever heard.

343

Running to the window, he opened it, and put out his head. No fog, no mist, no night; clear, bright, stirring, golden day!

"What's to-day?" cried Scrooge, calling downward to a boy in Sunday clothes, who perhaps had loitered in to look about him.

"Eh?"

"What's to-day, my fine fellow?"

"To-day! Why, CHRISTMAS DAY."

"It's Christmas day! I haven't missed it. Hallo, my fine fellow!"

"Hallo!"

"Do you know the Poulterer's, in the next street but one, at the corner?"

"I should hope I did."

"An intelligent boy! A remarkable boy! Do you know whether they've sold the prize turkey that was hanging up there? Not the little prize turkey, — the big one?"

"What, the one as big as me?"

"What a delightful boy! It's a pleasure to talk to him. Yes, my boy!"

"It's hanging there now."

"Is it? Go and buy it. I am in earnest. Go and buy it, and tell 'em to bring it here, that I may give them the direction where to take it. Come back with the man, and I'll give you a shilling. Come back with him in less than five minutes, and I'll give you half a crown!"

The boy was off like a shot.

344

"I'll send it to Bob Cratchit's! He shan't know who sends it. It's twice the size of Tiny Tim. Joe Miller never made such a joke as sending it to Bob's will be!"

The hand in which he wrote the address was not a steady one; but write it he did, somehow, and went downstairs to open the street door, ready for the coming of the poulterer's man.

It *was* a turkey! He never could have stood upon his legs, that bird. He would have snapped 'em short off in a minute, like sticks of sealing wax.

Scrooge dressed himself "all in his best," and at last got out into the streets. The people were by this time pouring forth, as he had seen them with the Ghost of Christmas Present; and, walking with his hands behind him, Scrooge regarded every one with a delighted smile. He looked so irresistibly pleasant, in a word, that three or four good-humored fellows said, "Good morning, sir! A Merry Christmas to you!" and Scrooge said often afterwards, that, of all the blithe sounds he had ever heard, those were the blithest in his ears.

In the afternoon he turned his steps towards his nephew's house.

He passed the door a dozen times before he had the courage to go up and knock. But he made a dash, and did it.

"Is your master at home, my dear?" said Scrooge to the girl. Nice girl! Very.

"Yes, sir."

"Where is he?"

"He's in the dining-room, sir, along with Mistress."

"He knows me," said Scrooge, with his hand already on the dining-room lock, "I'll go in here."

He turned it gently and sidled his face in, round the door. They were looking at the table (which was spread out in great array); for these young housekeepers are always nervous on such points, and like to see that everything is right.

C. E. Brock.

HE TURNED IT GENTLY AND SIDLED HIS FACE IN, ROUND THE DOOR.

"Fred!" said Scrooge.

"Why, bless my soul!" cried Fred, "who's that?"

"It's I. Your uncle Scrooge. I have come to dinner. Will you let me in, Fred?"

Let him in! It is a mercy he didn't shake his arm off. He was at home in five minutes. Nothing could be heartier. His niece looked just the same. So did Topper when *he* came. So did the plump sister when *she* came. So did every one when *they* came. Wonderful party, wonderful games, wonderful unanimity, won-der-ful happiness!

But he was early at the office next morning. Oh, he was

early there! If he could only be there first, and catch Bob Cratchit coming late! That was the thing he had set his heart upon.

And he did it. The clock struck nine. No Bob. A quarter past. No Bob. Bob was full eighteen and a half minutes behind his time. Scrooge sat with his door wide open, that he might see him come into the Tank.

Bob's hat was off before he opened the door; his comforter, too. He was on his stool in a jiffy; driving away with his pen, as if he were trying to overtake nine o'clock.

"Hallo!" growled Scrooge in his accustomed voice, as near as he could feign it. "What do you mean by coming here at this time of day?"

"I am very sorry, sir. I *am* behind my time."

"You are? Yes. I think you are. Step this way, if you please."

"It's only once a year, sir. It shall not be repeated. I was making rather merry yesterday, sir."

"Now, I'll tell you what, my friend. I am not going to stand this sort of thing any longer. And therefore," Scrooge continued, leaping from his stool, and giving Bob such a dig in the waistcoat that he staggered back into the Tank again,— "and therefore, I am about to raise your salary!"

Bob trembled, and got a little nearer to the ruler.

"A Merry Christmas, Bob!" said Scrooge, with an earnestness that could not be mistaken, as he clapped him on the back. "A merrier Christmas, Bob, my good fellow, than I have given you for many a year! I'll raise your salary, and endeavor to assist your struggling family, and we will discuss your affairs this very afternoon, Bob! Make up the fires, and buy a second coal-scuttle before you dot another *i*, Bob Cratchit!"

Scrooge was better than his word. He did it all, and infinitely more; and to Tiny Tim, he was a second father. He became as good a friend, as good a master, and as good a man as the good old city knew, or any other good old city, town, or borough in the good old world. Some people laughed to see the alteration in him; but his own heart laughed, and that was quite enough for him.

He had no further intercourse with spirits; but it was always said of him that he knew how to keep Christmas well, if any man alive possessed the knowledge. May that be truly said of us, and all of us! And so, as Tiny Tim observed, "God Bless us, every one!"

> "God Bless us, every one!" prayed Tiny Tim,
> Crippled and dwarfed of body, yet so tall
> Of soul, we tiptoe earth to look on him
> High towering over all.

—James Whitcomb Riley.

THE CLOSING YEAR

George Dennison Prentice

dirge	scythe	serried	empires
knell	condor	pinions	skeleton
Andes	carnage	plumage	cadences

348

'Tis midnight's holy hour, and silence now
Is brooding like a gentle spirit o'er
The still and pulseless world.   Hark ! on the winds
The bell's deep tones are swelling, — 'tis the knell
Of the departed year.   No funeral train
Is sweeping past ; yet, on the stream and wood,
With melancholy light, the moonbeams rest
Like a pale, spotless shroud ; the air is stirred
As by a mourner's sigh ; and on yon cloud
That floats so still and placidly through heaven,
The spirits of the seasons seem to stand, —
Young Spring, bright Summer, Autumn's solemn form,
And Winter with its aged locks, — and breathe,
In mournful cadences that come abroad
Like the far wind-harp's wild and touching wail,
A melancholy dirge o'er the dead year,
Gone from the earth forever.

                                    'Tis a time
For memory and for tears.   Within the deep,
Still chambers of the heart, a specter dim,
Whose tones are like the wizard's voice of Time
Heard from the tomb of ages, points its cold
And solemn finger to the beautiful
And holy visions that have passed away
And left no shadow of their loveliness
On the dead waste of life.   That specter lifts

The coffin lid of Hope, and Joy, and Love,
And, bending mournfully above the pale,
Sweet forms that slumber there, scatters dead flowers
O'er what has passed to nothingness.

                                    The year
Has gone, and with it many a glorious throng
Of happy dreams.   Its mark is on each brow,
Its shadow in each heart.   In its swift course
It waved its scepter o'er the beautiful,
And they are not.   It laid its pallid hand
Upon the strong man, and the haughty form
Is fallen, and the flashing eye is dim.
It trod the hall of revelry, where thronged
The bright and joyous, and the tearful wail
Of stricken ones is heard where erst the song
And reckless shout resounded.

                                It passed o'er
The battle plain where sword and spear and shield
Flashed in the light of midday, and the strength
Of serried hosts is shivered, and the grass,
Green from the soil of carnage, waves above
The crushed and mouldering skeleton.   It came,
And faded like a wreath of mist at eve;
Yet ere it melted in the viewless air,
It heralded its millions to their home
In the dim land of dreams.

Remorseless Time!
Fierce spirit of the glass and scythe ! What power
Can stay him in his silent course, or melt
His iron heart to pity ? On, still on,
He presses, and forever. The proud bird,
The condor of the Andes, that can soar
Through heaven's unfathomable depths, or brave
The fury of the northern hurricane,
And bathe his plumage in the thunder's home,
Furls his broad wings at nightfall, and sinks down
To rest upon his mountain crag — but Time
Knows not the weight of sleep or weariness,
And night's deep darkness has no chain to bind
His rushing pinions.

Revolutions sweep
O'er the earth, like troubled visions o'er the breast
Of dreaming sorrow ; cities rise and sink
Like bubbles on the water ; fiery isles
Spring blazing from the ocean, and go back
To their mysterious caverns ; mountains rear
To heaven their bald and blackened cliffs, and bow
Their tall heads to the plain ; new empires rise,
Gathering the strength of hoary centuries,
And rush down like the Alpine avalanche,
Startling the nations ; and the very stars,
Yon bright and burning blazonry of God,

Glitter awhile in their eternal depths;
And, like the Pleiades, loveliest of their train,
Shoot from their glorious spheres, and pass away
To darkle in the trackless void: yet Time,
Time the tomb-builder, holds his fierce career,
Dark, stern, all-pitiless, and pauses not
Amid the mighty wrecks that strew his path
To sit and muse, like other conquerors,
Upon the fearful ruin he has wrought.

THE LITTLE BOY IN THE BALCONY

Henry W. Grady

Coney	robust	petulance	ventilation
Rector	balcony	projecting	kaleidoscope
Avenue	emulate	restaurants	combinations

My special amusement in New York is riding on the elevated
railway. It is curious to note how little one can see on the
crowded sidewalks of this city. It is simply a rush of the same
people, hurrying this way or that on the same errands, doing
the same shopping or eating at the same restaurants. It is a
kaleidoscope with infinite combinations, but with the same
effects. You see it to-day, and it is the same as yesterday.
Occasionally, in the multitude you hit upon an odd detail, such
as a prim little dog that sits upright all day and holds in its
mouth a cup for pennies for its blind master, or an old book-
seller with a grand head and the deliberate motions of a scholar

moldering in a stall; but the general effect is one of sameness and soon tires and bewilders.

Once on the elevated road, however, a new world is opened, full of the most interesting objects. The cars sweep by the upper stories of the houses, and, running never too swiftly to allow observation, disclose the secrets of a thousand homes, bringing to view people and things never dreamed of by the giddy, restless crowd that sends its impatient murmur from the streets below. In a course of several months' pretty steady riding from Twenty-third Street, which is the station for the Fifth Avenue Hotel, to Rector, which overlooks Wall Street, I have made many acquaintances along the route; and on reaching the city my first curiosity is in their behalf.

One of these is a boy about six years of age, — a youngster that is very precious to one. I first saw this boy on a little balcony about three feet by four, projecting from the window of a poverty-stricken fourth floor. He was leaning over the railing, his white, thoughtful head just clearing the top, holding a short round stick in his hand. The little fellow made a pathetic picture, all alone there above the street, so friendless and desolate; and his pale face came between me and my business many a time that day. On going up town that evening just as night was falling, I saw him still at his place, white and patient and silent. Every day afterwards I saw him there, always with a short stick in his hand. Occasionally, he would walk around the balcony rattling the stick in a solemn manner against the railing, or poke it across from one corner to another and sit on it. This was the only playing I ever saw him do, and the stick was the only plaything that he had. But he was never without it. His little hand always held it, and I pictured him every morning when he woke from his joyless sleep, picking up his plaything and going out to his balcony, as other boys go to play. Or perhaps he slept with it, as little ones do with dolls and whip-tops.

I could see that the room beyond the window was bare. I never saw any one in it. The heat must have been terrible, for it could have had no ventilation. Once I missed the boy from the balcony, but saw his white head, moving about slowly in the dusk of the room. Gradually the little fellow became a burden to me. I found myself continually thinking of him, and becoming troubled with that remorse that thoughtful people feel even for suffering for which they are not in the slightest degree responsible. Not that I had ever seen any suffering on his face. It was patient, thoughtful, serious, but with never a sign of petulance. What thoughts filled that young head, what complaint or questioning were living behind that white face, no one could guess. In an older person the face would have betokened a resignation that found peace in the hope of things hereafter. In this child, without hope, it was sad beyond expression.

One day as I passed, I nodded at him. He made no sign in return. I repeated the nod on another trip, waving my hand at him, and his pale lips trembled into a smile, but a smile that was soberness itself. Wherever I went that day, that smile went with me. Wherever I saw children playing in the parks, or trotting along with their hands nestled in strong fingers that guided and protected, I thought of that tiny watcher in the balcony, — joyless, hopeless, friendless, — a desolate mite, hanging between the blue sky and the gladsome streets, now lifting his wistful face to the peaceful heights of the one, and now looking with grave wonder on the ceaseless tumult of the other. At length — but why go any further? Why is it necessary to tell that the boy had no father, that his mother had been bed-ridden from his birth, that his sister pasted labels in a drug house, and that he had been thus left to himself all day? It is sufficient to say that I went to Coney Island yesterday, and forgot the heat in the sharp ocean breezes; that I watched the bathers and the children; listened to the crisp, lingering music of the waves as they sang to the beach; ate a robust lunch on the pier; wandered in and out among the booths, tents, and hubbub; and that through all these manifold pleasures I had a companion that enjoyed them with a gravity that I can never hope to emulate, but with a soulfulness that was touching; and that as I came back in the boat, the breezes singing through the cordage, music floating from the fore deck, and the sun lighting with its dying rays the shipping that covered the river, there was sitting in front of me a very pale but very happy bit of a boy, opened-eyed with wonder, but sober and self-contained, clasping tightly in his little fingers a short battered stick. And finally that whenever I pass by a certain overhanging balcony now, I am sure of a smile from an intimate and esteemed little friend who lives there.

WILLIAM TELL ON THE MOUNTAINS

JAMES SHERIDAN KNOWLES

buoyed   scaling   thraldom

Ye crags and peaks, I'm with you once again!
I hold to you the hands you first beheld,
To show they still are free! Methinks I hear
A spirit in your echoes answer me,
And bid your tenant welcome home again.
O sacred forms, how fair, how proud you look!
How high you lift your heads into the sky!
How huge you are! how mighty, and how free!

Ye are the things that tower, that shine; whose smile
Makes glad, whose frown is terrible; whose forms,
Robed or unrobed, do all the impress wear
Of awe divine! Ye guards of liberty,
I'm with you once again! I call to you
With all my voice! I hold my hands to you,
To show they still are free. I rush to you
As though I could embrace you!

Scaling yonder peak,
I saw an eagle wheeling, near its brow,
O'er the abyss. His broad expanded wings
Lay calm and motionless upon the air,
As if he floated there without their aid,

By the sole act of his unlorded will,
Which buoyed him proudly up! Instinctively
I bent my bow; yet wheeled he, heeding not
The death that threatened him: I could not shoot!
'Twas liberty! I turned my bow aside
And let him soar away.

Once Switzerland was free! Oh, with what pride
I used to walk these hills, look up to heaven,
And bless God that it was so! It was free!
From end to end, from cliff to lake, 'twas free!
Free as our torrents are, that leap our rocks
And plow our valleys without asking leave;
Or as our peaks, that wear their caps of snow
In very presence of the regal sun!

How happy was I in it then! I loved
Its very storms! Aye, often have I sat
In my boat at night, when, midway o'er the lake,
The stars went out, and down the mountain gorge
The wind came roaring — sat in it, and eyed
The thunder breaking from his cloud, and smiled
To see him shake his lightnings o'er my head,
And think I had no master save his own!

On yonder jutting cliff, round which a track
Up hither winds, whose base is but the brow
To such another one, with scanty room
For two to pass abreast. O'ertaken there

357

By the mountain-blast, I've laid me flat along;
And, while gust followed gust more furiously,
As if 'twould sweep me o'er the horrid brink,
I have thought of other lands, whose storms
Are summer-flaws to those of mine, and just
Have wished me there, — the thought that mine was free
Has checked that wish, and I have raised my head,
And cried in thraldom to that furious wind,
"Blow on! This is the land of liberty!"

THE TWO ROADS

Jean Paul Richter

errors   Von Arden

It was New Year's night; and Von Arden, having fallen into an unquiet slumber, dreamed that he was an aged man standing at a window. He raised his mournful eyes toward the deep blue sky, where the stars were floating like white lilies on the surface of a clear, calm lake. Then he cast them on the earth, where a few more hopeless beings than he now moved toward their certain goal — the tomb.

Already, as it seemed to him, he had passed sixty of the stages which lead to it, and he had brought from his journey nothing but errors and remorse. His health was destroyed, his mind vacant, his heart sorrowful, and his old age devoid of comfort.

The days of his youth rose up in a vision before him, and he recalled the solemn moment when his father had placed him at the entrance of two roads, — *one* leading into a peaceful, sunny land, covered with a fertile harvest and resounding with soft, sweet songs; the *other* leading the wanderer into a deep, dark cave, whence there was no issue, where poison flowed instead of water, and where serpents hissed and crawled.

He looked toward the sky and cried out in his agony: " O days of my youth, return!   O my father, place me once more at the entrance to life that I may choose the better way!"   But the days of his youth and his father had both passed away.

He saw wandering lights float away over dark marshes and then disappear. These were the days of his wasted life. He saw a star fall from heaven and vanish in darkness. This was an emblem of his life; and the sharp arrows of unavailing remorse struck home to his heart. Then he remembered his early companions who entered on life with him, but who, having trod the paths of virtue and of labor, were now honored and happy on this New Year's night.

The clock in the high church tower struck; and the sound, falling on his ear, recalled his parents' early love for him, their erring son; the lessons they had taught him; the prayers they had offered up on his behalf. Overwhelmed with shame and grief, he dared no longer look toward that heaven where his father dwelt; his darkened eyes dropped tears, and with one despairing effort he cried aloud, " Come back, my early days! Come back!"

And his youth did return; for all this was but a dream which visited his slumbers on New Year's night. He was still young; his faults alone were real. He thanked God fervently that time was still his own; that he had not yet entered the deep, dark cavern, but that he was free to tread the road leading to the peaceful land where sunny harvests wave.

Ye who still linger on the threshold of life, doubting which path to choose, remember that when years are passed, and your feet stumble on the dark mountain, you will cry bitterly, but cry in vain: " O youth, return! Oh, give me back my early days!"

ABOU BEN ADHEM

Leigh Hunt

Abou Ben Adhem (may his tribe increase!)
Awoke one night from a deep dream of peace,
And saw within the moonlight of his room,
Making it rich, and like a lily in bloom,
An angel writing in a book of gold.
Exceeding peace had made Ben Adhem bold,
And, to the presence in the room, he said,
"What writest thou?" The vision raised its head,
And, with a look made all of sweet accord,
Answered, "The names of those who love the Lord!"
"And is mine one?" asked Abou.—"Nay, not so,"
Replied the angel. Abou spake more low,
But cheerily still; and said—"I pray thee, then,
Write me as one that loves his fellow-men."

The angel wrote and vanished. The next night
It came again, with a great wakening light,
And showed the names whom love of God had blest;
And lo! Ben Adhem's name led all the rest!

Edgar Allan Poe

foster	luting	Lafayette	Baltimore
chords	Virginia	Richmond	mendicant

Edgar Allan Poe was born in Boston, Massachusetts, in 1809. His father was an actor and his mother was an actress. They both died in Richmond, Virginia, when Edgar was only two years old, leaving three children to the charity of the world.

His grandfather, General David Poe of Baltimore, was a Revolutionary hero, over whose grave Lafayette, as he kissed the sod, declared, "Here lies a noble heart."

Little Edgar soon won the attention of Mr. John Allan, a wealthy gentleman living at Richmond, who adopted the little fellow when he was only three years old. His foster parents were very kind and indulgent; and the result was that this bright, beautiful little boy was sadly spoiled in his luxurious new home.

He soon showed a love of poetry and early learned to repeat long passages to visitors, with such appreciation of their meaning as to delight his hearers. He began to write poems to his playmates before he was ten years old.

His works include a long list of brilliant short stories, such as "The Oval Portrait," "A Manuscript Found in a Bottle," and "The Gold Bug," and the famous poems, "The Raven," "The Bells," and "Annabel Lee."

Poe was married in Baltimore to his cousin, Virginia Clemm. Their short married life was a happy one, for the poet was devoted to his wife, who was an invalid. She died when she was only twenty-five years of age. In his poem "Annabel Lee" he touchingly describes her loving character.

In 1849, in the fortieth year of his age, and two years after the death of his young wife, his fitful, troubled life ended at Baltimore. The pathos of it

Edgar Allan Poe.

is well summed up in the inscription on a memorial tablet erected to him in the New York Museum of Art: "He was great in his genius, unhappy in his life, wretched in his death, but in his fame, immortal."

No singer of old story
    Luting accustomed lays,
No harper for new glory,
    No mendicant for praise;
He struck high chords and splendid,
Wherein were fiercely blended
Tones that unfinished ended
    With his unfinished days.

— JOHN HENRY BONER.

Through many a year his fame has grown
    Like midnight, vast; like starlight, sweet,—
Till now his genius fills a throne,
    And homage makes his realm complete.

— WILLIAM WINTER.

ANNABEL LEE

EDGAR ALLAN POE

Lee   seraphs
Annabel   coveted
kinsman   sepulcher

It was many and many a year ago,
    In a kingdom by the sea,
That a maiden there lived whom you may know
    By the name of Annabel Lee;
And this maiden she lived with no other thought
    Than to love and be loved by me.

I was a child and she was a child,
　　In this kingdom by the sea:
But we loved with a love that was more than love—
　　I and my Annabel Lee;
With a love that the wingèd seraphs of heaven
　　Coveted her and me.

And this was the reason that, long ago,
　　In this kingdom by the sea,
A wind blew out of a cloud, chilling
　　My beautiful Annabel Lee;
So that her highborn kinsman came
　　And bore her away from me,
To shut her up in a sepulcher
　　In this kingdom by the sea.

The angels, not half so happy in heaven,
　　Went envying her and me;
Yes,— that was the reason (as all men know,
　　In this kingdom by the sea)
That the wind came out of the cloud by night,
　　Chilling and killing my Annabel Lee.

But our love it was stronger by far than the love
　　Of those who were older than we,—
　　Of many far wiser than we;—
And neither the angels in heaven above
　　Nor the demons down under the sea

Can ever dissever my soul from the soul
  Of the beautiful Annabel Lee;

For the moon never beams without bringing me dreams
  Of the beautiful Annabel Lee;
And the stars never rise but I feel the bright eyes
  Of the beautiful Annabel Lee;
And so, all the nighttide, I lie down by the side
Of my darling, my darling, my life and my bride,
  In the sepulcher there by the sea,
  In her tomb by the sounding sea.

THE BELLS

EDGAR ALLAN POE

pæan	Ghouls	euphony	voluminously
Runic	sledges	wrangling	expostulation
brazen	menace	palpitating	tintinnabulation

I

Hear the sledges with the bells, —
  Silver bells!
What a world of merriment their melody foretells!
  How they tinkle, tinkle, tinkle,
   In the icy air of night!
  While the stars that oversprinkle
  All the heavens seem to twinkle
   With a crystalline delight;
  Keeping time, time, time,
  In a sort of Runic rhyme,

To the tintinnabulation that so musically wells
From the bells, bells, bells, bells,
Bells, bells, bells —
From the jingling and the tinkling of the bells.

II

Hear the mellow wedding bells, —
Golden bells!
What a world of happiness their harmony foretells!
Through the balmy air of night
How they ring out their delight!
From the molten-golden notes,
And all in tune,
What a liquid ditty floats
To the turtledove that listens, while she gloats
On the moon!
Oh, from out the sounding cells
What a gush of euphony voluminously wells!
How it swells!
How it dwells
On the future! how it tells
Of the rapture that impels
To the swinging and the ringing
Of the bells, bells, bells,
Of the bells, bells, bells, bells,
Bells, bells, bells —
To the rhyming and the chiming of the bells!

III

Hear the loud alarum bells —
Brazen bells!
What a tale of terror, now, their turbulency tells!
In the startled ear of night
How they scream out their affright!
Too much horrified to speak,
They can only shriek, shriek,
Out of tune,
In a clamorous appealing to the mercy of the fire,
In a mad expostulation with the deaf and frantic fire,
Leaping higher, higher, higher,
With a desperate desire, —
And a resolute endeavor
Now, — now to sit, or never,
By the side of the pale-faced moon.
Oh, the bells, bells, bells!
Of despair!
How they clang, and clash, and roar!
What a horror they outpour
On the bosom of the palpitating air!
Yet the ear it fully knows,
By the twanging —
And the clanging —
How the danger ebbs and flows;
Yet the ear distinctly tells —

In the jangling
And the wrangling
How the danger sinks and swells,
By the sinking or the swelling in the anger of the bells;
Of the bells —
Of the bells, bells, bells, bells,
Bells, bells, bells —
In the clamor and the clangor of the bells!

IV

Hear the tolling of the bells, —
Iron bells!
What a world of solemn thought their melody compels!
In the silence of the night
How we shiver with affright
At the melancholy menace of their tone!
For every sound that floats
From the rust within their throats
Is a groan.
And the people — ah, the people, —
They that dwell up in the steeple
All alone,
And who tolling, tolling, tolling,
In that muffled monotone,
Feel the glory in so rolling
On the human heart a stone, —
They are neither man nor woman, —

They are neither brute nor human,
    They are Ghouls;
And their king it is who tolls;
And he rolls, rolls, rolls,
            Rolls
        A pæan from the bells!
        And his merry bosom swells
        With the pæan of the bells!
        And he dances, and he yells;
    Keeping time, time, time,
In a sort of Runic rhyme,
        To the pæan of the bells, —
            Of the bells;
        Keeping time, time, time,
    In a sort of Runic rhyme,
        To the throbbing of the bells; —
Of the bells, bells, bells, —
        To the sobbing of the bells;
    Keeping time, time, time,
        As he knells, knells, knells,
    In a happy Runic rhyme,
            To the rolling of the bells;
    Of the bells, bells, bells —
        To the rolling of the bells;
    Of the bells, bells, bells, bells, —
        Bells, bells, bells, —
To the moaning and the groaning of the bells.

THE GREAT STONE FACE

Nathaniel Hawthorne

PART I

Titan	edifice	affirmed	harbingers
Midas	portico	Allegory	beseeching
sordid	purport	precipice	sculptured
Ralph	sterling	prophetic	unobtrusive
rumor	studded	semblance	upholsterers
Waldo	exterior	variegated	physiognomy
chaotic	Emerson	commodity	perpendicular

This story is from Hawthorne's "The Snow Image and Other Twice-Told Tales." In the mountains of New Hampshire there is a Great Stone Face, called the "Old Man of the Mountains." It is only the rocky top of a mountain outlined against the sky; but as we look, we are startled to see the heap of rocks taking the shape of a human face, with long nose, deep eyes, and high forehead. There is no doubt that it suggested this story; but we may well believe that Hawthorne's intimate friend, Ralph Waldo Emerson, was the real inspiration of the Allegory of the "Great Stone Face."

One afternoon, when the sun was going down, a mother and her little boy sat at the door of their cottage, talking about the Great Stone Face. They had but to lift their eyes, and there it was plainly to be seen, though miles away, with the sunshine brightening all its features.

And what was the Great Stone Face?

The Great Stone Face was a work of Nature, in a mood of majestic playfulness, formed on the perpendicular side of a

"Old Man of the Mountains."

mountain, by some immense rocks, which had been thrown together in such a position as, when viewed at a proper distance, precisely to resemble the features of the human countenance. It seemed as if an enormous giant, or a Titan, had sculptured his own likeness on the precipice. There was the broad arch of the forehead, a hundred feet in height; the nose, with its long bridge; and the vast lips, which, if they could have spoken, would have rolled their thunder accents from one end of the valley to the other. True it is, that if the spectator approached too near, he lost the outline of the gigantic visage, and could discern only a heap of ponderous and gigantic rocks, piled in chaotic ruin one upon another. Retracing his steps, however, the wondrous features would again be seen; and the farther he withdrew from them, the more like a human face did they appear; until, as it grew dim in the distance, with the clouds and glorified vapor of the mountains clustering about it, the Great Stone Face seemed positively to be alive.

It was a happy lot for children to grow up to manhood or womanhood with the Great Stone Face before their eyes, for all the features were noble, and the expression was at once grand and sweet, as if it were the glow of a vast, warm heart, which embraced all mankind in its affections, and had room for more. It was an education only to look at it.

As we began with saying, a mother and her little boy sat at their cottage door, gazing at the Great Stone Face, and talking about it. The child's name was Ernest.

"Mother," said he, while the Titanic visage smiled on him,

"I wish that it could speak, for it looks so very kindly that its voice must needs be pleasant. If I were to see a man with such a face, I should love him dearly."

"If an old prophecy should come to pass," answered his mother, "we may see a man, some time or other, with exactly such a face as that."

"What prophecy do you mean, dear Mother?" eagerly inquired Ernest. "Pray tell me all about it!"

So his mother told him a story that her own mother had told to her, when she herself was younger than little Ernest; a story, not of things that were past, but of what was yet to come; a story, nevertheless, so very old that even the Indians, who formally inhabited this valley, had heard it from their forefathers, to whom, as they affirmed, it had been murmured by the mountain streams, and whispered by the wind among the tree tops. The purport was, that at some future day, a child should be born hereabouts, who was destined to become the greatest and noblest personage of his time, and whose countenance, in manhood, should bear an exact resemblance to the Great Stone Face.

"O Mother, dear Mother!" cried Ernest, clapping his hands above his head, "I do hope that I shall live to see him!"

His mother was an affectionate and thoughtful woman, and felt that it was wisest not to discourage the generous hopes of her little boy. So she only said to him, "Perhaps you may."

And Ernest never forgot the story that his mother told him. It was always in his mind, whenever he looked upon the Great

Stone Face. He spent his childhood in the log cottage where he was born, and was dutiful to his mother, and helpful to her in many things, assisting her much with his little hands, and more with his loving heart. In this manner, from a happy, yet often pensive child, he grew up to be a mild, quiet, unobtrusive boy, and sun-browned with labor in the fields, but with more intelligence brightening his face than is seen in many lads who have been taught at famous schools. Yet Ernest had had no teacher, save only that the Great Stone Face became one to him. When the toil of the day was over, he would gaze at it for hours, until he began to imagine that those vast features recognized him, and gave him a smile of kindness and encouragement, in response to his own look of veneration. We must not take upon us to affirm that this was a mistake, although the Face may have looked no more kindly at Ernest than at all the world besides. But the secret was, that the boy's tender and confiding simplicity discerned what other people could not see; and thus the love, which was meant for all, became his alone.

About this time there went a rumor throughout the valley that the great man, foretold from ages long ago, who was to bear a resemblance to the Great Stone Face, had appeared at last. It seems that, many years before, a young man had left the valley and settled at a distant seaport, where, after getting together a little money, he had set up as a shopkeeper. His name — but I could never learn whether it was his real one, or a nickname that had grown out of his habits and success in life — was Gathergold. All the countries of the globe appeared to join hands for the mere purpose of adding heap after heap to the mountainous accumulation of this one man's wealth. Be the original commodity what it might, it was gold within his grasp. It might be said of him, as of Midas in the fable, that whatever he touched with his finger immediately glistened, and grew yellow, and was changed at once into sterling metal, or, which suited him still better, into piles of coin. And, when Mr. Gathergold had become so very rich that it would have taken him a hundred years only to count his wealth, he bethought himself of his native valley, and resolved to go back thither, and end his days where he was born. With this purpose in view, he sent a skillful architect to build him such a palace as should be fit for a man of his vast wealth to live in.

As I have said above, it had already been rumored in the valley that Mr. Gathergold had turned out to be the prophetic personage so long and vainly looked for, and that his visage was the perfect and undeniable likeness of the Great Stone Face. People were the more ready to believe that this must needs be the fact, when they beheld the splendid edifice that rose, as if by enchantment, on the site of his father's old weather-beaten farmhouse. The exterior was of marble, so dazzlingly white that it seemed as though the whole structure might melt away in the sunshine, like those humbler ones which Mr. Gathergold, in his young playdays, had been accustomed to build of snow. It had a richly ornamented portico, supported by tall pillars, beneath which was a lofty door, studded with silver knobs, and made of a kind of variegated wood that had been brought from beyond the sea. The windows, from the floor to the ceiling of each stately apartment, were composed, respectively, of but one enormous pane of glass. Hardly anybody had been permitted to see the interior of this palace; but it was reported, and with good semblance of truth, to be far more gorgeous than the outside, insomuch that whatever was iron or brass in other houses was silver or gold in this; and Mr. Gathergold's bedchamber, especially, made such a glittering appearance that no ordinary man would have been able to close his eyes there. But, on the other hand, Mr. Gathergold was now so accustomed to wealth that perhaps he could not have closed his eyes unless where the gleam of it was certain to find its way beneath his eyelids.

In due time, the mansion was finished; next came the up-holsterers, with magnificent furniture; then, a whole troop of black and white servants, the harbingers of Mr. Gathergold, who, in his own majestic person, was expected to arrive at sunset. Our friend Ernest, meanwhile, had been deeply stirred by the idea that the great man, the noble man, the man of prophecy, after so many ages of delay, was at length to appear in his native valley. He knew, boy as he was, that there were a thousand ways in which Mr. Gathergold, with his vast wealth, might transform himself into an angel of beneficence, and assume a control over human affairs as wide and benignant as the smile of the Great Stone Face. Full of faith and hope, Ernest doubted not that what the people said was true, and that now he was to behold the living likeness of those wondrous features on the mountain side. While the boy was still gazing up the valley, and fancying, as he always did, that the Great Stone Face returned his gaze and looked kindly at him, the rumbling of wheels was heard, approaching swiftly along the winding road.

"Here he comes!" cried a group of people who were assembled to witness the arrival. "Here comes the great Mr. Gathergold!"

A carriage, drawn by four horses, dashed round the turn of the road. Within it, thrust partly out of the window, appeared the physiognomy of a little old man, with a skin as yellow as gold. He had a low forehead, small, sharp eyes, puckered about with innumerable wrinkles, and very thin lips, which he made still thinner by pressing them forcibly together.

"The very image of the Great Stone Face!" shouted the people. "Sure enough, the old prophecy is true; and the great man has come, at last!"

And, what greatly perplexed Ernest, they seemed actually to believe that here was the likeness which they spoke of. By the roadside there chanced to be an old beggar woman and two little beggar children, stragglers from some far-off region, who, as the carriage rolled onward, held out their hands and lifted up their doleful voices, most piteously beseeching charity. A yellow claw — the very same that had clawed together so much wealth — poked itself out of the coach window, and dropped some copper coins upon the ground; so that, though the great man's name seems to have been Gathergold, he might just as suitably have been nicknamed Scattercopper. Still, nevertheless, with an earnest shout, and evidently with as much good faith as ever, the people bellowed, —

"He is the very image of the Great Stone Face!"

But Ernest turned sadly from the wrinkled shrewdness of that sordid visage, and gazed up the valley, where, amid a gathering mist, gilded by the last sunbeams, he could still distinguish those glorious features which had impressed themselves into his soul. Their aspect cheered him. What did the benign lips seem to say?

"He will come! Fear not, Ernest; the man will come!"

PART II

Phiz	sheriff	flaunting	illustrious
veteran	enlisted	cavalcade	reverberate
warrior	faculties	vociferous	illuminated
turmoil	conceded	potentates	accomodation
betwixt	barouche	aid-de-camp	enthusiastically

The years went on, and Ernest ceased to be a boy. He had grown to be a young man now. He attracted little notice from the other inhabitants of the valley; for they saw nothing remarkable in his way of life, save that, when the labor of the day was over, he still loved to go apart and gaze and meditate upon the Great Stone Face. According to their idea of the matter, it was a folly, indeed, but pardonable, inasmuch as Ernest was industrious, kind, and neighborly, and neglected no duty for the sake of indulging this idle habit. They knew not that the Great Stone Face had become a teacher to him, and that the sentiment which was expressed in it would enlarge the young man's heart, and fill it with wider and deeper sympathies than other hearts.

378

They knew not that thence would come a better wisdom than could be learned from books, and a better life than could be molded on the example of other human lives. Neither did Ernest know that the thoughts and affections which came to him so naturally, in the fields and at the fireside, were of a higher tone than those which all men shared with him. A simple soul, — simple as when his mother first taught him the old prophecy, — he beheld the marvelous features beaming down the valley, and still wondered that their human counterpart was so long in making his appearance.

By this time poor Mr. Gathergold was dead and buried; and the oddest part of the matter was, that his wealth, which was the body and spirit of his existence, had disappeared before his death, leaving nothing of him but a living skeleton, covered over with a wrinkled, yellow skin. Since the melting away of his gold, it had been very generally conceded that there was no such striking resemblance, after all, betwixt the ignoble features of the ruined merchant and that majestic face upon the mountain side. So the people ceased to honor him during his lifetime, and quietly consigned him to forgetfulness after his decease. Once in a while, it is true, his memory was brought up in connection with the magnificent palace which he had built, and which had long ago been turned into a hotel for the accommodation of strangers, multitudes of whom came, every summer, to visit that famous natural curiosity, the Great Stone Face. The man of prophecy was yet to come.

It so happened that a native-born son of the valley, many

years before, had enlisted as a soldier, and after a great deal of hard fighting had now become an illustrious commander. Whatever he may be called in history, he was known in the camps and on the battle field under the nickname of Old Blood-and-Thunder. This war-worn veteran, being now infirm with age and wounds, and weary of the turmoil of a military life, and of the roll of the drum and the clangor of the trumpet, which had so long been ringing in his ears, had lately signified a purpose of returning to his native valley, hoping to find repose where he remembered to have left it. The inhabitants, his old neighbors and their grown-up children, were resolved to welcome the renowned warrior with a salute of cannon and a public dinner; and all the more enthusiastically, it being affirmed that now, at last, the likeness of the Great Stone Face had actually appeared. An aid-de-camp of Old Blood-and-Thunder, traveling through the valley, was said to have been struck with the resemblance. Moreover the school-mates and early acquaintances of the general were ready to testify, on oath, that, to the best of their recollection, the general had been exceedingly like the majestic image, even when a boy, only that the idea had never occurred to them at that period. Great, therefore, was the excitement throughout the valley; and many people, who had never once thought of glancing at the Great Stone Face for years before, now spent their time in gazing at it, for the sake of knowing exactly how General Blood-and-Thunder looked.

On the day of the great festival, Ernest, and all the other people of the valley, left their work, and proceeded to the spot where the sylvan banquet had been prepared. Our friend Ernest raised himself on his tiptoes, in hopes to get a glimpse of the celebrated guest. But there was a mighty crowd about the tables anxious to hear the toasts and speeches, and to catch any word that might fall from the general in reply; and a volunteer company, doing duty as a guard, pricked ruthlessly with their bayonets at any particularly quiet person among the throng. So Ernest, being of an unobtrusive character, was thrust quite into the background, where he could see no more of Old Blood-and-Thunder's physiognomy than if it had been still blazing on the battle field. To console himself he turned towards the Great Stone Face, which like a faithful and long-remembered friend, looked back and smiled upon him through the vista of the forest. Meantime, however, he could overhear the remarks of various individuals, who were comparing the features of the hero with the face on the distant mountain side.

" 'Tis the same face, to a hair!" cried one man, cutting a caper for joy.

" Wonderfully like, that's a fact!" responded another.

" Like! why, I call it Old Blood-and-Thunder himself, in a monstrous looking-glass!" cried a third. "And why not? He's the greatest man of this or any other age, beyond a doubt."

" The general! the general!" was now the cry. "Hush! silence! Old Blood-and-Thunder's going to make a speech."

Even so; for, the cloth being removed, the general's health had been drunk amid shouts of applause, and he now stood upon his feet to thank the company. Ernest saw him. There he was, over the shoulders of the crowd. And there, too, visible in the same glance, through the vista of the forest, appeared the Great Stone Face! And was there, indeed, such a resemblance as the crowd had testified? Alas, Ernest could not recognize it! He beheld a war-worn and weather-beaten countenance, full of energy, and expressive of an iron will; but the gentle wisdom, the deep, broad, tender sympathies, were altogether wanting in Old Blood-and-Thunder's visage; and even if the Great Stone Face had assumed his look of stern command, the milder traits would still have tempered it.

"This is not the man of prophecy," sighed Ernest to himself, as he made his way out of the throng. "And must the world wait longer yet?"

"Fear not, Ernest," said his heart, even as if the Great Face were whispering him, — "fear not, Ernest; he will come."

More years sped swiftly and tranquilly away. Ernest still dwelt in his native valley, and was now a man of middle age. By imperceptible degrees, he had become known among the people. Now, as heretofore, he labored for his bread, and was the same simple-hearted man that he had always been. But he had thought and felt so much, he had given so many of the best hours of his life to unworldly hopes for some great good to mankind, that it seemed as though he had been talking with the angels, and had imbibed a portion of their wisdom unawares. It was visible in the calm beneficence of his daily life, the quiet stream of which had made a wide green margin all along its course. Not a day passed by, that the world was not the better because this man, humble as he was, had lived. He never stepped aside from his own path, yet would always reach a blessing to his neighbor.

When the people's minds had had a little time to cool, they were ready enough to acknowledge their mistake in imagining a similarity between General Blood-and-Thunder's physiognomy and the benign visage on the mountain side. But now, again, there were reports and many paragraphs in the newspapers, affirming that the likeness of the Great Stone Face had appeared upon the broad shoulders of a certain eminent statesman. He, like Mr. Gathergold and Old Blood-and-Thunder, was a native of the valley, but had left it in his early days, and taken up the trades of law and politics. Instead of the rich man's wealth and the warrior's sword, he had but a tongue, and it was mightier than both together. So wonderfully eloquent was he, that whatever he might choose to say, his hearers had no choice but to believe him; wrong looked like right, and right, like wrong; for when it pleased him, he could make a kind of illuminated fog with his mere breath, and obscure the natural daylight with it. His tongue, indeed, was a magic instrument: sometimes it rumbled like the thunder; sometimes it warbled like the sweetest music. It was the blast of war, — the song of peace; and it seemed to have a heart in it, when there was no such matter. In good truth, he was a wonderous man; and when his tongue had acquired him all other imaginable success, — when it had been heard in halls of state, and in the courts of princes and potentates, — after it had made him known all over the world, even as a voice crying from shore to shore, — it finally persuaded his countrymen to select him for the Presidency. Before this time, — indeed, as soon as he began to grow celebrated, — his admirers had found out the resemblance between him and the Great Stone Face; and so much were they struck by it, that throughout the country this distinguished gentleman was known by the name of Old Stony Phiz.

While his friends were doing their best to make him President, Old Stony Phiz, as he was called, set out on a visit to the valley where he was born. Of course, he had no other object than to shake hands with his fellow-citizens, and neither thought nor cared about any effect which his progress through the country might have upon the election. Magnificent preparations were made to receive the illustrious statesman; a cavalcade of horsemen set forth to meet him at the boundary line of the State, and all the people left their business and gathered along the wayside to see him pass. Among these was Ernest. Though more than once disappointed, as we have seen, he had such a hopeful and confiding nature that he was always ready to believe in whatever seemed beautiful and good. He kept his heart continually open, and thus was sure to catch the blessing from on high, when it should come. So now again, as buoyantly as ever, he went forth to behold the likeness of the Great Stone Face.

The cavalcade came prancing along the road, with a great clattering of hoofs and a mighty cloud of dust, which rose up so dense and high that the visage of the mountain side was completely hidden from Ernest's eyes. All the great men of the neighborhood were there on horseback: militia officers, in uniform; the member of Congress; the sheriff of the county; the editors of newspapers; and many a farmer, too, had mounted his patient steed, with his Sunday coat upon his back. It really was a very brilliant spectacle, especially as there were numerous banners flaunting over the cavalcade, on some of which were gorgeous portraits of the illustrious statesman and the Great Stone Face, smiling familiarly at one another, like two brothers. If the pictures were to be trusted, the resemblance, it must be confessed, was marvelous. We must not forget to mention that there was a band of music, which made the echoes of the mountains ring and reverberate with the loud triumph of its strains; so that airy and soul-thrilling melodies broke out among all the heights and hollows, as if every nook of his native valley had found a voice, to welcome the distinguished guest. But the grandest effect was when the far-off mountain precipice flung back the music; for then the Great Stone Face itself seemed to be swelling the triumphant chorus, in acknowledgment that, at length, the man of prophecy was come.

All this while the people were throwing up their hats and shouting, with enthusiasm so contagious that the heart of Ernest kindled up, and he likewise threw up his hat, and shouted, as loudly as the loudest, "Huzza for the great man! Huzza for Old Stony Phiz!" But as yet he had not seen him.

"Here he is, now!" cried those who stood near Ernest. "There! There! Look at Old Stony Phiz and then at the Old

Man of the Mountain, and see if they are not as like as two twin brothers!"

In the midst of all this gallant array, came an open barouche, drawn by four white horses; and in the barouche, with his massive head uncovered, sat the illustrious statesman, Old Stony Phiz himself.

"Confess it," said one of Ernest's neighbors to him, "the Great Stone Face has met its match at last!"

Now, it must be owned that, at his first glimpse of the countenance which was bowing and smiling from the barouche, Ernest did fancy that there was a resemblance between it and the old familiar face upon the mountain side. The brow, with its massive depth and loftiness, and all the other features, indeed, were bold and strong. But the grand expression of a divine sympathy, which illuminated the mountain visage, might here be sought in vain. Something had been originally left out, or had departed. And therefore the marvelously gifted statesman had always a weary gloom in the deep caverns of his eyes, as of a child that has outgrown its playthings, or a man of mighty faculties and little aims, whose life, with all its high performances, was vague and empty, because no high purpose had endowed it with reality.

Still, Ernest's neighbor was thrusting his elbow into his side, and pressing him for an answer.

"Confess! confess! Is not he the very picture of your Old Man of the Mountain?"

"No!" said Ernest, bluntly, "I see little or no likeness."

"Then so much the worse for the Great Stone Face!" answered his neighbor; and again he set up a shout for Old Stony Phiz.

But Ernest turned away, melancholy, and almost despondent: for this was the saddest of his disappointments, to behold a man who might have fulfilled the prophecy, and had not willed to do so. Meantime, the cavalcade, the banners, the music, and the barouches swept past him, with the vociferous crowd in the rear, leaving the dust to settle down, and the Great Stone Face to be revealed again, with the grandeur that it had worn for untold centuries.

"Lo, here I am, Ernest!" the benign lips seemed to say. "I have waited longer than thou, and am not yet weary. Fear not; the man will come."

PART III

pulpit	festoons	celestial
imbued	tapestry	interpret
stanzas	audience	philanthropist

The years hurried onward, treading in their haste on one another's heels. And now they began to bring white hairs, and scatter them over the head of Ernest; they made wrinkles across his forehead, and furrows in his cheeks. He was an aged man. But not in vain had he grown old: more than the white hairs on his head were the sage thoughts in his mind; his wrinkles and furrows were inscriptions that Time had graved, and in which he had written legends of wisdom that had been tested by the tenor of a life. And Ernest had ceased to be obscure. Unsought for, undesired, had come the fame which so many seek, and made him known in the great world, beyond the limits of the valley in which he had dwelt so quietly. College professors, and even the active men of cities, came from far to see and converse with Ernest; for the report had gone abroad that this simple husbandman had ideas unlike those of other men, not gained from books, but of a higher tone, — a tranquil and familiar majesty, as if he had been talking with the angels as his daily friends. Whether it were sage, statesman, or philanthropist, Ernest received these visitors with the gentle sincerity that had characterized him from boyhood, and spoke freely with them of whatever came uppermost, or lay deepest in his heart or their own. While they talked together, his face would kindle, unawares, and shine upon them, as with a mild evening light. Pensive with the fullness of such discourse, his guests took leave and went their way; and passing up the valley, paused to look at the Great Stone Face, imagining that they had seen its likeness in a human countenance, but could not remember where.

While Ernest had been growing up and growing old, a bountiful Providence had granted a new poet to this earth. He, likewise, was a native of the valley, but had spent the greater part of his life at a distance from that romantic region, pouring out his sweet music amid the bustle and din of cities. Often, however, did the mountains which had been familiar to him in his childhood lift their snowy peaks into the clear atmosphere of his poetry. Neither was the Great Stone Face forgotten, for the poet had celebrated it in an ode, which was grand enough to have been uttered by its own majestic lips. This man of genius, we may say, had come down from heaven with wonderful endowments. If he sang of a mountain, the eyes of all mankind beheld a mightier grandeur reposing on its breast, or soaring to its summit, than had before been seen there. If his theme were a lovely lake, a celestial smile had now been thrown over it, to gleam forever on its surface. If it were the vast old sea, even the deep immensity of its dread bosom seemed to swell the higher, as if moved by the emotions of the song. Thus the world assumed another and a better aspect from the hour that the poet blessed it with his happy eyes. The Creator had bestowed him, as the last best touch to his own handiwork. Creation was not finished till the poet came to interpret, and so complete it.

The songs of this poet found their way to Ernest. He read them after his customary toil, seated on the bench before his cottage door, where for such a length of time he had filled his repose with thought, by gazing at the Great Stone Face. And now, as he read stanzas that caused the soul to thrill within him, he lifted his eyes to the vast countenance beaming on him so benignantly.

"O majestic friend," he murmured, addressing the Great Stone Face, "is not this man worthy to resemble thee?"

The Face seemed to smile, but answered not a word.

Now it happened that the poet, though he dwelt so far away, had not only heard of Ernest, but had meditated much upon his character, until he deemed nothing so desirable as to meet this man, whose untaught wisdom walked hand in hand with the noble simplicity of his life. One summer morning, therefore, he took passage by the railroad, and, in the decline of the afternoon, alighted from the cars at no great distance from Ernest's cottage. The great hotel, which had formerly been the palace of Mr. Gathergold, was close at hand, but the poet, with his carpet-bag on his arm, inquired at once where Ernest dwelt, and was resolved to be accepted as his guest.

Approaching the door, he there found the good old man, holding a volume in his hand, which alternately he read, and then, with a finger between the leaves, looked lovingly at the Great Stone Face.

"Good evening," said the poet. "Can you give a traveler a night's lodging?"

"Willingly," answered Ernest; and then he added, smiling, "methinks I never saw the Great Stone Face look so hospitably at a stranger."

The poet sat down on the bench beside him, and he and Ernest talked together. Often had the poet conversed with the wittiest and the wisest, but never before with a man like Ernest, whose thoughts and feelings gushed up with such a natural freedom, and who made great truths so familiar by his simple utterance of them. Angels, as had been so often said, seemed to have wrought with him at his labor in the fields; angels seemed to have sat with him by the fireside. So thought the poet. And Ernest, on the other hand, was moved and agitated by the living images which the poet flung out of his mind, and which peopled all the air about the cottage door with shapes of beauty.

As Ernest listened to the poet, he imagined that the Great Stone Face was bending forward to listen, too. He gazed earnesty into the poet's glowing eyes.

" Who are you, my strangely gifted guest?" he said.

The poet laid his finger on the volume that Ernest had been reading.

" You have read these poems," said he. " You know me, then, — for I wrote them."

Again, and still more earnestly than before, Ernest examined the poet's features; then turned toward the Great Stone Face; then back to his guest. But his countenance fell; he shook his head, and sighed.

" Wherefore are you sad?" inquired the poet.

" Because," replied Ernest, " all through life I have awaited the fulfillment of a prophecy; and, when I read these poems, I hoped that it might be fulfilled in you."

" You hoped," answered the poet, faintly smiling, " to find in me the likeness of the Great Stone Face. And you are disappointed, as formerly with Mr. Gathergold, and Old Blood-and-Thunder, and Old Stony Phiz. Yes, Ernest, it is my doom. You must add my name to the illustrious three, and record another failure of your hopes. For — in shame and sadness do I speak it, Ernest — I am not worthy."

" And why?" asked Ernest. He pointed to the volume. " Are not those thoughts divine?"

" You can hear in them the far-off echo of a heavenly song," replied the poet. " But my life, dear Ernest, has not corresponded with my thought. I have had grand dreams, but they have been only dreams, because I have lived — and that, too, by my own choice — among poor and mean realities. Sometimes even — shall I dare to say it? — I lack faith in the grandeur, the beauty, and the goodness, which my own works are said to have made more evident in nature and in human life. Why, then, pure seeker of the good and true, shouldst thou hope to find me in yonder image of the divine?"

The poet spoke sadly, and his eyes were dim with tears; so, likewise, were those of Ernest.

At the hour of sunset, as had long been his frequent custom, Ernest was to speak to an assemblage of the neighboring inhabitants in the open air. He and the poet, arm in arm, still talking together as they went along, proceeded to the spot. It was a small nook among the hills, with a gray precipice behind, the stern front of which was relieved by the pleasant foliage of many creeping plants that made a tapestry for the naked rock by hanging their festoons from all its rugged angles. At a small elevation above the ground, set in a rich framework of verdure, there appeared a niche, spacious enough to admit a human figure. Into this natural pulpit Ernest ascended, and threw a look of familiar kindness around upon his audience. They stood, or sat, or reclined upon the grass, as seemed good to each, with the departing sunshine falling over them, and mingling its subdued cheerfulness with the solemnity of a grove of ancient trees, beneath and amid the boughs of which the golden rays were constrained to pass. In another direction was seen the

Great Stone Face, with the same cheer, combined with the same solemnity, in its benignant aspect.

Ernest began to speak, giving to the people of what was in his heart and mind. His words had power, because they accorded with his thoughts; and his thoughts had reality and depth, because they harmonized with the life which he had always lived. It was not mere breath that this preacher uttered; they were the words of life, because a life of good deeds and holy love was melted into them. Pearls, pure and rich, had been dissolved into this precious draught. The poet, as he listened, felt that the being and character of Ernest were a nobler strain of poetry than he had ever written. His eyes glistening with tears, he gazed reverentially at the venerable man, and said within himself that never was there an aspect so worthy of a prophet and a sage as that mild, sweet, thoughtful countenance, with the glory of white hair diffused about it. At a distance, but distinctly to be seen, high up in the golden light of the setting sun, appeared the Great Stone Face, with hoary mists around it, like the white hairs around the brow of Ernest. Its look of grand beneficence seemed to embrace the world.

At that moment, in sympathy with a thought which he was about to utter, the face of Ernest assumed a grandeur of expression, so imbued with benevolence, that the poet, by an irresistible impulse, threw his arms aloft, and shouted, —

"Behold! Behold! Ernest is himself the likeness of the Great Stone Face!"

Then all the people looked, and saw that what the deep-sighted poet said was true. The prophecy was fulfilled. But Ernest, having finished what he had to say, took the poet's arm, and walked slowly homeward, still hoping that some wiser and better man than himself would by and by appear bearing a resemblance to the Great Stone Face.

OH, WHY SHOULD THE SPIRIT OF MORTAL BE PROUD?

WILLIAM KNOX

bier	miter	transient
Knox	Israel	

William Knox was a Scotch poet who was born in 1789 and died in 1825. "The Lonely Hearth," and "The Songs of Israel," from which the following poem is taken, are the most noted of his works. Sir Walter Scott was an admirer of Knox's poems, and he befriended the author when his habits brought him into need.

This poem was a great favorite of Abraham Lincoln's. It was first shown to him by a friend when he was a young man, and he afterwards learned it by heart. When he was President of the United States he said to a friend: "I would give a great deal to know who wrote it, but I have never been able to find out." But he did afterwards learn the name of the author.

Oh, why should the spirit of mortal be proud?
Like a swift-fleeting meteor, a fast-flying cloud,
A flash of the lightning, a break of the wave,
Man passes from life to his rest in the grave.

The leaves of the oak and the willow shall fade,
Be scattered around, and together be laid;
And the young and the old, the low and the high,
Shall molder to dust and together shall lie.

The infant a mother attended and loved,
The mother that infant's affection who proved,
The father that mother and infant who blest, —
Each, all, are away to their dwellings of rest.

The maid on whose brow, on whose cheek, in whose eye,
Shone beauty and pleasure, — her triumphs are by;
And the memories of those who loved her and praised,
Are alike from the minds of the living erased.

The hand of the king, that the scepter hath borne;
The brow of the priest, that the miter hath worn;
The eye of the sage, and the heart of the brave, —
Are hidden and lost in the depths of the grave.

The peasant, whose lot was to sow and to reap,
The herdsman, who climbed with his goats up the steep,
The beggar, who wandered in search of his bread,
Have faded away like the grass that we tread.

The saint, who enjoyed the communion of Heaven,
The sinner, who dared to remain unforgiven,
The wise and the foolish, the guilty and just,
Have quietly mingled their bones in the dust.

So the multitude goes, like the flower or the weed,
That withers away to let others succeed;
So the multitude comes, even those we behold,
To repeat every tale that has often been told.

For we are the same that our fathers have been;
We see the same sights that our fathers have seen;
We drink the same stream, we see the same sun,
And run the same course that our fathers have run.

The thoughts we are thinking our fathers would think;
From the death we are shrinking our fathers would shrink;
To the life we are clinging they also would cling,
But it speeds from us all like a bird on the wing.

They loved, but the story we cannot unfold;
They scorned, but the heart of the haughty is cold;
They grieved, but no wail from their slumbers will come;
They joyed, but the tongue of their gladness is dumb.

They died, ah! they died; and we things that are now,
Who walk on the turf that lies over their brow,
And make in their dwelling a transient abode,
Meet the things that they met on their pilgrimage road.

Yea, hope and despondency, pleasure and pain,
Are mingled together like sunshine and rain;
And the smile and the tear, the song and the dirge,
Still follow each other like surge upon surge.

'Tis the wink of an eye; 'tis the draught of a breath
From the blossom of health to the paleness of death,
From the gilded saloon to the bier and the shroud;
Oh, why should the spirit of mortal be proud?

EULOGY ON JAMES A. GARFIELD

JAMES GILLESPIE BLAINE

decree	baffled	sundering	aspirations
frenzy	Garfield	sustaining	premonition
mystic	assassins	foreboding	relinquishment

Surely, if happiness can ever come from the honors or triumphs of this world, on that quiet July morning James A. Garfield may well have been a happy man. No foreboding of evil haunted him; no slightest premonition of danger clouded his sky. His terrible fate was upon him in an instant. One moment he stood erect, strong, confident in the years stretching peacefully out before him. The next he lay wounded, bleeding, helpless, doomed to weary weeks of torture, to silence and the grave.

Great in life, he was surpassingly great in death. For no cause, in the very frenzy of wantonness and wickedness, by the red hand of murder, he was thrust from the full tide of this world's interest, from its hopes, its aspirations, its victories, into the visible presence of death, — and he did not quail.

Not alone for one short moment in which, stunned and dazed, he could give up life, hardly aware of its relinquishment, but through days of deadly languor, through weeks of agony, that was not less agony because silently borne, with clear sight and calm courage, he looked into his open grave. What blight and ruin met his anguished eyes, whose lips may tell? What brilliant, broken plans, what baffled, high ambitions, what sundering of strong, warm manhood's friendships, what bitter rending of sweet household ties!

Behind him a proud, expectant nation, a great host of sustaining friends, a cherished and happy mother, wearing the full, rich honors of her early toil and tears; the wife of his youth, whose whole life lay in his; the little boys, not yet emerged from childhood's day of frolic; the fair, young daughter; the sturdy sons, just springing into closest companionship, claiming every day, and every day rewarding a father's love and care; and in his heart, eager, rejoicing power to meet all demands. Before him, desolation and great darkness! And his soul was not shaken.

His countrymen were thrilled with instant, profound, and universal sympathy. Masterful in his mortal weakness, he became the center of a nation's love, enshrined in the prayers of a world. But all the love and all the sympathy could not share with him his suffering. He trod the wine-press alone. With unfaltering front he faced death. With unfailing tenderness he took leave of life. Above the demoniac hiss of the assassin's bullet, he heard the voice of God. With simple resignation he bowed to the Divine decree.

As the end drew near, his early craving for the sea returned. The stately mansion of power had been to him the wearisome hospital of pain, and he begged to be taken from its prison walls, from its oppressive, stifling air, from its homelessness and its hopelessness. Gently, silently the love of a great people bore the pale sufferer to the longed-for healing of the sea, to live or to die, as God should will, within sight of its heaving billows, within sound of its manifold voices.

With wan, fevered face tenderly lifted to the cooling breeze, he looked out wistfully upon the ocean's changing wonders; on its far sails whitening in the morning light; on its restless waves, rolling shoreward to break and die beneath the noonday sun; on the red clouds of evening, arching low to the horizon; on the serene and shining pathway of the stars.

Let us think that his dying eyes read a mystic meaning which only the rapt and parting soul may know. Let us believe that in the silence of the receding world he heard the great waves breaking on a farther shore, and felt already upon his wasted brow the breath of the eternal morning.

A PSALM OF LIFE

HENRY WADSWORTH LONGFELLOW

bivouac

Tell me not, in mournful numbers,
  "Life is but an empty dream!"
For the soul is dead that slumbers,
  And things are not what they seem.

Life is real! Life is earnest!
  And the grave is not its goal;
"Dust thou art, to dust returnest,"
  Was not spoken of the soul.

Not enjoyment, and not sorrow,
　　Is our destined end or way;
But to act, that each to-morrow
　　Find us farther than to-day.

Art is long, and Time is fleeting,
　　And our hearts, though stout and brave,
Still, like muffled drums, are beating
　　Funeral marches to the grave.

In the world's broad field of battle,
　　In the bivouac of Life,
Be not like dumb, driven cattle;
　　Be a hero in the strife!

Trust no Future, howe'er pleasant!
　　Let the dead Past bury its dead!
Act, act in the living Present!
　　Heart within, and God o'erhead!

Lives of great men all remind us
　　We can make our lives sublime,
And, departing, leave behind us
　　Footprints on the sands of time;

Footprints, that perhaps another,
　　Sailing o'er life's solemn main,
A forlorn and shipwrecked brother,
　　Seeing, shall take heart again.

Let us, then, be up and doing,
   With a heart for any fate;
Still achieving, still pursuing,
   Learn to labor and to wait.

THANATOPSIS

William Cullen Bryant

Barcan   patriarchs   quarry-slave
caravan   decorations

To him who, in the love of Nature, holds
Communion with her visible forms, she speaks
A various language; for his gayer hours
She has a voice of gladness, and a smile
And eloquence of beauty; and she glides
Into his darker musings with a mild
And healing sympathy, that steals away
Their sharpness, ere he is aware. When thoughts
Of the last bitter hour come like a blight
Over thy spirit, and sad images
Of the stern agony, and shroud, and pall,
And breathless darkness, and the narrow house,
Make thee to shudder, and grow sick at heart; —
Go forth, under the open sky, and list
To Nature's teachings, while from all around —
Earth and her waters, and the depths of air —
Comes a still voice —

Yet a few days, and thee
The all-beholding sun shall see no more
In all his course; nor yet in the cold ground,
Where thy pale form was laid, with many tears,
Nor in the embrace of ocean, shall exist
Thy image. Ea ch, that nourished thee, shall claim
Thy growth, to be resolved to earth again;
And, lost each human trace, surrendering up
Thine individual being, shalt thou go
To mix forever with the elements,
To be a brother to the insensible rock
And to the sluggish clod, which the rude swain
Turns with his share, and treads upon. The oak
Shall send his roots abroad, and pierce thy mold.

Yet not to thine eternal resting-place
Shalt thou retire alone, nor couldst thou wish
Couch more magnificent. Thou shalt lie down
With patriarchs of the infant world, — with kings,
The powerful of the earth, — the wise, the good,
Fair forms, and hoary seers of ages past,
All in one mighty sepulcher. The hills
Rock-ribbed and ancient as the sun, — the vales
Stretching in pensive quietness between;
The venerable woods — rivers that move
In majesty, and the complaining brooks
That make the meadows green; and, poured round all,

Old ocean's gray and melancholy waste, —
Are but the solemn decorations all
Of the great tomb of man. The golden sun,
The planets, all the infinite host of heaven,
Are shining on the sad abodes of death,
Through the still lapse of ages. All that tread
The globe are but a handful to the tribes
That slumber in its bosom. — Take the wings
Of morning, pierce the Barcan wilderness,
Or lose thyself in the continuous woods
Where rolls the Oregon, and hears no sound,
Save his own dashings, — yet the dead are there:
And millions in those solitudes, since first
The flight of years began, have laid them down
In their last sleep — the dead reign there alone.
So shalt thou rest, and what if thou withdraw
In silence from the living, and no friend
Take note of thy departure? All that breathe
Will share thy destiny. The gay will laugh
When thou art gone, the solemn brood of care
Plod on, and each one as before will chase
His favorite phantom ; yet all these shall leave
Their mirth and their employments, and shall come
And make their bed with thee. As the long train
Of ages glides away, the sons of men, —
The youth in life's fresh spring, and he who goes
In the full strength of years, matron and maid,

The speechless babe, and the gray-headed man —
Shall one by one be gathered to thy side,
By those who in their turn shall follow them.

So live, that when thy summons comes to join
The innumerable caravan, which moves
To that mysterious realm, where each shall take
His chamber in the silent halls of death,
Thou go not, like the quarry-slave at night,
Scourged to his dungeon, but, sustained and soothed
By an unfaltering trust, approach thy grave
Like one who wraps the drapery of his couch
About him, and lies down to pleasant dreams.

Reprinted from Bryant's Complete Poetical Works, by permission of D. Appleton and Company.

THE LEGEND OF SLEEPY HOLLOW

Washington Irving

Crane	elapsed	inferior	spluttering
Irving	pervade	vicinity	sequestered
parade	Hessian	sojourned	surrounding
reverie	uncouth	anecdotes	speculations
spindle	curdling	vegetating	topsy-turvey
damsels	elegance	Tarrytown	maintenance
revenue	behooved	subsequent	superstitions
Ichabod	Hendrick	Connecticut	Greensburgh

In 1783 a son was born in a New York home. "Washington's work is ended," said his mother, "and this child shall be named after him." And so the boy was called Washington Irving.

Washington Irving.

When, six years later, all New York was enthusiastically greeting the first President of the United States, a Scotch servant in the Irving family followed the President into a shop and approaching him, said, "Please your honor, here's a bairn was named for you." Washington kindly placed his hand on the head of the little boy, then in his first trousers, little dreaming that he was blessing his future biographer. But it seemed eminently fitting that this boy, who became known as the Father of American Letters, should write the biography of the man whose name he bore, and whom we know as the Father of his Country.

"The Sketch Book" is a collection of short tales, sketches, and essays, published in 1820. Most of the sketches are descriptive of English manners and scenery, but it contained two well-known stories of American life, "Rip Van Winkle," and "The Legend of Sleepy Hollow."

Sunnyside, the beautiful home of Washington Irving, is at Tarrytown-on-the-Hudson. Just before his death he finished the "Life of Washington." He died in 1859, and was buried on a hill overlooking the river and a portion of Sleepy Hollow Valley.

THE SCHOOLMASTER

In the bosom of one of those spacious coves which indent the eastern shore of the Hudson, there lies a small market town, which by some is called Greensburgh, but which is more generally and properly known by the name of Tarrytown. Not far from this village, perhaps about two miles, there is a little valley, which is one of the quietest places in the whole world. A small brook glides through it, with just murmur enough to lull one to repose; and the occasional whistle of a quail or the tapping of a woodpecker is almost the only sound that ever breaks in upon the uniform tranquillity.

If ever I should wish for a retreat, whither I might steal from the world and its distractions, and dream quietly away the remnant of a troubled life, I know of none more promising than this little valley.

From the listless repose of the place, and the peculiar character of its inhabitants, who are descendents from the original Dutch settlers, this sequestered glen has long been known by the name of Sleepy Hollow, and its rustic lads are called the Sleepy Hollow Boys throughout all the neighboring country. A drowsy, dreamy influence seems to hang over the land, and to pervade the very atmosphere. Some say that the place was bewitched by a high German doctor during the early days of the settlement; others, that an old Indian chief, the prophet or wizard of his tribe, held his powwows there before the country was discovered by Master Hendrick Hudson. Certain it is the place still continues under the sway of some witching power, which holds a spell over the minds of the good people, causing them to walk in a continual reverie. They are given to all kinds of marvelous beliefs, are subject to trances and visions, and frequently see strange sights, and hear music and voices in the air. The whole neighborhood abounds with local tales, haunted spots, and twilight superstitions; stars shoot and meteors glare oftener across the valley than in any other part of the country, and the nightmare, with her whole nine fold, seems to make it the favorite scene of her gambols.

Though years have elapsed since I trod the drowsy shades of Sleepy Hollow, yet I question whether I should not still find the same trees and the same families vegetating in its sheltered bosom.

In this by-place of nature, in a remote period of American history, there lived a worthy man whose name was Ichabod Crane. He sojourned, or, as he expressed it, "tarried," in Sleepy Hollow, for the purpose of instructing the children of the vicinity. He was a native of Connecticut. He was tall but exceedingly lank, with narrow shoulders, long arms and legs, hands that dangled a mile out of his sleeves, feet that might have served for shovels, and his whole frame was most loosely hung together. His head was small, and flat at the top, with huge ears, large green glassy eyes, and a long snipe nose, which looked like a weathercock perched upon his spindle neck to tell which way the wind blew. To see him striding along the profile of a hill on a windy day, with his clothes bagging and fluttering about him, one might have mistaken him for some scarecrow eloped from a cornfield.

His schoolhouse was a low building of one large room, rudely constructed of logs. It stood in a rather lonely but pleasant situation, just at the foot of a woody hill, with a brook running close by, and a birch tree growing at one end of it. Hence the low murmur of his pupils' voices, conning over their lessons, might be heard in a drowsy summer's day, like the hum of a beehive; interrupted now and then by the voice of the master, or by the appalling sound of the birch as he urged some tardy loiterer along the flowery path of knowledge.

When school hours were over, the teacher forgot that he was master, and was even the companion and playmate of the larger boys; and on holiday afternoons would go home with some of the smaller ones, who happened to have pretty sisters, or good housewives for mothers, noted for the comforts of the cupboard. Indeed, it behooved him to keep on good terms with his pupils. The revenue arising from his school was small, and would have been scarcely sufficient to furnish him with daily bread. But to help out his maintenance, he was, according to the country custom in those parts, boarded and lodged at the houses of the farmers whose children he instructed. With these he lived successively a week at a time; thus going the rounds of the neighborhood, with all his worldly effects tied up in a cotton handkerchief.

He had various ways of rendering himself both useful and agreeable. He assisted the farmers occasionally in the lighter labors of their farms, helped to make hay, mended the fences, took the horses to water, drove the cows from pasture, and cut wood for the winter fire. He found favor in the eyes of the mothers by petting the children, particularly the youngest; and he would sit with a child on one knee, and rock a cradle with his foot for whole hours together.

The schoolmaster is generally a man of some importance in the female circle of a rural neighborhood, being considered a kind of idle, gentlemanlike personage, of vastly superior taste and accomplishments to the rough country swains, and, indeed, inferior in learning only to the parson. His appearance, therefore, is apt to occasion some little stir at the tea-table of a farmhouse, and the addition of an extra dish of cakes or sweetmeats or the parade of a silver teapot. Our man of letters, therefore, was peculiarly happy in the smiles of all the country damsels. How he would figure among them in the churchyard between services on Sundays! gathering grapes for them from the wild vines that overran the surrounding trees; reciting for their amusement all the epitaphs on the tombstones; or sauntering, with a whole bevy of them, along the banks of the adjacent mill pond; while the more bashful country bumpkins hung sheepishly back, envying his superior elegance and address.

Another of his sources of pleasure was to pass long winter evenings with the old Dutch wives, as they sat spinning by the fire, with a row of apples roasting and spluttering along the hearth, and to listen to their marvelous tales of ghosts and goblins, and haunted fields, and haunted brooks, and haunted bridges, and haunted houses, and particularly of the headless horseman, or Galloping Hessian of the Hollow, as they sometimes called him. He would delight them equally by his anecdotes of witchcraft, and would frighten them woefully with speculations upon comets and shooting stars, and with the alarming fact that the world did absolutely turn round, and that they were half the time topsy-turvey!

But if there was a pleasure in all this, while snugly cuddling in the chimney corner of a room that was all of a ruddy glow from the crackling wood fire, and where, of course, no specter dared to show its face, it was dearly purchased by the terrors of his subsequent walk homeward. What fearful shapes and shadows beset his path amidst the dim and ghastly glare of a snowy night! With what wistful look did he eye every trembling ray of light streaming across waste fields from distant window! How often was he appalled by some shrub covered with snow, which, like a sheeted specter, beset his very path! How often did he shrink with curdling awe at the sound of his own steps on the frosty crust beneath his feet, and dread to look over his shoulder, lest he should behold some uncouth being tramping close behind him! And how often was he thrown into complete dismay by some rushing blast, howling among the trees, in the idea that it was the Galloping Hessian on one of his nightly scourings!

The Invitation

ferule	cavalier	opulence	racketing
legion	quilting	slapjacks	furbishing
sundry	despotic	tow-cloth	application
genuine	Katrina	garnished	Van Tassel's
pommel	bestrode	enthroned	emancipation
Mynheer	banquets	screaming	knight-errant

On a fine autumnal afternoon, Ichabod, in pensive mood, sat enthroned on the lofty stool whence he usually watched all the concerns of his little literary realm. In his hand he swayed a ferule, that scepter of despotic power; the birch of justice reposed on three nails behind the throne, a constant terror to evildoers; while on the desk before him might be seen sundry contraband articles and prohibited weapons, detected upon the persons of idle urchins, such as half-munched apples, popguns, whirligigs, and fly-cages. His scholars were all busily intent upon their books, or slyly whispering behind them with one eye kept upon the master; and a kind of buzzing stillness reigned throughout the schoolroom. It was suddenly interrupted by the appearance of a negro, in tow-cloth jacket and trousers, a round-crowned fragment of a hat, like the cap of Mercury, and mounted on the back of a ragged, wild, half-broken colt, which he managed with a rope by way of halter. He came clattering up to the school door, with an invitation to Ichabod to attend a merrymaking, or " quilting frolic," to be held that evening at Mynheer Van Tassel's; and having delivered his message, he dashed over the brook, and was seen scampering away up the Hollow, full of the importance and hurry of his mission.

All was now bustle and hubbub in the late quiet schoolroom. The scholars were hurried through their lessons without stopping at trifles; those who were nimble skipped over half, and those who were slow were hurried along by a smart application of the rod. Books were flung aside without being put away on the shelves; inkstands were overturned, benches thrown down, and the whole school was turned loose an hour before the usual time, bursting forth like a legion of young imps, yelping and racketing about the green in joy at their early emancipation.

The gallant Ichabod now spent at least an extra half-hour at his toilet, brushing and furbishing his best, and, indeed, only suit of rusty black, and arranging his locks by a bit of broken looking-glass that hung up in the schoolhouse. That he might make his appearance at the party in the true style of a cavalier, he borrowed a horse from the farmer with whom he was boarding, and thus gallantly mounted, rode forth like a knight-errant in quest of adventures. The animal he bestrode was a broken-down plow-horse, that had outlived almost everything but his viciousness. He was gaunt and shagged, with a slender neck and a head like a hammer; his rusty mane and tail were tangled and knotted with burrs; one eye had lost its pupil, and was glaring and spectral; but the other had the gleam of a genuine devil in it. Still he must have had fire and mettle in his day, if we may judge from the name he bore of Gunpowder.

Ichabod was a suitable figure for such a steed. He rode with short stirrups, which brought his knees nearly up to the pommel of the saddle; his sharp elbows stuck out like grasshoppers'; he carried his whip perpendicularly in his hand, like a scepter; and, as his horse jogged on, the motion of his arms was not unlike the flapping of a pair of wings. A small woolen hat rested on the top of his nose, for so his scanty strip of forehead might be called; and the skirts of his black coat fluttered out almost to the horse's tail. Such was the appearance of Ichabod and his steed, as they shambled out of the gate and along the highway; and it was altogether such an apparition as is seldom to be met with in broad daylight.

It was, as I have said, a fine autumnal day; the sky was clear and serene, and nature wore that rich and golden livery which we always associate with the idea of abundance. The forests had put on their sober brown and yellow, while some trees of the tenderer kind had been nipped by the frosts into brilliant dyes of orange, purple, and scarlet. Streaming files of wild ducks began to make their appearance high in the air; the bark of the squirrel might be heard from the groves of beech and hickory nuts, and the pensive whistle of the quail at intervals from the neighboring stubble-field.

The small birds were taking their farewell banquets. In the fullness of their revelry they fluttered, chirping and frolicking, from bush to bush and tree to tree, gay and happy from the very profusion and variety around them. There were the twittering blackbirds flying in sable clouds; and the golden-winged woodpecker, with his crimson crest, and splendid plumage; and the cedar bird, with its red-tipped wings and yellow-tipped tail, and its little cap of feathers; and the blue jay, in his gay light blue coat and white underclothes, screaming and chattering, nodding and bobbing and bowing, and pretending to be on good terms with every songster of the grove.

As Ichabod jogged slowly on his way, his eye ranged with delight over the treasures of jolly autumn. On all sides he beheld vast stores of apples, some hanging in oppressive opulence on the trees, some gathered into baskets and barrels for the market, others heaped up in rich piles for the ciderpress. Farther on he beheld great fields of Indian corn, with its golden ears peeping from their leafy coverts, and holding out the promise of cakes and hasty pudding; and the yellow pumpkins lying beneath them, turning up their fair round yellow sides to the sun, and giving ample prospects of the most luxurious of pies; and anon he passed the fragrant buckwheat fields, breathing the odor of the beehive; and, as he beheld them, soft anticipations stole over his mind of dainty slapjacks, well buttered, and garnished with honey, by the delicate little dimpled hand of Katrina, the daughter of Mynheer Van Tassel.

Thus feeding his mind with many sweet thoughts and " sugared suppositions," he journeyed along the sides of a range of hills which look out upon some of the goodliest scenes of the mighty Hudson. The sun gradually wheeled his broad disk down into the west. A few amber clouds floated in the sky, without a breath of air to move them. The horizon was of a fine golden tint, changing gradually into a pure apple-green, and from that into the deep blue of the midheaven. A slanting ray lingered on the woody crests of the precipices that overhung some parts of the river, giving greater depth to the dark gray and purple of their rocky sides.

The " Quilting Frolic "

foray	cruller	tethered	petticoats
calico	flogger	adjacent	antiquated
casual	dilated	itinerant	enraptured
piazza	broiled	St. Vitus	innovations
doling	smitten	preserved	enumerated
Baltus	quinces	patrolling	Brom Bones
queued	pyramid	sumptuous	Major Andrè

It was toward evening that Ichabod arrived at the castle of the Herr Van Tassel, which he found thronged with the pride and flower of the adjacent country: old farmers, in homespun coats and breeches, blue stockings, huge shoes, and magnificent pewter buckles; their brisk little dames, in close crimped caps, long-waisted short gowns, homespun petticoats, with scissors and pincushions, and gay calico pockets hanging on the outside; buxom lasses, almost as antiquated in their style of dressing as their mothers, excepting where a straw hat, a fine ribbon, or perhaps a white frock, showed signs of city innovations; the sons, in short, square-skirted coats with rows of stupendous brass buttons, and their hair generally queued in the fashion of the times, especially if they could procure an eelskin for the purpose, it being esteemed throughout the country as a potent nourisher and strengthener of the hair.

Brom Bones, however, was the hero of the scene, having come to the gathering on his favorite steed Daredevil, a creature, like his rider, full of mettle and mischief, and which no one but him could manage. He was, in fact, noted for preferring vicious animals, given to all kinds of tricks, which kept the rider in constant risk of his neck; for he held a tractable, well-broken horse as unworthy of a lad of spirit.

Fain would I pause to dwell upon the world of charms that burst upon the enraptured gaze of my hero as he entered the state parlor of Van Tassel's mansion, — not those of the bevy of buxom lasses, with their luxurious display of red and white, but the ample charms of a genuine Dutch country tea-table, in the sumptuous time of autumn. Such heaped-up platters of cakes of various and almost indescribable kinds, known only to experienced Dutch housewives! There was the doughty doughnut, and the crisp and crumbling cruller; sweet-cakes and short-cakes, ginger-cakes and honey-cakes, and the whole family of cakes. And then there were apple pies and peach pies and pumpkin pies; besides slices of ham and smoked beef; and, moreover, dishes of preserved plums and peaches and pears and quinces, not to mention broiled shad and roasted chickens, together with bowls of milk and cream, all mingled higgledy-piggledy, pretty much as I have enumerated them, with the motherly teapot sending up its clouds of vapor from the midst! I want breath and time to describe this banquet as it deserves, and am too eager to get on with my story. Happily, Ichabod Crane was not in so great a hurry as his historian, but did ample justice to every dainty.

He was a kind and thankful creature, whose heart dilated in proportion as his skin was filled with good cheer, and whose spirits rose with eating. He could not help, too, rolling his large eyes round him as he ate, and chuckling with the possibility that he might one day be lord of all this scene of almost unimaginable luxury and splendor.

Old Baltus Van Tassel moved about among his guests with a face dilated with content and good humor, round and jolly as the harvest moon. His hospitable attentions were brief, but expressive, being confined to a shake of the hand, a slap on the shoulder, a loud laugh, and a pressing invitation to " fall to, and help themselves."

And now the sound of music from the common room or hall summoned to the dance. The musician was an old, gray-headed

417

negro, who had been the itinerant orchestra of the neighborhood for more than half a century. His instrument was as old and battered as he. The greater part of the time he scraped on two or three strings, accompanying every movement of the bow with a motion of the head, bowing almost to the ground and stamping with his foot whenever a fresh couple were to start.

Ichabod prided himself upon his dancing. Not a limb, not a fiber about him was idle; and to have seen his loosely hung frame in full motion, clattering about the room, you would have thought St. Vitus himself, that blessed patron of the dance, was figuring before you in person. He was the admiration of all the negroes, who, having gathered, of all ages and sizes, from the farm and the neighborhood, stood forming a pyramid of shining black faces at every door and window, gazing with delight at the scene, rolling their white eyeballs, and showing grinning rows of ivory from ear to ear. How could the flogger of urchins be otherwise than animated and joyous? Pretty Katrina Van Tassel, the lady of his heart, was his partner in the dance, and, smiling graciously in reply to all his gallant remarks; while Brom Bones, sorely smitten with love and jealousy, sat brooding by himself in one corner.

When the dance was at an end, Ichabod was attracted to a circle of the older folks, who, with Mynheer Van Tassel, sat smoking at one end of the piazza, gossiping over former times, and drawing out long stories about the war. But all these were nothing to the tales of ghosts and apparitions that succeeded. The neighborhood is rich in legendary treasures of the kind.

The immediate cause, however, of the prevalence of supernatural stories in these parts, was doubtless owing to the vicinity of Sleepy Hollow. There was a contagion in the very air that blew from that haunted region; it breathed forth an atmosphere of dreams and fancies infecting all the land. Several of the Sleepy Hollow people were present at Van Tassel's; and, as usual, were doling out their wild and wonderful legends. Many dismal tales were told about funeral trains, and mourning cries and wailings heard and seen about the great tree where the unfortunate Major André was taken, and which stood in the neighborhood. Some mention was made also of the woman in white that haunted the dark glen at Raven Rock, and was often heard to shriek on winter nights before a storm, having perished in the snow. The chief part of the stories, however, turned upon the favorite specter of Sleepy Hollow, the headless horseman, who had been heard several times of late, patrolling the country, and who, it was said, tethered his horse nightly among the graves in the churchyard.

The sequestered situation of this church seems always to have made it a favorite haunt of troubled spirits. To look upon its grass-grown yard, where the sunbeams seem to sleep so quietly, one would think that there at least the dead might rest in peace. On one side of the church extends a wide woody dell, along which raves a large brook among broken rocks and trunks of fallen trees. Over a deep black part of the stream, not far from the church, was formerly thrown a wooden bridge; the road that led to it, and the bridge itself, were thickly shaded by overhanging trees, which cast a gloom about it, even in the daytime, but occasioned a fearful darkness at night. Such was one of the favorite haunts of the headless horseman, and the place where he was most frequently encountered. The tale was told of a man who once met the horseman returning from his foray into Sleepy Hollow, and who was obliged to get up behind him ; how they galloped over bush and brake, over hill and swamp, until they reached the bridge, when the horseman suddenly turned into a skeleton, threw the man into the brook, and sprang away over the tree tops with a clap of thunder.

This story was immediately matched by a thrice marvelous adventure of Brom Bones, who made light of the Galloping Hessian as an arrant jockey. He affirmed that, on returning one night from the neighboring village of Sing-Sing, he had been overtaken by this midnight trooper ; that he had offered to race with him for a bowl of punch, and that he should have won it too, for Daredevil beat the goblin horse all hollow, — but that just as they came to the church bridge, the Hessian bolted, and vanished in a flash of fire.

All these tales, told in that drowsy undertone with which men talk in the dark, the countenances of the listeners only now and then receiving a casual gleam from the glare of a pipe, sank deep in the mind of Ichabod. He repaid them in kind with many marvelous events that had taken place in his native state of Connecticut, and with fearful sights that he had seen in his nightly walks about Sleepy Hollow.

The revel now gradually broke up. The old farmers gathered

together their families in their wagons, and were heard for some time rattling along the hollow roads and over the distant hills. Some of the damsels mounted on pillions behind their favorite swains, and their light-hearted laughter, mingling with the clatter of hoofs, echoed along the silent woodlands, sounding fainter and fainter until they gradually died away, and the late scene of noise and frolic was all silent and deserted. Ichabod only lingered behind, according to the custom of country lovers, to have a parting word with pretty Katrina. What passed at this interview I will not pretend to say, for in fact I do not know. Something, however, must have gone wrong, for he certainly sallied forth, after no great interval, with an air quite desolate and chopfallen.

The Headless Horseman

girths	missile	diligent	pedagogue
flimsy	scathed	snorting	dimensions
lateral	gutteral	snuffling	ascertained
parched	cranium	scramble	electioneered
asunder	identical	sprawling	investigation

It was the very witching time of night that Ichabod, heavy-hearted and crestfallen, pursued his travels homewards, along the sides of the lofty hills which rise above Tarrytown, and which he had traversed so cheerily in the afternoon. The hour was as dismal as he. In the dead hush of midnight he could even hear the barking of the watchdog from the opposite shore

421

of the Hudson; but it was so vague and faint as only to give an idea of his distance from this faithful companion of man. No signs of life occurred near him, but occasionally the melancholy chirp of a cricket, or perhaps the gutteral twang of a bullfrog from a neighboring marsh, as if sleeping uncomfortably, and turning suddenly in his bed.

All the stories of ghosts and goblins that he had heard in the afternoon now came crowding upon his recollection. The night grew darker and darker; the stars seemed to sink deeper in the sky, and driving clouds occasionally hid them from his sight. He had never felt so lonely and dismal. He was, moreover, approaching the very place where many of the scenes of the ghost stories had been laid. In the center of the road stood an enormous tulip tree, which towered like a giant above the other trees of the neighborhood, and formed a kind of landmark. Its limbs were gnarled and fantastic, large enough to form trunks for ordinary trees, twisting down almost to the earth, and rising again into the air.

As Ichabod approached this fearful tree he began to whistle: he thought his whistle was answered; it was but a blast sweeping sharply through the dry branches. As he approached a little nearer, he thought he saw something white hanging in the midst of the tree: he paused and ceased whistling; but on looking more narrowly, perceived that it was a place where the tree had been scathed by lightning, and the white wood laid bare. Suddenly he heard a groan; his teeth chattered and his knees smote against the saddle. It was but the rubbing of one huge bough upon another, as they were swayed about by the breeze. He passed the tree in safety, but new perils lay before him.

About two hundred yards from the tree a small brook crossed the road, and ran into a marshy and thickly wooded glen. A few rough logs, laid side by side, served for a bridge over this stream. On that side of the road where the brook entered the wood, a group of oaks and chestnuts, matted thick with wild grapevines, threw a gloom over it. To pass this bridge was the severest trial. It was at this identical spot that the unfortunate Andrè was captured, and under the covert of those chestnuts and vines were the sturdy yeomen concealed who surprised him. This has ever since been considered a haunted stream, and fearful are the feelings of the schoolboy who has to pass it alone after dark.

As he approached the stream, his heart began to thump; he summoned up, however, all his resolution, gave his horse half a score of kicks in the ribs, and attempted to dash briskly across the bridge; but, instead of starting forward, the perverse old animal made a lateral movement, and ran broadside against the fence. Ichabod, whose fears increased with the delay, jerked the reins on the other side, and kicked lustily with the contrary foot; it was all in vain. His steed started, it is true; but it was only to plunge to the opposite side of the road into a thicket of brambles. The schoolmaster now bestowed both whip and heel upon the ribs of old Gunpowder, who dashed forward, snuffling and snorting, but came to a stand just by the bridge with a suddenness that had nearly sent his rider sprawling over his head. Just at this moment a plashy tramp by the side of the bridge caught the sensitive ear of Ichabod. In the dark shadow of the grove, on the margin of the brook, he beheld something huge, misshapen, black, and towering. It stirred not, but seemed gathered up in the gloom, like some gigantic monster ready to spring upon the traveler.

The hair of the affrighted pedagogue rose upon his head with terror. What was to be done? To turn and fly was now too late; and, besides, what chance was there of escaping ghost or goblin, if such it was, which could ride upon the wings of the wind? Summoning up, therefore, a show of courage, he demanded in stammering accents, "Who are you?" He received no reply. He repeated his demand in a still more agitated voice. Still there was no answer. Once more he cudgeled the sides of Gunpowder, and, shutting his eyes, broke forth into a psalm tune. Just then the shadowy object of alarm put itself in motion, and with a scramble and a bound stood at once in the middle of the road. Though the night was dark and dismal, yet the form of the unknown might now in some degree be ascertained. He appeared to be a horseman of large dimensions, and mounted on a black horse of powerful frame. He made no offer of molestation or sociability, but kept aloof on one side of the road, jogging along on the blind side of old Gunpowder, who had now got over his fright and waywardness.

Ichabod, who had no relish for this strange midnight companion, and bethought himself of the adventure of Brom Bones and the Headless Horseman, now quickened his steed in hopes of leaving him behind. The stranger, however, quickened his horse to an equal pace. Ichabod pulled up and fell into a walk, thinking to lag behind; the other did the same. His heart began to sink within him; he endeavored to resume his psalm tune, but his parched tongue clave to the roof of his mouth. There was something in the moody and dogged silence of his companion that was mysterious and appalling. It was soon fearfully accounted for. On mounting a rising ground, which brought the figure of his fellow-traveler in relief against the sky, Ichabod was horror-struck on perceiving that he was headless! But his horror was still more increased on observing that the head, which should have rested on his shoulders, was carried before him on the pommel of the saddle: his terror rose to desperation; he rained a shower of kicks and blows upon Gunpowder, hoping by a sudden movement to give his companion the slip, but the specter started full jump with him. Away then they dashed, through thick and thin, stones flying, and sparks flashing, at every bound. Ichabod's flimsy garments fluttered in the air, as he stretched his long lank body away over his horse's head in the eagerness of his flight.

They had now reached the road which turns off to Sleepy Hollow; but Gunpowder, who seemed possessed with a demon, instead of keeping up it, made an opposite turn, and plunged headlong down the hill to the left. This road leads through a sandy hollow, shaded by trees for about a quarter of a mile, where it crosses the bridge famous in goblin story; and just beyond swells the green knoll on which stands the whitewashed church.

Just as he had got halfway through the hollow, the girths of the saddle gave way, and he felt it slipping from under him. He seized it by the pommel and endeavored to hold it firm, but in vain; and he had just time to save himself by clasping old Gunpowder round the neck, when the saddle fell to the earth, and was trampled under foot by his pursuer. For a moment the terror of its owner's wrath passed across his mind, — for it was his Sunday saddle, — but this was no time for petty fears. He had much ado to maintain his seat, sometimes slipping on one side, sometimes on the other, and sometimes jolted on the high ridge of the horse's backbone with a violence that he verily feared would cleave him asunder.

An opening in the trees now cheered him with the hope that the church bridge was at hand. The wavering reflection of a silver star in the bosom of the brook told him that he was not mistaken. He saw the walls of the church dimly glaring under the trees beyond. "If I can but reach that bridge," thought Ichabod, "I am safe." Just then he heard the black steed panting and blowing close behind him; he even fancied that he felt his hot breath. Another kick in the ribs, and old Gunpowder sprang upon the bridge; he thundered over the resounding planks; he gained the opposite side: and now Ichabod cast a look behind, to see if his pursuer should vanish in a flash of fire and brimstone. Just then he saw the goblin rising in his stirrups and in the very act of hurling his head at him. Ichabod endeavored to dodge the horrible missile, but too late. It encountered his cranium with a tremendous crash; he was tumbled headlong into the dust, and Gunpowder, the black steed, and the goblin rider passed by like a whirlwind.

The next morning the old horse was found, without his saddle, and with the bridle under his feet, soberly cropping the grass at his master's gate. Ichabod did not make his appearance at breakfast. Dinner hour came; but no Ichabod! The boys assembled at the schoolhouse, and strolled idly about the banks of the brook; but no schoolmaster. An inquiry was set on foot, and after diligent investigation they came upon his traces. In one part of the road leading to the church was found the saddle trampled in the dirt; the tracks of horses' hoofs, deeply dented in the road, and evidently at furious speed, were traced to the bridge, beyond which, on the bank of a broad part of the brook where the water ran deep and black, was found the hat of the unfortunate Ichabod, and close beside it a shattered pumpkin.

The brook was searched, but the body of the schoolmaster was not to be discovered. As he was a bachelor, and in nobody's debt, nobody troubled his head any more about him. The school was removed to a different quarter of the hollow, and another pedagogue reigned in his stead.

It is true, an old farmer, who had been down to New York on a visit several years after, and from whom this account of the ghostly adventure was received, brought home the intelligence that Ichabod Crane was still alive; that he had left the neigborhood, partly through fear of the goblin and the farmer whose horse he had ridden, and partly for other reasons; that he had changed his quarters to a distant part of the country; had kept school and studied law at the same time; had been admitted to the bar, turned politician, electioneered, written for the newspapers, and finally had been made a justice of the Ten-pound Court. Brom Bones, too, who shortly after his rival's disappearance conducted the blooming Katrina in triumph to the altar, was observed to look exceedingly knowing whenever the story of Ichabod was related, and always burst into a hearty laugh at the mention of the pumpkin; which led some to suspect that he knew more about the matter than he chose to tell.

The old country wives, however, who are the best judges of these matters, maintain to this day that Ichabod was spirited away by supernatural means; and it is a favorite story, often told about the neighborhood round the winter evening fire. The bridge became more than ever an object of superstitious awe; and that may be the reason why the road has been altered of late years, so as to approach the church by the border of the mill pond. The schoolhouse, being deserted, soon fell to decay, and was reported to be haunted by the ghost of the unfortunate pedagogue; and the plowboy, loitering homeward of a still summer evening, has often fancied his voice at a distance, chanting a melancholy psalm tune among the tranquil solitudes of Sleepy Hollow.

THE HUSKERS

JOHN GREENLEAF WHITTIER

sleek   bleaching   chastened

It was late in mild October, and the long autumnal rain
Had left the summer harvest fields all green with grass again;
The first sharp frost had fallen, leaving all the woodlands gay
With the hues of summer's rainbow, or the meadow flowers of May.

Through a thin, dry mist, that morning, the sun rose broad and red,
At first a rayless disk of fire, he brightened as he sped;
Yet, even his noontide glory fell chastened and subdued,
On the cornfields and the orchards, and the softly pictured wood.

And all that quiet afternoon, slow sloping to the night,
He wove with golden shuttle the haze with yellow light;
Slanting through the painted beeches, he glorified the hill;
And beneath it, pond and meadow lay brighter, greener still.

And shouting boys in woodland haunts caught glimpses of that sky,
Flecked by the many tinted leaves, and laughed, they knew not why;
And schoolgirls gay with aster flowers, beside the meadow brooks,
Mingled the glow of autumn with the sunshine of sweet looks.

From spire and barn looked westerly the patient weathercocks;
But even the birches on the hill stood motionless as rocks.
No sound was in the woodlands, save the squirrel's dropping shell,
And the yellow leaves among the boughs, low rustling as they fell.

The summer grains were harvested; the stubble fields lay dry,
Where June winds rolled, in light and shade, the pale green waves
  of rye;

But still, on gentle hill slopes, in valleys fringed with wood,
Ungathered, bleaching in the sun, the heavy corn crop stood.

Bent low, by autumn's wind and rain, through husks that, dry and
     sere,
Unfolded from their ripened charge, shone out the yellow ear;
Beneath, the turnip lay concealed, in many a verdant fold,
And glistened in the slanting light the pumpkin's sphere of gold.

There wrought the busy harvesters; and many a creaking wain
Bore slowly to the long barn floor its load of husk and grain;
Till broad and red, as when he rose, the sun sank down at last,
And like a merry guest's farewell, the day in brightness passed.

And lo! as through the western pines, on meadow, stream, and pond,
Flamed the red radiance of a sky, set all afire beyond,
Slowly o'er the eastern sea bluffs a milder glory shone,
And the sunset and the moonrise were mingled into one!

As thus into the quiet night the twilight lapsed away,
And deeper in the brightening moon the tranquil shadows lay;
From many a brown old farmhouse, and hamlet without name,
Their milking and their home tasks done, the merry huskers came.

Swung o'er the heaped-up harvest, from pitchforks in the mow,
Shone dimly down the lanterns on the pleasant scene below;
The growing pile of husks behind, the golden ears before,
And laughing eyes and busy hands and brown cheeks glimmering o'er.

Half hidden, in a quiet nook, serene of look and heart,
Talking their old times over, the old men sat apart;
While up and down the unhusked pile, or nestling in its shade,
At hide and seek, with laugh and shout, the happy children played.

Urged by the good host's daughter, a maiden young and fair,
Lifting to light her sweet blue eyes and pride of soft brown hair,
The master of the village school, sleek of hair and smooth of tongue,
To the quaint tune of some old psalm, a husking-ballad sung.

THE WHITE–FOOTED DEER

WILLIAM CULLEN BRYANT

mead   crescent   sprouting
twang   pheasant   whippoorwill

It was a hundred years ago,
   When, by the woodland ways,
The traveler saw the wild deer drink,
   Or crop the birchen sprays.

Beneath a hill, whose rocky side
   O'erbowered a grassy mead,
And fenced a cottage from the wind
   A deer was wont to feed.

She only came when on the cliffs
   The evening moonlight lay,
And no man knew the secret haunts
   In which she walked by day.

White were her feet, her forehead showed
   A spot of silvery white,
That seemed to glimmer like a star
   In autumn's hazy night.

T. *Schmitzberger.*

AUTUMN GOLD.

And here, when sang the whippoorwill,
  She cropped the sprouting leaves,
And here her rustling steps were heard
  On still October eves.

But when the broad midsummer moon
  Rose o'er that grassy lawn,
Beside the silver-footed deer
  There grazed a spotted fawn.

The cottage dame forbade her son
  To aim the rifle here;
"It were a sin," she said, "to harm
  Or fright that friendly deer.

"This spot has been my pleasant home
  Ten peaceful years and more;
And ever, when the moonlight shines,
  She feeds before our door.

"The red men say that here she walked
  A thousand moons ago;
They never raise the war whoop here,
  And never twang the bow.

"I love to watch her as she feeds,
  And think that all is well
While such a gentle creature haunts
  The place in which we dwell."

The youth obeyed, and sought for game
  In forests far away,
Where, deep in silence and in moss
  The ancient woodland lay.

But once, in autumn's golden time,
  He ranged the wild in vain,
Nor roused the pheasant nor the deer,
  And wandered home again.

The crescent moon and crimson eve
  Shone with a mingled light;
The deer upon the grassy mead,
  Was feeding full in sight.

He raised the rifle to his eye,
  And from the cliffs around
A sudden echo, shrill and sharp,
  Gave back its deadly sound.

Away, into the neighboring wood,
  The startled creature flew,
And crimson drops at morning lay
  Amid the glimmering dew.

Next evening shone the waxing moon
  As sweetly as before;
The deer upon the grassy mead
  Was seen again no more.

But ere that crescent moon was old,
  By night the red men came,
And burnt the cottage to the ground,
  And slew the youth and dame.

Now woods have overgrown the mead,
  And hid the cliffs from sight;
And shrieks the hovering hawk at noon,
  And prowls the fox at night.

Reprinted from Bryant's Complete Poetical Works, by permission of D. Appleton and Company.

RALPH WALDO EMERSON

Thoreau	sentinels
studious	Shakespeare

Ralph Waldo Emerson was born in Boston, Massachusetts, in 1803. He entered Harvard College when he was fourteen years old; and at that time he was a quiet boy who never jested or joined in any boyish sports: "By degrees," says one of his classmates, "the more studious members of his class began to seek him out. They found him to be unusually thoughtful and well read. He knew Shakespeare almost by heart."

Emerson wrote essays more helpful than most sermons; poems full of power and sweetness; and, better than any song or sermon, he lived a life so noble, true, and beautiful, that its influence was felt on both sides of the sea. In a letter to a friend, Lowell writes: "I hope you have seen something of Emerson, who is as sweet and wholesome as an Indian-summer afternoon."

For nearly half a century, Emerson was one of the leaders of American thought. He made his home in the historic town of Concord, Massachusetts. His last public appearance was at the funeral of his friend Longfellow. On Sunday, April 30, 1882, all that was mortal of Ralph Waldo Emerson was borne by loving hands up the wooded hillside in Sleepy Hollow Cemetery, and tenderly laid to rest on the brow of the hill in the midst of the tall forest pines which stand like sentinels to guard this hallowed ground.

On the well-known and well-worn " Ridge Path " that leads up the hillside to Emerson's grave, the literary pilgrim of to-day lingers reverently at the graves of Emerson's distinguished friends and neighbors, Hawthorne, Thoreau, Louisa M. Alcott, and others hardly less famous. And as he walks slowly and reverently down the hillside, the trees, the air, and the sky, all seem to whisper : —

> " So nigh is grandeur to our dust,
> So near is God to man,
> When Duty whispers low, *Thou must,*
> The youth replies, *I can.*"

MANNERS

Ralph Waldo Emerson

basis	pollute	dialect	superficial
mien	leprosy	utilities	distempers
usage	routine	rational	paramount
talent	nobility	committee	rheumatism
ocular	awarding	democracy	peremptorily

Nature tells every secret once. Yes ; but in man she tells it all the time, by form, gesture, mien, face, and parts of the face, and by the whole action of the machine. The visible carriage or action of the individual, we call manners. What are they but thought entering the hands and the feet and controlling the movements of the body, the speech, and the behavior?

436

RALPH WALDO EMERSON.

There is always a best way of doing everything, if it be but to boil an egg. Manners are the happy ways of doing things; each once a stroke of genius or of love, now repeated or hardened into usage. They form at last a rich varnish, with which the routine of life is washed, and its details adorned. If they are superficial, so are the dewdrops which give such a depth to the morning meadows.

The power of manners is incessant, — an element as unconcealable as fire. The nobility cannot in any country be disguised, and no more in a republic or a democracy, than in a kingdom. No man can resist their influence. There are certain manners which are learned in good society, of that force, that if a person have them, he or she must be considered, and is everywhere welcome, though without beauty, or wealth, or genius. Give a boy address and accomplishments, and you give him the mastery of palaces and fortunes, wherever he goes. He has not the trouble of earning or owning them; they solicit him to enter and possess.

Every day bears witness to their gentle rule. Your manners are always under examination, and by committees little suspected, — a police in citizens' clothes, — but are awarding or denying you very high prizes when you least think of it.

We talk much of utilities, but 'tis our manners that associate us. In hours of business, we go to him who knows, or has, or does this or that which we want, and we do not let our taste or feeling stand in the way. But this activity over, we wish for those whom we can be at ease with; those who will go where we go, whose manners do not offend us, whose social tone chimes with ours.

The eyes of men converse as much as their tongues, with the advantage, that the ocular dialect needs no dictionary, but is understood all the world over. When the eyes say one thing, and the tongue another, a practiced man relies on the language of the first. You can read in the eyes of your companion, whether your argument hits him, though his tongue will not confess it. There is a look by which a man shows he is going to say a good thing, and a look when he has said it. Vain and forgotten are all the fine offers and offices of hospitality, if there is no holiday in the eye. 'Tis very certain that each man carries in his eye the exact indication of his rank in the immense scale of men, and we are always learning to read it.

The basis of good manners is self-reliance. Those who are not self-possessed obtrude and pain us. Some men appear to feel that they belong to a low caste. They fear to offend, they bend and apologize, and walk through life with a timid step. As we sometimes dream that we are in a well-dressed company without any coat, so Godfrey acts ever as if he suffered from some mortifying circumstance. The hero should find himself at home, wherever he is; and he should impart comfort by his own security and good nature to all beholders. The hero is suffered to be himself.

I have seen manners that make a similar impression with personal beauty. But they must always show self-control. Then they must be inspired by the good heart. There is no beautifier of complexion, or form, or behavior, like the wish to scatter joy and not pain around us. 'Tis good to give a stranger a meal or a night's lodging. 'Tis better to be hospitable to his good meaning and thought, and give courage to a companion. We must be as courteous to a man as we are to a picture, which we are willing to give the advantage of a good light.

Special precepts are not to be thought of : the talent of well-doing contains them all. Every hour will show a duty as paramount as that of my whim just now ; and yet I will write it, — that there is one topic peremptorily forbidden to all well-bred, to all rational mortals, namely, their distempers.

If you have not slept, or if you have slept, or if you have headache, or rheumatism, or leprosy, or thunderstroke, I beseech you, by all angels, to hold your peace, and not pollute the morning, to which all the housemates bring serene and pleasant thoughts, by groans. Love the day. Do not leave the sky out of your landscape.

EACH AND ALL

Ralph Waldo Emerson

| deity | sexton | heifer |
| clown | enamel | inhaled |

Little thinks, in the field, yon red-cloaked clown
Of thee from the hilltop looking down;
The heifer that lows in the upland farm,
Far-heard, lows not thine ear to charm;
The sexton, tolling his bell at noon,
Deems not that Great Napoleon

440

Stops his horse, and lists with delight,
Whilst his files sweep round yon Alpine height;
Nor knowest thou what argument
Thy life to thy neighbor's creed has lent.
All are needed by each one;
Nothing is fair or good alone.

I thought the sparrow's note from heaven,
Singing at dawn on the alder bough;
I brought him home, in his nest, at even;
He sings his song, but it pleases not now,
For I did not bring home the river and sky;
He sang to my ear; they sang to my eye.
The delicate shells lay on the shore:
The bubbles of the latest wave
Fresh pearls to their enamel gave;
And the bellowing of the savage sea
Greeted their safe escape to me.
I wiped away the weeds and foam,
I fetched my sea-born treasures home;
But the poor, unsightly, noisome things
Had left their beauty on the shore
With the sun and the sand and the wild uproar.

Then I said, " I covet truth;
Beauty is unripe childhood's cheat;
I leave it behind with the games of youth."

441

As I spoke, beneath my feet
The ground pine curled its pretty wreath,
Running over the club moss burrs;
I inhaled the violet's breath;
Around me stood the oaks and firs;
Pine cones and acorns lay on the ground;
Over me soared the eternal sky,
Full of light and of deity;
Again I saw, again I heard,
The rolling river, the morning bird;
Beauty through my senses stole;
I yielded myself to the perfect whole.

William Shakespeare

| religion | modern | Hathaway |
| interweave | Stratford | contemporary |

William Shakespeare was born in the little village of Stratford-on-Avon, in England, in 1564. As a boy, he went to the village school, learning " little Latin and less Greek," and helped in his father's shop. When he was in his nineteenth year he married Anne Hathaway, who was several years his senior, and a few years later he set out to seek his fortune in London.

This is all we know of his early days, and of his life in the great city we know as little. It is strange that no one thought, in the time that he lived, of writing his history, so that we might know as much about him as we do of most other great men.

It is certain that Shakespeare's education went on after he left school; that he learned something from everything he saw about him and from all that he read. Even the trees in the forests and the streams in the meadows taught him lessons about nature.

442

WILLIAM SHAKESPEARE.

The name of Shakespeare is the greatest in our literature; it is the greatest in all literature. And so far from Shakespeare's being the least known, he is the one person, in all modern history, known to us. "Shakespeare is of no age. He speaks a language which thrills in our blood in spite of the separation of over two hundred years. His thoughts, passions, feelings, strains of fancy, all are of this day as they were of his own; and his genius may be contemporary with the mind of every generation for a thousand years to come."

Shakespeare is really the only biographer of Shakespeare; and even he can tell us nothing until we have learned to read and understand his writings. In his writings we have really the information, which, if we were about to meet the man and deal with him, would be most important for us to know. " In his works we have his recorded convictions on those questions which knock for answer at every heart, — on life and death, on love, on wealth and poverty, on the prizes of life, and the ways whereby we come at them; on the characters of men, and the influences which affect their fortunes; and on those mysterious powers which defy our science and which yet interweave their malice and their gift in our brightest hours.

"What point of morals, of manners, of economy, of philosophy, of religion, of taste, of the conduct of life, has he not settled? What mystery has he not signified his knowledge of?"

The last few years of his life were spent at Stratford-on-Avon, the home of his childhood. He died in the year 1616, at the age of fifty two years.

GOOD NAME

William Shakespeare

filches   enriches

Good name in man and woman, dear my lord,
Is the immediate jewel of their souls;
Who steals my purse steals trash; 'tis something, nothing;
'Twas mine, 'tis his, and has been slave to thousands;

But he that filches from me my good name
Robs me of that which not enriches him,
And makes me poor indeed.

— From " Othello."

THE QUALITY OF MERCY

William Shakespeare

attribute   salvation

The quality of mercy is not strain'd,
It droppeth as the gentle rain from heaven
Upon the place beneath; it is twice blest;
It blesseth him that gives and him that takes:
'Tis mightiest in the mightiest; it becomes
The thronèd monarch better than his crown;
His scepter shows the force of temporal power,
The attribute to awe and majesty,
Wherein doth sit the dread and fear of kings;
But mercy is above his sceptered sway;
It is enthroned in the hearts of kings,
It is an attribute to God himself;
And earthly power doth then show likest God's
When mercy seasons justice. Therefore, Jew,
Though justice be thy plea, consider this,
That, in the course of justice, none of us
Should see salvation ; we do pray for mercy;
And that same prayer doth teach us all to render
The deeds of mercy.

— From " The Merchant of Venice."

POLONIUS' ADVICE TO HIS SON

WILLIAM SHAKESPEARE

vulgar   gaudy   grapple
censure   apparel   unfledged

        Give thy thoughts no tongue,
Nor any unproportion'd thought his act.
Be thou familiar, but by no means vulgar.
The friends thou hast, and their adoption tried,
Grapple them to thy soul with hoops of steel;
But do not dull thy palm with entertainment
Of each new-hatch'd, unfledged comrade. Beware
Of entrance to a quarrel; but, being in,
Bear't that th' opposèd may beware of thee.
Give every man thine ear, but few thy voice:
Take each man's censure, but reserve thy judgment.
Costly thy habit as thy purse can buy,
But not express'd in fancy; rich, not gaudy:
For the apparel oft proclaims the man;
And they in France of the best rank and station
Are most select and generous, chief in that.
Neither a borrower nor a lender be:
For loan oft loses both itself and friend;
And borrowing dulls the edge of husbandry.
This above all: To thine own self be true;
And it must follow, as the night the day,
Thou canst not then be false to any man.
                    — From " Hamlet."

HASTE NOT, REST NOT

JOHANN WOLFGANG VON GOETHE

atone   betide

motto   conflicts

Without haste! without rest!
Bind the motto to thy breast;
Bear it with thee as a spell;
Storm or sunshine, guard it well!
Heed not flowers that round thee bloom;
Bear it onward to the tomb!

Haste not! let no thoughtless deed
Mar fore'er the spirit's speed;
Ponder well and know the right,
Onward, then, with all thy might!
Haste not! years can ne'er atone
For one reckless action done.

Rest not! life is sweeping by,
Do and dare, before you die;
Something mighty and sublime
Leave behind to conquer time;
Glorious 'tis to live for aye,
When these forms have passed away!

Haste not! rest not! calmly wait,
Meekly bear the storms of fate;
Duty be thy polar guide; —
Do the right, whate'er betide!
Haste not! rest not! conflicts past,
God shall crown thy work at last.